Brand Marks

The brand-marks shown on the front end-paper are distinctive stud- and breed-marks which were in use in the second half of the nineteenth century. Most of them are no longer in existence

Row 1
1–15: East Indian
16–20: Stud brand-marks of Little Russia; Count Rossumovsky, Apostolo, Countess Orlov, Emperor Alexander, Count Rossumovsky at Boro, Count Rossumovsky at Szorbau, Count Basinov

Row 2
1–7: Brand-marks of German States: Redvienen, Lopshorn, progeny of Prussian primary sires and regional mares, Lippe-Detmold, progeny of Brandenburg sires and regional mares, progeny of Saxon sires and regional mares, old mark followed by new mark
8–17: German private stud-farms: Ivenack, Walda, Carolath, Certzen, Stapelburg, Sachsen; regional stud-farms: Hanover, Kingdom of Hanover, Altstädt, Anhalt Dessau 18–19: Bohemian private stud-farms: Kamenitz, Oposchna
20–22: Spanish brand-marks: Seville stallion centre, Benjumea, Ciguri

Row 3
1–20: Russian stud-farms
21–22: Thessaly-Macedonia

Row 4
1–22: Transylvanian and Hungarian private stud-farms: Gross-Bum, Borkenyes, Frata, Marton, Katsko, Zaja, Berkes, Daniel, Buza, Möves, Stökefalva (2), Kyraly, Sibo, Bagos, Skerei, Datos, Kerestes, Magyar Benye, Kemeny, Banfy, Valaszut

Row 5
1–22: Transylvanian and Hungarian private stud-farms: Gorgeny (2), Abafaja, Mopial, Szurdok, Töleky, Sulelmed, Kessibuz-Urmeny, Ozora, Kerliskyi, Peter, Horvathy, Töleky, Maros-Ejessoe, Edö-Szt-Gyurgy, Teleky, Weisskirchen, Radnoth, Weisskirchen, Köresd, Klein-Bum, Daniel

Row 6
1–3: Austrian court stud-farms: Kladrub, Lipizza, Koptschan
4–9: Austrian military stud-farms: Babolna, Mezöhegyes, Nemoschitz, Biber, Ossiach, Radautz
10–22: Prussian central and regional stud-farms: Trakehnen, Graditz, Beberbeck, Lithauen, Marienwerder, Zirke Regional Stud, Leubus, Lindenau, Neustadt, Warendorf, Wickrath, Vessra, Zirke

Row 7
1–22: Prussian private stud-farms: Wilkischken, Fowegen, Wigerlinnen, Schönbruch, Juditten, Knauten, Preuken, Lamgarben, Budopöhnen, Geritten, Dwarischken, Sedargen, Lendiken, Hassort Kattenau, Miodunsken, Czichen, Strelken, Leuken, Heidekrug, Klein Genie, Hassort

Row 8
1–22: Prussian private stud-farms: Kordmedin, Juckeln, Meier, Drygallen, Szirguspöhnen, Polmingkehmen, Netinnen, Weeszenhof, Drosdowen, Granden, Waldeck, Löbegallen, Königsfelde, Staneitschen, Kirschnehmen, Dressler, Gerschullen, Plicken, Georgenburg, Julienfelde, Goritten, Dombrowsken

Row 9
1–22: Prussian private stud-farms: Grabentin, Kinschen, Eszerischken, Lugowen, Kisselkehmen, Trautlade, Krerrin, Grünwaitschen, Bärwalde, Sesslacken, Grünhof, Berken, Puspern, Galben, Grumbkowkaiten, Pogrimmen, Degesen, Lambgarden, Buglinen, Tarpuschken, Botkeim, Taplacken

Row 10
1–22: Prussian private stud-farms: Wandlack, Wehlau, Prekuls, Mertensdorf, Wedern, Pyragynen, Cordehnen, Gelgodischken, Schlodin, Rantenburg, Steinort, Toussainen, Dennewitz, Sanditten, Wicken, Friedrichstein, Springlacken, Baubeln, Friedrichsgabe, Perwalkischken, Schrengen, Scantlack

Rows 11–13
1–22: Circassian and Turcoman brand-marks

Most of the brand-marks illustrated are taken from the book: *Gestütsbrandzeichen der Staats- und Privatgestüte Europas und des Orients* (Stud Brand-marks of State-Owned and Private Stud-farms of Europe and the Orient), by C. Bräuer, published in 1877 (Collection of the Library of Deutsches Pferdemuseum e.V.)

Great
Stud-Farms

of the World

Preface by
HRH Prince Philip, Duke of Edinburgh

with 811 illustrations, 320 in color

Monique and Hans D. Dossenbach, Hans Joachim Köhler

Great Stud-Farms
of the World

William Morrow & Company, Inc.

Text contributions

HISTORY OF HORSE BREEDING: Hans D. Dossenbach.
FRANCE: D. Bechean La Fonta, Director, UNIC,
with Louis Reillier, Michel Jussiaux, Michel de
Thoré, L. de Villeneuve, Christian Depuille, Hans D.
Dossenbach, Emmanuel Bodard, Mme René
Aumont, Henri Pellerin. GERMANY: Hans Joachim
Köhler, with Johannes Grelle, Dr Lehmann, Dr B.
Bade, Dr Wenzler, Dr Cranz, W. Finkh, Gudrun
Schultz, Martin Beckmann, Andreas Löwe.
DENMARK: I. C. Christensen, with Jörgen Paulsen.
SWEDEN: O. Kjellander. ENGLAND: Allan Smith,
with Hanspeter Meier, Michael Ross, P. Doyle, Tony
Jakobson, Michael Oswald. IRELAND: Hanspeter
Meier, with Lord and Lady Hemphill. SPAIN: Duke
of Aguilar, with Horse-breeding Directorate,
Madrid, Luis de Ybarra e Ybarra, Juan del Cid
Galonge. SWITZERLAND: Max E. Ammann. ITALY:
Andreas Zindel. YUGOSLAVIA: Hans D. Dossenbach.
AUSTRIA: Hofrat Dr H. Lerner. HUNGARY: Ivan A.
Hatos. CZECHOSLOVAKIA: Jaromír Dušek, with
Vladimir Hucko, Dr Alfred Stiene. POLAND: Hans D.
Dossenbach, with Antoni Pacynski,
A. Krzysztalowicz, Bronislaw Stepniak. SOVIET
UNION: Hans D. Dossenbach. NEAR EAST: Elsie
Streiff. JAPAN: Japan Light Breed Horse Association.
AUSTRALIA AND NEW ZEALAND: Dr Victor C. Spiers,
Lex Nichols. ARGENTINA: Christoph Wegemann.
USA: Hans D. Dossenbach, with Margaret B. Glass,
Jane Atkinson, Stephen M. Brown, Barbara W.
Noviello, Mary Jane Gallaher. BREEDS AND TYPES:
Hans D. Dossenbach, Hans Joachim Köhler. HORSE
BREEDING TODAY: Hans Joachim Köhler.

Illustrations

Monique and Hans D. Dossenbach. Additional
illustration material: Pablo Imthurn, Marco Tissi,
Werner Menzendorf, O. Kjellander,
Militärbibliothek Bern, Hans R. Schläpfer, Japan
Light Breed Horse Assn., Maximilian Bruggmann,
Tony Jakobson, Jaromír Dušek, J. Revayova, Agence
de Presse P. Bertrand & Fils, Irish Horse Board, Irish
Tourist Board, Lex Nichols, Mary Brogan, Turkish
Ministry of Agriculture, Royal Stables, Jordan,
Bilke-Archiv, Elisabeth Weiland, Austrian Ministry
of Agriculture, A. Koren, Royal Studs, Rosenborg
Castle, Denmark, Jörgen Paulsen, Jytte Lemkow,
I. C. Christensen, Ruth Rogers, Equine Research
Station Newmarket, The British Racehorse, Radio
Times Hulton Picture Library, Elsie Streiff, Hans
Bendel.

Acknowledgments

Special thanks are due to the following: Robert
Buchmüller, who, together with Hans D.
Dossenbach, was responsible for the conception and
design of the book; Hanspeter Meier, who
contributed much of the text and participated in the
editorial work. Frau Elsie Streiff helped with texts,
illustrations and administrative work. Dr Hans
Ulrich Staub answered countless enquiries. The
celebrated horse painter Ingo Kublischek made his
portraits of *Grundy*, *Mill Reef*, *Star Appeal* and
Galipolis available for reproduction and painted
Anilin and *Ribot* especially for this book.

This book was compiled in cooperation with the
German Horse Museum (Deutsches Pferdemuseum),
Verden a.d. Aller.

Contents

Preface
by HRH Prince Philip, Duke of Edinburgh
President of the Fédération Equestre Internationale

Of all the many animals domesticated by man the horse has been given the first place in his esteem. In transport, agriculture, war, sport and pleasure the horse has given quite exceptional service and it has been rewarded with the most lavish facilities for breeding, training and stabling.

In pictures and in words by authors with unique experience and knowledge, this splendid book provides a fascinating insight into the life and work of some of the great studs of the world. The introductory chapter on the history of horse breeding and the chapters on breeds and veterinary science give perspective to the main subject and ensure that this book will provide both pleasure and interest to all who count themselves friends of the horse.

The history of horse breeding

The stud-farm

It is still uncertain when, why and how the horse was first domesticated and the mutually beneficial partnership between man and horse began. It was certainly long after man took the dog as his companion, about 9000 years ago. However, it must be some 5000 or 6000 years since the horse entered the service of man, probably in the steppes north of the Caucasus, inhabited by the warlike Indo-Germanic race.

The road from the early stage of keeping half-wild horses to the breeding centres which we now know as stud-farms was a long one. The demand for improvement in the quality of horses and the continual increase in the number of their uses imposed the need for true selective breeding and the production of different types.

The term 'stud-farm' corresponds to a clearly defined concept only to the extent that it always implies the breeding of horses, and indeed breeding with particular uses in mind. In Germany, for example, in the unrestricted stud-farm (*Wildgestüt*) a herd of mares is kept with a selected stallion all through the year or during the mating season, without any control. The provincial stud-farm (*Landgestüt*) is a state institution which controls horse breeding throughout a province or district; it serves as a base for the so-called state sires (*Landbeschäler*) who during the mating season are sent out to covering stations round the country and placed at the disposal of private breeders to serve their mares. A breeding centre which is stocked with top-class so-called foundation mares and stallions – primary sires (*Hauptbeschäler*) – and produces the stallions for the stallion centres, is designated as a primary stud-farm (*Hauptgestüt*); such stud-farms are also usually state-controlled. Finally the private stud-farm, holding mares but not necessarily stallions, is found everywhere, producing, for example, Thoroughbreds or trotters. In England and in most countries outside Europe this last is the only system of horse breeding practised.

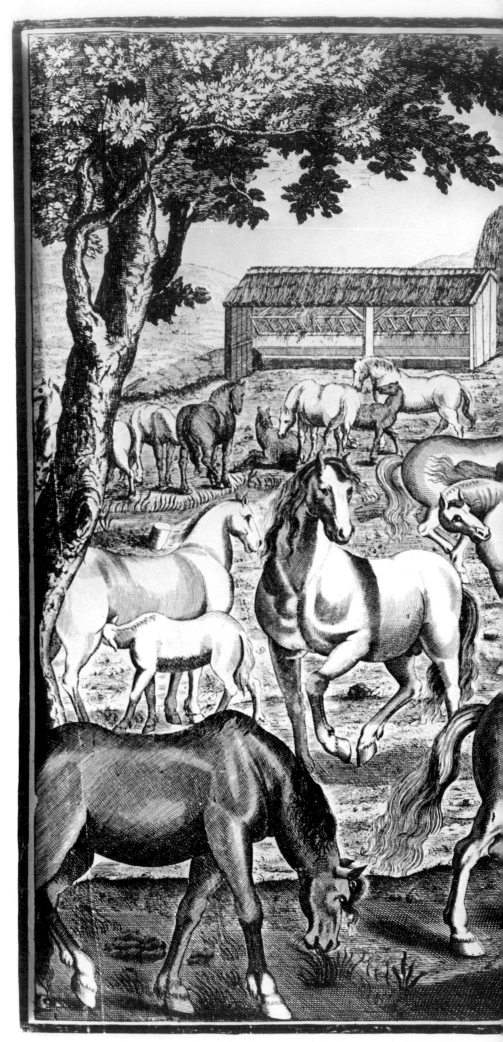

(p. 6) The horse's head and the 'golden bee' at the main entrance to the French stud-farm at Le Pin, the 'Horse Versailles'.

'The Stud-Farm': an illustration from the riding manual, *Nouvelle méthode pour dresser les chevaux* by William Cavendish, Duke of Newcastle, published in 1700.

Das Gestütt
LesHaras.

In the second half of the nineteenth century the American palaeontologist Othniel Charles Marsh discovered in the Tertiary geological strata of North America the most complete series of fossils of a family of mammals. These excavations, which were later supplemented by numerous finds in various parts of the world, provided an extraordinarily clear picture of the evolution of the horse.

The oldest known stage, illustrated (below, left), was the little prehistoric proto-horse of the genus *Hyracotherium*, which lived some sixty to fifty millions of years ago. *Hyracotherium*, about the size of a hare, still had four toes on its front feet and three on its back feet; these kept it from sinking into the swampy

ground. With its head carried low, its high, sloping loins and its sharply angled hind legs, it was much more like an African duiker than a horse. The brain structure is similar to that of marsupials or insectivores, but the molars are recognizable as the basic arrangement of the horse's dentition.

The genera *Orohippus* and *Epihippus*, which lived in the late Eocene period about fifty to forty million years ago, constituted the transition to *Mesohippus*, shown here (below, centre). In *Mesohippus* an equine shape is clearly visible, although the croup is still distinctly elevated and no withers are noticeable. This animal still had three toes, but the middle one had become distinctly dominant. With a height of about 50 cm (20

inches), it was still a mini-horse. During its existence in the south-west of North America in the Oligocene period forty to twenty-five million years ago, the land became drier, and in Europe the prehistoric horses died out. The various genera that existed in the subsequent geological period, the Miocene, from twenty-five to ten million years ago, included *Merychippus*, shown here (below, right).

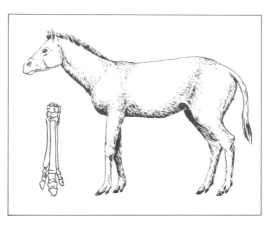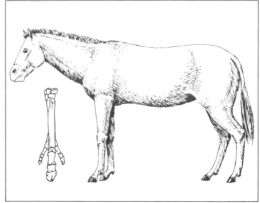

Evolution

Well over a hundred years ago, at the time when Darwin's theory of evolution had completely shattered the existing mental picture of the world, and while in the American West the scene was dominated by the wars with the Indians, the gold rush and the great cattle trek, two men were quietly at work there, searching for bones in the geological strata formed millions of years before and now laid open by erosion and excavations. These two men were Othniel Charles Marsh and Edward Drinker Cope. Marsh was the more successful; the result of his activity was the most complete series of fossils of a family of mammals yet to become available for research on evolution. From this collection the development of the horse can be followed with scarcely a break from *Hyracotherium*, no bigger than a hare, to a recognizable horse equal in size to a zebra.

This example, now a classic, still retains its importance today, although a great many of later fossil finds indicate that the evolution did not proceed in quite such a straight line as it appeared to Marsh.

Even in earliest times, the many different kinds of horse-like animals showed a strong migratory tendency. Members of several species forsook the North American soil, crossed via the land-link then still existing from Alaska to northern Siberia, and spread out from there over Asia and Europe. At least two species migrated to South

America. But they all died out. And lastly solid-hoofed animals of the most highly developed genus, *Equus*, also crossed the Behring link. While they spread out over Asia, Europe and North Africa, giving rise to a whole series of species and sub-species, in America – their ancient homeland – horses became extinct.

At the present time six species of *Equus* are still extant in the wild: the horse, the Grevy zebra, the mountain zebra, the steppe zebra, and the wild asses of

Asia and Africa. Of these species, only the steppe zebra is still common. Mountain and Grevy zebras are quite rare, both kinds of wild ass are almost extinct, and only a single sub-species of the wild horse, *Equus przewalskii*, is still in existence, probably only in zoos (see p. 268).

When the wild horse spread over the whole of Asia and Europe and over the northern part of Africa it naturally encountered a very wide range of living conditions to which it had to adapt. As

Whereas *Merychippus* still had two distinct residual toes, in the Pliocene epoch horses developed into definite solid-hoofed animals. Two genera are known to have existed in the Pliocene epoch, from ten to one million years ago: *Hipparion*, standing about 1 m or 40 inches, which spread over North America, Europe, Asia and North Africa; and *Pliohippus* (below, left), shown here, which was about 15 cm (6 inches) taller and appears to have inhabited only North America. Like all the preceding types which had taken the Behring road from their original home in North America to Asia and Europe, the Pliocene horses also died out in the Old World; only in North America did their evolution continue.

In the Pleistocene, one million to ten thousand years ago, the south-west of North America was the home of *Plesihippus*, depicted here (below, right); it does not appear to have spread very far, and in time became extinct. During the same period, however, *Equus* appeared. Like various earlier types of horse, these animals migrated to Asia and Europe via the land link then still existing, and spread to North Africa; there, unlike their predecessors, they survived through thousands of years to our own time, while America's wild horses finally died out.

Today only one genus remains of the family of early horses: *Equus*, which includes three species of zebra, two species of ass and one species of horse.
Of the many geographical races only the Eastern Wild Horse of the Steppes, or Przewalski's horse remains, illustrated here (below, right); and even this type is probably to be found only in zoos. It may, however, be assumed that the numerous breeds of domestic horses have evolved from various wild races. Long-vanished primeval types did indeed show affinities with 'ram's-head' horses and northern ponies, with cold-bloods like the Clydesdale (p. 10, below) and with the high-bred Arab horse (bottom).

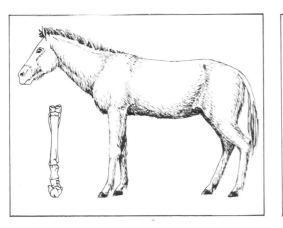

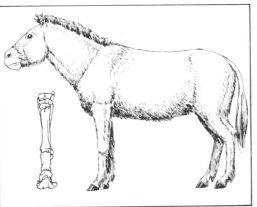

with all other widely dispersed animals, various sub-species or geographical types developed; some of these were very strongly differentiated as regards size, anatomical features and behaviour. At least four clearly differentiated fundamental breeds appeared, with numerous intermediate variations.

The smallest of these was a primitive pony, the ancestor of all the northern ponies. The anatomical features of the English Exmoor pony are almost exactly

like those of this primeval pony. The second fundamental northern breed was a tundra horse, generally standing about 135 centimetres (13–14 hands), but in some variants about 180 centimetres (18 hands). Its characteristics are seen in the cold-blood breeds. Very different from this stocky animal, with its barrel-shaped body and neck carried low, is the breed which adapted itself to the arid steppes and desert regions of southern Asia. Like the other grazing animals of this habitat, for example

the gazelles, it did not need particularly large digestive organs or powerful jaws and teeth. When danger threatened there was nowhere to hide; flight was the only escape. Thus a slender animal evolved, swift as the wind, always on the alert, with hindquarters capable of an astonishing thrust and neck carried high. This little prehistoric horse may be accepted as the original progenitor of the Arab breed.

The typical horse of the second fundamental southern breed was considerably larger and was distinguished above all by its long 'ram's head'. This race spread out from southern Asia over southern Europe and North Africa and attained its most clearly individual form in the west. It determined the basic features of the Barbs and Andalusians and their descendant breeds.

By far the majority of the horses which first became domesticated were either of the 'Tarpan' or 'Przewalski' type, although no doubt other prehistoric types were also included. In the first few centuries after the birth of Christ all the warlike nomads in Europe still had small, tough ponies of primitive type. With many of these tribes it was the custom to bury the fallen warrior's horse with him; this custom has led to many important historical discoveries. The skeleton (below, left) dates from the fourth century and was found in a burial ground at Klein-Fliess near Tapiau in East Prussia. It wore a noseband (a), a ring-snaffle (b) and fastenings of bronze.

In contrast, the antique relief sculpture of a horse (right) shows great nobility of type.

(Below, right) *Equi mauri* was the name given by the Romans to the horses of the Moors. These horses were considerably larger than the ponies of the European nomads, although this picture certainly exaggerates the size greatly.

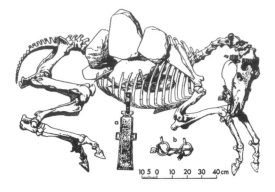

In the service of man

In the literature on the history of the horse it is nearly always asserted that the horse was used for driving before it was ridden. However, all that can be taken as certain is that in war, horses drew chariots before they carried warriors. Writings on tablets dating from about 1800 BC make frequent mention of horse-drawn war chariots of the Indo-Germanic tribes. The peoples to the south of the Caucasus were at first helpless against the warriors from the north, until they also built war chariots. This happened in Egypt and Troy around 1580 BC, in Greece and India around 1500 BC.

On the other hand, a small Sumerian tablet dating from the third millennium BC shows a rider on an animal resembling a horse, while a sculpture from about the same period represents a horseman from southern Arabia. Others are depicted in rock and cave drawings in the Pyrenees and

the Sahara, made four to five thousand years ago.

At the same time it is also known that as early as the fifth century BC cattle were used as draught and pack animals. It may therefore be assumed that soon after the domestication of horses in the fourth and third millennia attempts were made to use them in a similar manner. However, it is more than likely that at the same period the young herdsmen tending the cattle would ride on any tamed horses among the herd. Whether riding or driving came first remains uncertain.

In the hilly and marshy regions of central and western Europe it was not possible to use carts until the Romans had built roads, about two thousand years ago. In these regions, however, the horse had already been domesticated for some hundreds of years, though we have no evidence that it was also ridden.

Our first evidence of mounted troops comes from the Assyrians, in about 890 BC.

In ancient Rome warriors were already protecting particularly vulnerable parts of the body by metal plates. In the middle ages these developed into armour which became increasingly heavy, and which naturally called for stronger horses. With the advent of the age of chivalry there was a tremendous increase in the breeding of cold-bloods which, along with the development of the tournament, became very important in France (left).

The fighting tactics of the Eastern peoples consisted in lightning attacks. Their horses (above), far superior as regards speed and endurance, rendered them for a long time invincible.

The Assyrians, Persians and Gauls were already developing riding into an art; in this they were probably just as well versed as the Greeks, about whom, however, more is known, thanks to their voluminous literature. Xenophon's manual of equitation, for example, is *the* classic work on the art of riding.

It is hard to grasp the magnitude of the part played by the horse in the cultural history of mankind through more than 4000 years. Since the Indo-Germanic tribes abandoned the desiccating steppes to the north of the Caucasus and rode out in search of conquests, many great political upheavals have been decisively influenced by the horse. Without the horse the Roman domination of Europe would have been unthinkable; likewise the conquest of south-west Europe by the armies of Islam and that of eastern Europe by the Turks, the domination of South and Central America by the Spanish and the Portuguese, the Napoleonic campaigns, the colonization of the American West, and even many campaigns in the Second World War.

The horse also occupied a decisive position in the modernization of agriculture and forestry, as well as in transport and communications. Before the invention of the steam engine horses not only drew road vehicles of all kinds but also railway stock and ships – not without cause is the capacity of motors expressed in horse-power to this very day.

Until the twentieth century, the postal system was closely associated with the picturesque image of coach teams, which grew into a veritable legend with the American stage coaches (above).

As well as coaches, railway stock and ships, horses pulled whole houses, as illustrated in the scene (above, right) from Chicago in 1871.

(Right) The Place de l'Opéra in Paris, around 1880. Buses, trade vehicles, cabs and private carriages formed the picture in the streets of every big city at that time.

Chronology of the great stud-farms

The numbers in parentheses refer to the illustrations on these two pages.

1064 Einsiedeln (1)
1230 Córdoba (2)
1264 Georgenburg
1490 Beberbeck
1532 Frederiksborg (3)
1536 Rohrenfeld
1573 Marbach
1579 Kladrub
1580 Lipizza (4)
1658 Flyinge
1665 Harzburg
1666 Ivenack
1713 Lopshorn
1714 Le Pin (5)
1715 Redefin
1722 Graditz
1724 Beberbeck
1730 Triesdorf
1732 Trakehnen
1733 Moritzburg
1735 Celle (6)
1745 Pompadour (7)
1748 Strasbourg
1755 Zweibrücken (8)
1768 Dillenburg
1768 Rosières-aux-Salines
1769 Ansbach
1777 Marienwerder
1785 Mezöhegyes (9)
1788 Neustadt
1789 Lithuania
1792 Radautz
1797 Babolna
1798 Piber
1802 Bois-Roussel
1806 Saint-Lô (10)
1808 Darmstadt
1810 Broock
1812 Voronovo

1813 Streletzk
1817 Weil
1817 Ossiach
1817 Janow Podlaski
1818 Leubus
1824 Gudwallen
1825 Lamballe (11)
1825 Novo Alexandrovsk
1825 Neustrelitz
1829 Zirka
1836 Karlsruhe
1836 Gumniska
1838 Landshut
1838 Victot (12)
1839 Wickrath (13)
1844 Augsburg
1845 Khrenovoye
1849 Hampton Court
1849 Ansbach
1853 Kisber
1860 Pisa
1861 Ferrara
1866 Traventhal
1867 Nemoschitz
1869 Schlenderhan
1870 Kosel
1876 Labes
1877 Rastenburg
1877 Kreutz
1879 Walnut Hall
1880 Tiarel
1883 Stetchworth Park
1885 Gnesen
1885 Warendorf (14)
1890 Pisek
1891 Braunsberg
1893 Military Stud, Córdoba (later Jérez)
1894 Woodlands (15)
1899 Stargard
1900 Irish National Stud
1910 Darby Dan (16)
1912 Valdehelechoso
1920 Altefeld (17)
1921 Topolcianky
1925 Osnabrück
1926 Hanover Shoe (18)
1927 Someries
1928 Dalham Hall
1937 Spendthrift
1951 Silvasvarad (19)
1962 Moyglare
1966 National Stud, Newmarket

Horse transport

For thousands of years horses were the one and only means of transport. They carried men, military equipment and goods. Some horses performed exceptional feats. A few became famous – for example, Napoleon's Arab stallion *Vizir*, who carried his master from Paris to Moscow and back, or Tschiffely's two Criollos who, aged fifteen and sixteen, took their owner on a phenomenally exhausting ride from Buenos Aires to New York which took $2\frac{3}{4}$ years and arrived there in perfect health. Nothing is recorded about the 100,000 Mongolian ponies which helped Genghis Khan conquer the greatest empire of all time, extending from the Pacific to the Mediterranean and from Siberia to the Himalayas.

And, of course, horses were also their own means of transport. It was taken for granted that the chargers of the medieval knights should travel from tournament to

tournament on their own legs; and similarly the sporting horses of later centuries were ridden to their events. But also in times of war whole stud-farms had to be evacuated and herds of valuable stallions, mares and foals had to be driven for distances which were often very great, for example from Lipizza to Mezöhegyes in Hungary, or, more recently, from Trakehnen in East Prussia to Schleswig.

The first serious transport problems arose when large stretches of water had to be crossed. The Vikings were probably the first to overcome this difficulty. In their shallow open vessels they ventured out from Scandinavia on long sea journeys with their cattle, sheep and ponies secured athwart amidships. With the Spaniards and Portuguese, and later also with the peoples of northern Europe, it was quite usual to take horses with them on their ships to the overseas colonies. The horses were hoisted up in wide sailcloth slings and had to remain suspended during the sea voyage,

usually lasting some months, and endure the oscillations caused by the motion of the sea.

With the passage of time the horse has been so completely superseded by motorized traffic that in highly civilized countries it cannot even transport itself except to a very limited extent. Even to get to a sporting event a few miles away horses are loaded into transporters to protect them from motor traffic.

(Above, left) *Transporting high-bred horses* is the title of Ammon the Younger's drawing showing stud horses on the move.

(Above, right) Loading horses onto a ship in England in the eighteenth century. As early as the fifteenth century the Spanish transported their horses to the New World on ships, suspended by wide belts.

(Left) Fully air-conditioned high-comfort horse transporter belonging to a Kentucky Thoroughbred stud-farm. Nowadays it is also quite common for valuable horses to be transported by air.

Leisure and sport

For thousands of years the horse has served man, in the sphere of battle and conquest, on journeys to new lands, in agriculture and in industry. For thousands of years it shared the history of the nations. And within a few decades it has now become superfluous, or practically so.

However, the horse has not died out or become a rarity to be marvelled at only in the zoo; its sphere of activity has merely changed. It has become the companion of man's leisure, the partner in his sporting competitions, or simply the comrade in his enjoyment of nature.

The multitude of leisure riders grows from year to year. The great majority of them come from towns, no doubt seeking to regain contact with nature. Equestrian sports are older than history, and were already practised in the form of races at the Olympic Games of antiquity; but they were always a subsidiary branch of equine

activity in comparison with the importance of war and work. Nowadays we have jumping competitions, dressage and cross-country trials, games with mounted players, driving events and horse-races attracting millions of enthusiastic spectators to crowd the world's showgrounds and racecourses and sit in front of television screens.

It is only the image that has changed. The horse lives on.

(Left) The Olympic dressage winner Christine Stückelberger on *Granat*.

(Below) For those riders who seek neither more nor less than contact with nature and living creatures, the value of all the unknown and unregistered horses and ponies cannot be overestimated.

(Centre) Show-jumping. The Swiss, Markus Fuchs, on the Irish hunter *Ballymena*.

(Bottom) Flat-racing, the oldest equestrian sport, which, with the English Thoroughbred, spread all round the world, is shown here at Santa Fé in New Mexico.

France

In 1950, among other brilliant victories in Great Britain, Marcel Boussac won the Gimcrack Stakes with his foal *Courtil*. In accordance with an old English tradition – of which the Gimcrack Club is itself a living symbol – he subsequently attended the 108th Annual Dinner in York as guest of honour. He was happy to take this opportunity to tell the racing world the reason for his success as breeder and owner of a racing stable. Many people may have thought that such victories must be based on an impenetrable secret.

Since legends die slowly, some may still be doubtful about the simple explanation which Boussac gave then, especially as here, more than in other spheres, the incalculable holds dominion.

The skilful application of long-established rules, comprehensive knowledge and strong empathy, coupled with inexhaustible energy, had led Boussac to the successful production of new cross-breeds from old strains whose value was already universally recognized. Pointing out that work is most successful when it is done with love, he summarized his method – also applicable to other fields than horse breeding – in the words: 'Work is the intelligent manipulation of nature.'

This seems to be the secret formula of all French breeders. From generation to generation, they have followed the strict rules embodied in the age-old tradition of stud-farm management established by Colbert in 1665, and by unremitting application they have learnt how to develop to the full those *grand-cru* horses whose high reputation has now spread throughout the world.

The range of French horses extends from heavy draught horses of various breeds and types, through versatile warm-bloods, to trotters and high-spirited Thoroughbreds, and is thus among the most comprehensive in the world.

The breeding of Arabs in France, which began with horses imported from the East, was located at first in the south-west, in the region of Pau and Tarbes and at Pompadour in the Limousin, the cradle of a whole series of famous breeding animals. New government imports, most recently in 1925, provided a regeneration of the blood and new genetic possibilities. The French purchasing commissions sought out their horses in the regions of Mosul, Baghdad, Jerusalem and Aleppo, where the qualities of the ancient noble races have been excellently preserved.

All other breeds of horse, including the cold-bloods, and particularly the English Thoroughbred, have in fact been developed by crossing an ordinary native breed with the Arab or with other breeds. At the present time many connoisseurs are endeavouring to breed Arabs again. As a foundation they are using the old strains from the south-west of France, where the blood has been renewed by private imports from England, Spain, Poland and the USA.

It was around 1780 that horse racing became fashionable in France. Sport, spectacle and amusement all in one, it rapidly attracted tremendous interest. The advances

Whereas the famous sixteenth-century masters of the noble art of equitation (Grisone, Pignatelli, etc.) often used horrifying methods to make horses obedient, the Frenchman Antoine de Pluvinel exhibited a quite different and much more humane attitude. He ran an 'Academy for young noblemen with particular emphasis on equitation' in Paris in the early seventeenth century, and wrote a book on equitation which was used as an instruction manual by all the European nobility of that era. The book was published in 1623 under the title *Manège du Roy* and was brought out again five years later as *L'Instruction du Roy en l'exercice de monter à cheval*. The book takes the form of a dialogue between Pluvinel and the young King Louis XIII, clearly a very enthusiastic pupil. The book is illustrated with a number of splendid engravings, some of which are reproduced here.

in bloodstock breeding afforded justification for races as tests of performance. Only horses successful on the racecourse were used for breeding. The history of the Turf and the development of bloodstock breeding were thus closely connected.

How things look in practice is best seen in those places where the pure-bred horses are reared – in the famous stud-farms of Normandy and the Ile-de-France, where nearly every loose-box has a history of its own.

Climbing the hill of Nonant-le-Pin in the Orne or of Cambremer in Calvados, the visitor sees the wide expanse of the pastures of the great French stud-farms, bordered with white fences.

Victot near Lisieux, an ancient spot with a magnificent small château and exceptionally beautiful stables in the Norman half-timbered style, gives a picture of the beginnings of bloodstock breeding in France.

In the impressive classical-modern

surroundings of Jardy, near Paris, lies the story of *Flying Fox*, the ancestor, through *Ajax*, of *Teddy*. *Teddy* came to the Bois-Roussel stud-farm near Sées, where he gave evidence of great vitality and breeding qualities. The story of Bois-Roussel is also the story of *Vatout* and all his illustrious descendants. The story of Jardy is indissolubly linked with that of *Ksar*, whose excellent characteristics – heart, courage, staying-power and racing spirit – persist in all parts of the world in *Tourbillon* and his sons. Such famous names as Messieurs de Meautry, near Deauville, and the well-known racing colours of Baron Edouard de Rothschild, must also be mentioned here.

The more recent history of bloodstock breeding in France is also that of the Fresnay-le-Buffard stud-farm between Argentan and Falaise, scene of Marcel Boussac's breeding activities, where everything, even nature, is subservient to the master. The example of Fresnay has indeed shown that protectionism

in breeding will sooner or later have a bad effect: the hothouse life is not in accordance with nature, and a breed of horses, like a human family, needs external influences to preserve it from decline.

After the Thoroughbred, next in importance in French bloodstock breeding is the trotter. The first trotter race here was run in 1836.

The French Trotter sprang from a local breed, the Anglo-Norman. By careful selection of Anglo-Normans with marked trotting proclivities and by frequent crossing with American Standard Trotters and English Thoroughbreds a race was produced which had a significant influence on trotter breeding in Italy, Germany, Belgium and Holland. The most important founders of the line were *Conquérant* and *Normand*, two sons of the Thoroughbred *Young Rattler*, together with *Phaeton*, a son of the Thoroughbred *The Norfolk Phenomenon*. Many more than half of all today's French

trotters can be traced back to *Conquérant*.

On average, the French Trotter is larger and of more harmonious proportions than the American Standard Trotter. His staying-power is generally greater, but his speed is somewhat lower. Trotter races in France are run both with the horse harnessed to a sulky and with a rider in the saddle.

As with the Thoroughbreds, the main centre for trotter breeding is Normandy, where the climatic and geological conditions are particularly suitable. The most important stud-farm in the history of trotter breeding in France is that of M. Orly-Roederer at Rouges-Terres.

With the increasing demand for multi-purpose saddle horses during the last twenty years, this branch of breeding is also experiencing new momentum. After the disbanding of mounted army units, which for hundreds of years had been by far the most important customers for saddle horses, this breed was in danger of extinction.

Two distinctly different races of saddle horses are bred in France: the Anglo-Norman, now also called French saddle horse, and the Anglo-Arab.

Multi-purpose horses were bred in Normandy as long ago as the twelfth century. English Thoroughbreds were introduced for the first time around 1800, and from 1830 onward the Normans were systematically improved by adding Thoroughbred blood. Thirty years later the Anglo-Norman was a firmly established breed. It was used primarily as a carriage horse and a lively working horse, and also for riding. During the last twenty years, breeding has been switched to the production of a well defined saddle horse with all the required points, and French show and army riders now have at their disposal a horse of splendid calibre.

(Below) The great riding-masters of the baroque period showed astonishing imagination in developing bits for dressage schools. The illustration shows two of Pluvinel's Turkish bits (*genettes*) from the seventeenth century.

(P. 21, opposite) French cold-bloods have influenced the breeding of working horses in all parts of the world, and Thoroughbreds and trotters which rank with the best in the world; moreover, among the show-jumpers, bred mainly from Anglo-Normans and Anglo-Arabs, are first-class animals.
This photograph captures a jump during a cross-country event.

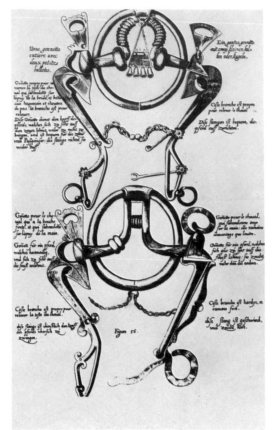

The Anglo-Norman breed did not only provide the basis for the French Trotter: it also played a considerable part in improving warm-blood breeds in other countries; for example the Hungarian Nonius, the Dutch

and Swedish warm-bloods, the Swiss breed at Einsiedeln and Avenches, and the German Oldenburger and Württemberger.

In France the Anglo-Norman breed spread beyond the confines of its original territory, as far as the Ain, Charolais, central and eastern France, Anjou and the Vendée.

In the south it is the Anglo-Arab that has spread throughout Charente and Limousin. This breed is distinguished by its elegant, aristocratic appearance, its speed and its endurance – clear reminders of its eastern origin. The Anglo-Arab, developed in France at the Pompadour stud-farm, has also passed on its qualities to stocks in other countries, for example in Spain and in Poland. In top-level sport, especially in show-jumping, Anglo-Arabs have demonstrated their great qualities on many occasions.

Cold-bloods, which until a few decades ago were dominant, are now of little significance. 'Heavy horses' is the term in current use, without further details of breed, perhaps to make it clear that they are destined for the weighing-machine rather than the harness. Nevertheless there are more opportunities in France than elsewhere in central Europe to admire the powerful forms of cold-blood horses. In the pastures of Huisme, in the Grand' Place at Landivisiau, high on the slopes of Picardy, on the hills of Bassigny and on the wide plateaux of the Doubs these horses still graze today: the magnificent Percherons, the impressive Bretons, the splendid Boulonnais, the heavy Ardennais and the primitive, lively Comtois. The farmers of France may feel proud to be breeding these horses now as they did in former times, when these stocks found their way across the seas and made their influence felt on nearly all the cold-blood breeds in the world.

Pompadour

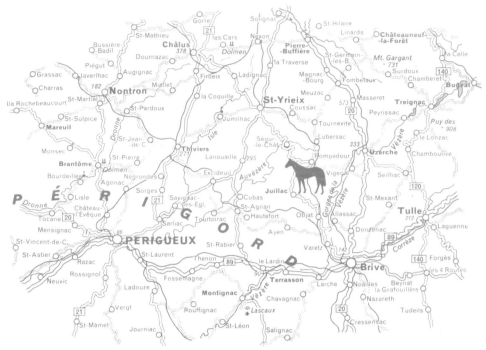

exchange for a piece of land at Amboise. As his great-grandfather had done at Le Pin, he turned the estate into a royal stud-farm. This was closed down several times, under different administrations, and then brought into operation again; it has been running without interruption since 1872. Very close to the château is Puy-Marmont, Pompadour's centre for breeding stallions. Alongside the extensive stables is a jumping course. Another sporting establishment is situated to the south of the château: the

The history of Pompadour goes back nearly a thousand years. The first château at Pompadour was built by Guy de Lastour in 1026. Since that period, partial destruction on several occasions has been followed by rebuilding and conversion. Louis XV acquired the château and the estate and on 24 July 1745 presented the entire property to his mistress, Madame Lenormand d'Etoiles, who at the same time also received the title, soon to become world-famous, of Marquise de Pompadour.

The Marquise, who never lived at Pompadour and apparently only made one short visit to her château, had the first stud-farm installed there, stocked with Arabs and Barbs. However, this breeding centre was not successful.

As time went on Madame Pompadour fell from favour with the King, and as a result experienced financial difficulties. On 24 May 1760 she sold her property to the Duke of Choiseuil-Stainville. This did not please Louis, and he re-acquired Pompadour in

(Above) Puy-Marmont, Pompadour's stallion stud-farm. At the centre of the three long stables is the office, which also contains the saddle-room (right). The collection of valuable harness equipment and trophies is well worth a visit.

(Top) Reliefs possibly dating from the fifteenth century, and belonging to the chapel. The chapel and three wings of the château were to a great extent destroyed during the Revolution.

(Above) The view through the main entrance towards the south façade, the only one to have been completely preserved since the fifteenth century. The ramparts, the moats and the ten turrets are also not much damaged. The other parts were rebuilt or restored in the eighteenth and nineteenth centuries.

(Right) Two high-class Arab stallions: the chesnut *Ba Toustein*, by *Djerba Oua* out of *Baccharanta*, by *Damour*, and the magnificent grey *Baj*, by *Negatiw* out of *Bajdara*.

racecourse. Set in delightful country, this is the most beautiful in France.

In the loose-boxes of the first stable on the right-hand side are the English Thorough-breds, the Arabs and the Anglo-Arabs.

A visit to the stable housing the draught horses demonstrates clearly that the breeding of cold-bloods is not confined to the north of France, even though all the breeds came from there originally. Here are to be found a magnificent array of Bretons, Percherons and Ardennais.

The carriage museum has preserved a collection of magnificent coaches, conjuring up the Belle Epoque.

Pompadour is the only one of France's national stud-farms to have, as well as the stallion centre, a breeding centre with mares. This is located at La Rivière, 4km (2½ miles) from Pompadour. The stables were built about a hundred years ago, among the partly renovated buildings of the little château of La Rivière. The stud-farm contains some 40 brood-mares, all Anglo-Arabs; Pompadour

ranks as one of the most important stud-farms in the world for this breed. In fact the French Anglo-Arab originated here. The breeding success must be credited to M. Gayot, who was the director of the stud-farm some 120 years ago.

(Above) Pompadour's herd of brood-mares consists exclusively of Anglo-Arabs, about forty in number. They are kept at La Rivière, 4 km (2½ miles) from the castle. The principal stable at La Rivière was built about a hundred years ago. The twenty-one loose-boxes are arranged so as to enclose the yard on three sides.

(Overleaf) The castle and entrance viewed from the south-west. The part shown here, dating from the fifteenth century, has been almost completely preserved.

Lamballe

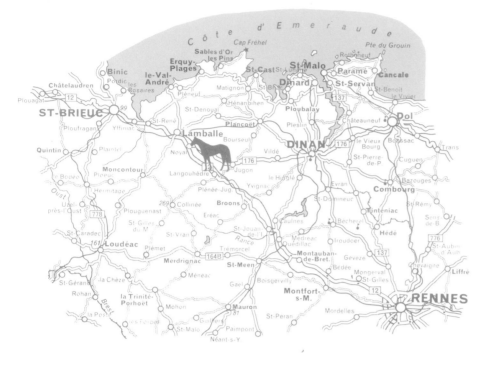

(Below) Near the entrance to the stud-farm, at Cavillon where the newer stables are located, is an old well, of a type common in the district.

(Bottom, left) The entrance to the stud-farm. In the distance is the office, set at right-angles to the other buildings.

(Bottom, right) The director's house, like most houses in Brittany, is built of large stone blocks.

From the days of Napoleon I onwards, the people of Lamballe in Brittany repeatedly petitioned for a stallion station to be established, advancing, among other reasons, the importance of the foal markets in this region. Thanks to the intercession of the district council of Dinan with the Minister of the Interior, on 16 January 1825 permission was granted by royal decree for the foundation of a stallion stud-farm. Shortly afterwards the old Saint-Martin barracks were purchased and stable No. 1 was erected.

The early years of the history of the Lamballe stud-farm cannot be described as exactly successful. A certain amount of opposition from the district council, four changes of director in the course of eight years, the fact that horse breeding in Brittany was at that time not yet firmly established, and the resulting failures all contributed to the closure of the stud-farm in 1833.

The local breeders took this decision very badly. Moreover, it soon became apparent

that no more suitable horses were available for cavalry remounts in the Côtes-du-Nord region. The stud-farm was therefore re-opened on 12 November 1842. The rapid increase in the number of stallions after the re-opening made it necessary to put up stable No. 2 in 1848. In the same year houses were built for the management staff.

In 1859 Lamballe's sphere of action was extended. Brest and Morlaix joined Côtes-du-Nord. In 1870 stable Nos 3, 4, 5, 6 and 7 were put up, bounding the great courtyard.

The war in that year swallowed up a great number of army horses. At the same time the Postier Breton proved very suitable for artillery teams, so breeding was rapidly increased. The stables which, including the new buildings, could accommodate 351 stallions, were no longer large enough. In 1918 Lamballe possessed 391 stallions. However, no more stables were built; instead, a number of stallions were transferred to the covering stations.

In 1918 the number of stallions gradually

started to decrease. From 1945 the reduction in the number of draught horses accelerated rapidly, and the number of riding-horses simultaneously increased, although not nearly to the same extent. In 1976 the stud-farm had 142 stallions available: during the covering season these are distributed among 44 stations.

From 1 July to 20 February they are kept at the breeding centre, where they are used for riding and driving. Tandem driving with two, four or more horses is particularly

popular here. Since 1900 attention has been paid to training drivers.

Every year races are held in the great Court of Honour, followed by team displays, including 2 tandem teams, 7 four-in-hands and 1 five-in-hand.

(Top) The great Court of Honour where the races and team displays are held.

(Centre) A Breton stallion of the heavy type in which neck, shoulder muscle formation and chest are especially powerful, while the limbs are short and sturdy. As well as this heavy type there is also the more agile hill type and the lighter Postier.

(Left) The water-tower.

(Above right) Anglo-Arab stallion.

(Below, right) Thoroughbred stallion.
In 1976 the following horses were standing at stud: 3 Thoroughbreds, 4 Anglo-Arabs, 3 Anglo-Normans, 1 French Trotter, 3 Connemara Ponies and 128 Bretons.

Saint-Lô

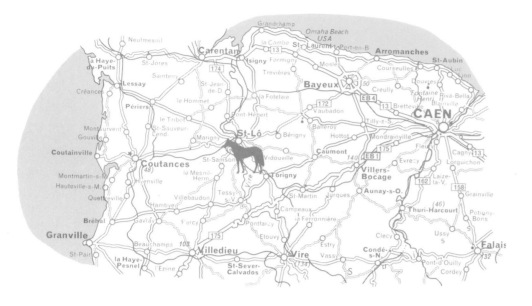

reduced to rubble and ashes. The grounds and the ruins of the old stud-farm were handed over to the local administration, which provided in exchange another, more suitably located, site on which various additional buildings were erected.

The majestic stud establishment consists principally of eight stable blocks surrounding the Court of Honour. On an adjacent piece of land are the new clinic, display and training ground and an area where young horses are put through jumping tests. At present, the stud-farm employs a staff of about ninety. They are responsible for looking after and working with the stallions, but on occasion are also assigned technical and administrative duties in connection with the care and control of riding-clubs and the advancement of horse breeding.

For the 1976 covering season the following stallions were available: 21 English Thoroughbreds, 10 French Trotters, 68 Anglo-Normans, 60 Norman Cobs, 24 Percherons, and 3 ponies: 186 altogether.

The Saint-Lô stud-farm was founded on the authority of an imperial decree dated 4 July 1806. It was erected on the site of the former Sainte-Croix monastery, and afforded accommodation for only 24 stallions.

In 1870 for the first time Saint-Lô began to be considered of some importance, and was enlarged. In 1874, after the reorganization of the National Stud Administration, the stock of stallions was fixed at 240, and consequently a great many changes had to be made.

Construction of the so-called 'new stud-farm' was started in 1882, and the installation was completed in 1898. Together, the old and new buildings could now take 330 stallions.

Later on the establishment had to be enlarged again, the peak number of stallions (422) being attained in 1912. On the evening of 6 June 1944 Saint-Lô was bombed. The old stud-farm was completely destroyed; of the new part, about half the stables, the saddlery and the adjutant's house were

(Above) Part of the stables at the new stud-farm erected between 1882 and 1898. The old stud-farm, built around 1810, was destroyed during the Second World War.

(Right) The riding-school.

28

From the end of June to the beginning of September, displays of stallions and teams were held in the Court of Honour every Saturday at 10 a.m.

English Thoroughbred

The qualities of this breed as a racehorse and its unique capacity for improving other breeds are recognized all over the world. As far as the stallions standing at Saint-Lô as

sires are concerned, it is not only racing performance that is important, but also appearance. The type of stallion in demand has a large build, with harmonious and elegant lines, and when crossed with a Norman mare should produce a definite improvement as regards character and points.

In recent years *Orange Peel*, *Ivanoë*, *Ultimate*, *Foudroyant II*, *Fra Diavolo* and *Rantzau* have distinguished themselves above all others for their excellent progeny.

French Trotter

This breed is of Norman origin and has been developed primarily by selection on racing performance. The first trotter races in France were held at Cherbourg in 1832. The initiator was an officer named Ephrem Honel, who four years later became director of the Saint-Lô stud-farm. Since these first beginnings the breed has improved steadily and has produced a series of great international favourites such as *Jamin*,

(Above) The Saint-Lô stud-farm as seen from the main entrance. In the centre, set back, is the director's house; to the right and left, parts of the stables.

(Left) Inside the stable of the Norman Cobs. In 1976 there were sixty stallions of this working breed in the stud-farm.

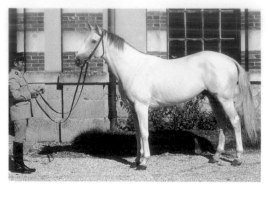

(Right) The English Thoroughbred stallion *Laigny*, born in 1967, by *La Varande* out of *Dogaresse*, by *Cobalt*.

(Below) The Anglo-Norman *Fort-de-la-Cour*, born in 1971, by *Surioso* out of *Une-de-la-Cour*, by *Débuché*.

(Below) The Anglo-Norman *Fend-l'Air*, born in 1971, by *Amour du Bois* out of *Magali*, by *Fra Diavolo*.

Roquepin and *Bellino II*. The most important trotter sires from Saint-Lô were *Javari* and *Harold D III*.

Anglo-Norman

This breed originated in La Manche. Every year the national sires for the whole of France are selected at the Saint-Lô stud-farm. The breeders from this area have always endeavoured to keep up with the volume and type of demand. In recent decades they have successfully switched their breeding activities from the earlier carriage horse to the show-jumper, which is now in great demand in many countries.

Recent favourites from Saint-Lô are *Plein d'Espoirs*, *Bel Avenir*, *Centaure du Bois*, *Diable Rouge* and *Ibrahim*.

Norman Cob

This rather large breed has always been used in the neighbourhood as a market- and farm-horse. It is very lively and is still widely used today in smaller businesses.

Percheron

Use of this heavy, imposing cold-blood is regrettably declining steadily, and it is being bred less and less. Among its most striking characteristics are the grey colour, which is very common, and the bright, expressive eyes.

(Above, left) The Percheron stallion *Dragon*, born in 1969, by *Tosca* out of *Sonora II*. In the background is the Director's house.

(Far left) The Norman Cob *Cyrus*, born in 1968, by *Ketupa* out of *Régence*, by *Koukou*.

(Left) The English Thoroughbred *Eclat*, born in 1963, by *Herbager* out of *Fée-du-Nil*, by *Free Man*.

Rosières-aux-Salines

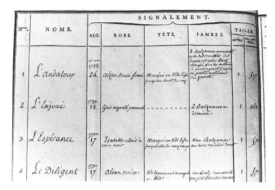

By 1760 the salt deposits of Rosières had become exhausted and the salt-works had to be closed. The buildings were put to use as accommodation for horses; the stables then built are still standing today.

In 1768 a royal stud-farm was established at Rosières; but in 1790, following the Revolution, the stud-farms were broken up as creations of the *ancien régime*. On 4 January 1791 the stud horses were sold.

A year later the victorious Revolutionary troops took over the stud-farm at

century mainly light riding-horses were bred. However, the local farmers began to look around for heavier horses. The type of horse in the stud-farm was gradually changed, and in 1850 the proportion of riding-horses among the stallions was only half, the other half being 'powerful draught horses'. The production of half-bloods stopped completely in 1929.

In the meantime the demand for heavier horses had continued to increase; they were needed for agriculture and for drawing

modern artillery weapons. Experiments led to the Ardennais breed being used more and more, and after 1945 only Ardennais stallions were standing at Rosières. However, their number was already beginning to decline.

In 1954 breeding was switched to horses for riding and sport, and the first Thoroughbred stallion arrived at Rosières. In 1976 the stock comprised 53 stallions, including 28 English Thoroughbreds.

Zweibrücken (Deux-Ponts) in western Germany and brought the breeding stallions and mares to Rosières. The Zweibrücken horses of those days had a very good reputation.

On 22 March 1795 Napoleon Bonaparte, as First Consul, gave orders for the re-opening of seven stud-farms, including Rosières. Stallions which had stood at the stud-farm previously were brought back from local breeders to join the Zweibrücken stock. In the first half of the nineteenth

(Top, right) Excerpt from the register of stallions dated 15 August 1807.

(Above) The director's house, erected in the middle of the nineteenth century to replace the derelict house of the governor of the salt-works.

(Above, right) The stables, built after 1760. Houses for the employees of the salt-works formerly stood here.

(Right) Anglo-Arab *Minon*, born in 1970, by *Unicol'Or* out of *Minette*, by *Nithard*.

(Far right) Thoroughbred stallion *Rainy Lake*, born in 1970, by *Val de Loir* out of *Silver Cloud*, by *Dan Cupid*.

Le Pin

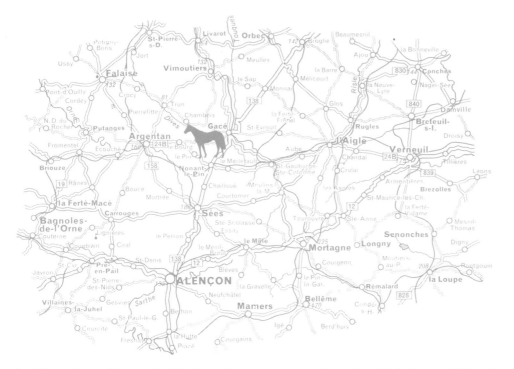

(Below) The entrance to the Pin stud-farm, the 'Horse Versailles', with its triumphal arch.

(Bottom) The horseshoe-shaped Court of Honour, known as the Cour Colbert after Louis XVI's great minister, viewed from the castle. In the distance, on each side of the entrance, are two lodges with small towers, one for the gate-keeper and the other serving as the office.

Le Pin is situated in the Le Merlerault district, long known for its lush pastures and excellent horses. In 1665 Louis XIV decided to move the first royal stud-farm from its site near Montfort l'Amaury to Le Pin. He bought the estate of his Counsellor of State, Bechameil, Marquis de Nointel, as well as a part of the Forest of Exmes.

It was not until 1715 that work was started, from plans designed by Mansard and Le Nôtre. Thirteen years later the whole magnificent establishment was completed,

in the form in which it can still be admired today – the great horseshoe-shaped Court of Honour, with the château across its lower end, the side yards, and the roomy stables built of natural stone and brick.

The first stallions arrived at Le Pin in 1730. Since then the stud-farm has remained faithful to its original purpose, although with varying fortunes. It has survived revolutions and wars, changes of regime and occupation by the army.

On 9 August 1865 Napoleon III honoured

the Le Pin races with his presence. This was an occasion for great festivities which are still remembered today.

Le Pin was created for work with horses and has constantly maintained that service. First as royal, then as imperial, and finally as national stud-farm, its continuity, so essential in horse breeding, has remained assured.

At the present time three institutions are combined under one management: the stallion station, the national stud school and the estate management.

(Right) One of the stables in the Court of Honour. Thirty trotter and Anglo-Norman stallions are housed here.

(Below) Two powerful stallions of the Percheron breed, one of the most important cold-blood breeds in the world.

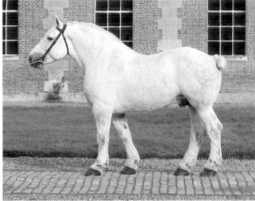

(Overleaf) The champion Thoroughbred *Carmarthen*, born in 1964, by *Devon* out of *Kuwait*, by *Persian Gulf*. In the background is the château.

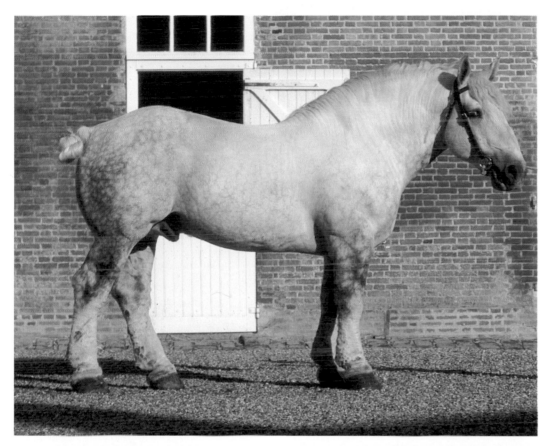

The stallion station is one of 23 establishments of this kind which are controlled by the Stud Service of the Ministry of Agriculture. In 1976 its stock comprised 83 stallions. During the covering season, from 20 February to the beginning of July, they are distributed among 25 covering stations. The region covered by Le Pin includes the Departments of Orne, Calvados, Eure and Seine-Maritime.

Apart from the direct influence which the stud-farm exerts by supplying breeders with first-class stallions at moderate prices, it also benefits breeding by the annual inspection of each individual breeding stallion; the inspection and certification of all Thoroughbred foals; and the organization of races for selecting horses and for the commercial benefit of the breeders. In addition the stud-farm gives support to societies for horse racing and riding sports.

The stud school was founded in 1823 by Barthélemy. After completing the course at the State Agricultural School, all the technical staff of the stud-farm received

(Above, left) The Anglo-Norman *Foudre de Guerre*, born in 1971, by *Nankin*, out of *Quenotte*, by *Gagne si Peu*.
(Above) The English Thoroughbred *Night and Day*, born in 1975, by *Soleil Levant* out of *Nuit de Noces*, by *Nosca*. He was set to sire Thoroughbreds and Anglo-Normans and produced *Danoso* among others.
(Left) The Anglo-Norman *Mexico*, born in 1956, by *Furioso XX* out of *Dame de Ranville*, by *Talisman*. His most famous brother on the paternal side is the Tokyo Gold Medal winner of 1964, *Lutteur*.
(Right) The Anglo-Norman *Emir du Mesnil*, born in 1970, by *Night and Day XX* out of *Ténébreuse*, by *Bel Avenir* or *L'Oudon*.

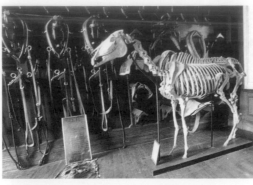

further training here. Nowadays engineers in the fields of agriculture, water management and forestry are able to take a practical course in stud work here. Also, school-leavers can take a three-year course here in horse management or farriery.

The Pin estate covers 1100 hectares (2718 acres); 300 hectares (741 acres) are forest and 700 hectares (1729 acres) pastureland, including 425 hectares (1050 acres) used by the Institute for Agricultural Research and 112 hectares (277 acres) for racecourses, exercise areas, roads and farms. A large number of events are organized on the sports ground every year. Another notable feature is the presence of an experimental herd of 25 mares for research in animal physiology.

(Above) The Cour Lambesc, named after the director of Le Pin from 1765 to 1790. The English Thoroughbred stable also bears this name.

(Above right; right) The covering hall, erected in 1882, exterior and interior views. The history of this hall, going back nearly a hundred years, is associated with many champions in different equestrian sports.

Eterpigny

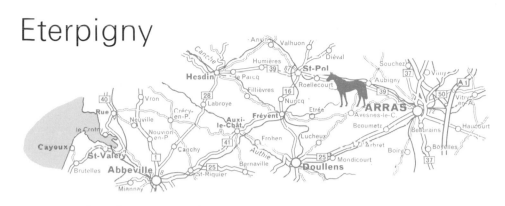

Eterpigny dates from ancient times as a property of the Barons of Herlincourt and lies 15km (9½ miles) to the west of Arras in the north of France.

Around the turn of the century this private stud-farm ranked as one of the best for Boulonnais horses. It was renowned for its high, airy stables and lush pastures. The horses reared here were so good that the owner received permission from the government to send stallions throughout the country to give covering services. The Baron usually kept some 20 Boulonnais breeding stallions and the same number of mares. Most of the time he also kept two Anglo-Normans for the use of local breeders. His Boulonnais brood-mares all worked on farms and only came to the stables a few days before foaling. With the foals at foot, only a week old, the mares were back at work, in the best of health. This cold-blood breed, originating from the Boulogne district, had received an infusion of eastern blood in early medieval times, or possibly even before that, and this had endowed it with a more attractive appearance and greater spirit and endurance. Further substantial additions of Arab blood towards the end of the last century gave rise to the predominance of the grey colour. Until then most Boulonnais had been bays or blacks.

(Top) Remains of the once famous stables of Eterpigny. The stud-farm was largely destroyed during the First World War. Since then the buildings have been restored only where needed; they are now used by a small agricultural concern. All the horses were taken to Germany during the war.

(Above, right) The château of the Barons of Herlincourt was also seized during the First World War and suffered under the occupation. Very little is left of the former splendour of this estate.

(Left) In the seventeenth century there were two types of Boulonnais horses: the small, nimbler type preferred by the dealers, with a height of about 160 cm (16 hands) and a weight of about 600 kg (94 st or 1320 lb); and the heavy farm-horse standing about 170 cm (16 hands 3 inches) and weighing 900 kg (141 st or 1980 lb). The two have now merged. The painting was done by Hans Bendel, an artist who specialized in horses.

(Overleaf) Percheron stallions at Le Pin.

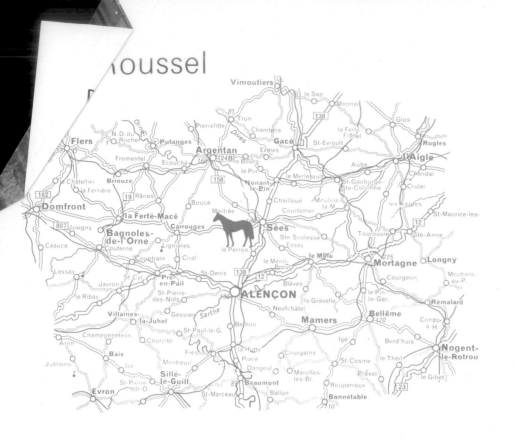

Honour for his cattle and at the same time his horse *Boiard* won the Jockey Club Prize, the Oaks, the Grand Prix de Paris and the Trial Stakes. In the following year the same horse went on to collect the Prix Cadran and the Ascot Gold Cup.

Apart from *Boiard*, the greatest horses to be born and reared at Bois-Roussel during the last century were *Vermouth*, *Bois-Roussel* and *Patricien*.

The breeding management remained in the hands of the Counts Roederer. For some years the stud-farm was leased to a M. Volterra, but was then taken over again by its owner, Mme de Rochefort, who, as mentioned above, disposed of it to Countess Batthyany in 1970.

With the change of ownership new horses were brought to Bois-Roussel. The new stable colours (orange and blue) soon became well-known. The most important winners from this stud-farm since 1970 are: *Pia*, winner of the Oaks, Lowther Stakes, Park Hill Stakes; *Samos*, Royal Oaks Prize, second in the Gold Cup, Gladiator Prize; *San San*,

The Bois-Roussel stud-farm was founded in 1802. Count Roederer, one of Napoleon I's ministers, received it as a gift from the Emperor in that year. The stud-farm remained for over 150 years in the family. In 1970 it was sold by the Countess of Rochefort to the Countess Margit Batthyany.

The new owner bears one of the best-known names in German bloodstock breeding. The international range of her activities had long been demonstrated by the pedigrees of her horses, and those at Bois-Roussel carry blood from countries which lead the world in horse breeding.

Bois-Roussel is situated in the parish of Bursard, 16 km (10 miles) from Alençon and in the vicinity of Sées, on the southern slopes of the Sarthe valley. The estate covers about 310 hectares (766 acres). Some 80 hectares (197 acres) are cultivated, mainly with oats, lucerne and barley, 185 hectares (457 acres) are pasture and the remainder is covered by forest and buildings.

The estate is surrounded by forests on three sides: to the south is the Forest of Perseigne, to the west the Forest of Ecouves and to the east the Forest of Bourse. This ensures that the climate at the stud-farm is particularly mild, with frequent falls of fine rain. The chalky soil guarantees a sound bone formation for the horses.

Situation and soil characteristics could scarcely be more favourable for a stud-farm. This was clear as early as 1873, when Count Roederer received the Agricultural Prize of

In 1976 five breeding stallions were standing at the stud-farm. The three most outstanding are illustrated here.

(Right) *Gift Card*, born in 1969, by *Dan Cupid* out of *Gracious Gift*, by *Princely Gift*, Winner in four races, placed twice.

(Above, left) *Bold Lad*, born in 1962 in the USA, by *Bold Ruler* out of *Misty Morn*, by *Princequillo*. Winner in fourteen races and placed three times. His most important offspring so far are *Niagara* and *Game Lad* in the USA and *Bold Fascinator*, *Marble Arch*, *Royal Family*, *Gentle Thoughts* and *Come Back* in Europe.

(Above) *Caro*, born in 1967, by *Fortino* out of *Chambord*, by *Chamossaire*, Winner in four races and fourth in the Prix de l'Arc de Triomphe.

Vermeille, Arc de Triomphe; *Mata Hari*, Filly Trials; *Caro*, Trials, Ispahan Prize, Harcourt, Dollar, Ganay; *Filiberto*, Morny Prize; *Arosa*, Queen Elizabeth II Cup; *Gift Card*, Perth Prize, Dollar, Prince of Wales Stakes; *Marduk*, German Derby, Grosser Preis von Baden, German St Leger; *No No Nanette*, Nonette Prize.

As regards the number of races won in France, the Batthyany stables took fourth place in 1971 and second place in 1972.

The equipment at the Bois-Roussel stud-farm has been brought right up to date. The 80 hectares (197 acres) under cultivation supply the greater part of the forage requirements for the horses. The stock comprises about 210 horses, some 60 of which are kept at two branch establishments. One of these, Mare-Dessous, with 28 loose-boxes, has facilities for quarantining sick horses and new arrivals from abroad. At the other branch, Les Fontaines, the yearlings are kept. This branch has 32 loose-boxes, a covered riding-track, a 1000-m (1100-yard)

exercise ground, and extensive pasturage. All the loose-boxes are disinfected once a week and whitewashed every year, thus reducing to a minimum the risk of transmitting diseases.

(Top) View of the extensive paddocks at Bois-Roussel, with the canals which make it possible to irrigate by sections.

(Above) Emanuel Bodard with the mare *Chambord*, born in 1955. Among her 16 offspring is the famous stallion *Caro*. Her greatest triumphs include the Fitzwilliam Stakes, the Royal Standard Stakes, the Newmarket Oaks and the Liverpool St Leger.

(Left) The Orangery, now the directorate building; behind it is the Countess Margit Batthyany's summer-house.

Victot

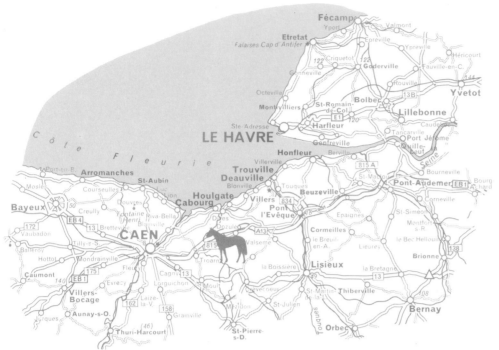

The Château de Victot was erected around 1575 on the site of a thirteenth-century fortress which had dominated the little valley of the Dorette.

At first there were two separate châteaux for father and son. In the eighteenth century these were linked by a slate-roofed section in the Norman style. The château was bought from the Boutin family of Sainte-Marie-le-Normand by the Aumont family, the Sieurs de la Fosse. Strong monarchists, they were horse breeders with a world-wide reputation.

The history of the Victot stud-farm is almost the history of racing in France, extending over more than a hundred years. It is true that the name Aumont does not appear in connection with racing until 1838, five years after the creation of the Jockey Club, when Eugène Aumont's colours (pink jacket and black cap) were worn at Chantilly and Caen.

But before then, Eugène's father, Alexandre Aumont, had been breeding horses all his life and had been the principal

supplier to Napoleon I's army. The prospects opened up by the creation of the Jockey Club encouraged his heir Eugène to start a racing stable.

Two years later, in 1840, his filly *Tontine* won the Jockey Club Prize. This victory annoyed the principal founding member of the Club, Lord Seymour, to such an extent that he turned his back on the Turf. Meanwhile, Eugène Aumont collected further laurels. Two horses from his stables, *Beggarman* and *Plover*, were winners, although in another's colours: Eugène had given up racing and had given his brother Alexandre a free hand.

At first, Alexandre bred riding-horses at Victot. After several study-trips to England he devoted himself exclusively to bloodstock breeding. In 1844 his own colours appeared on the scene: white jacket and green cap. They are the oldest in France, and are still worn. In the first year Alexandre's filly *Cavatine* took the third place in the Prix de Diane and came second in the Prix du Jockey Club.

In the following three years the Aumont stable beat all previous French records. In sixty-odd races it won 225,000 francs – an enormous sum at that time. One horse alone, *Fitz-Emilius*, won 100,000 francs.

For the Jockey Club of 1846 Aumont had two favourites in the running: *Premier Août* and *Liverpool*. His ambition was to win with *Liverpool*. *Premier Août*, alone in the lead, allowed *Liverpool* to pass. But the latter bolted at the last moment and was overtaken by *Meudon*, an outsider, who was however also from the Aumont stable. Later, *Premier Août* won five other races, and *Liverpool* four.

The enormous success achieved in such a short time was undoubtedly in part attributable to the trainer, Tom Hurst; shortly afterwards, however, he became un-cooperative, and, since Alexandre Aumont could see no other way of getting rid of him, in October 1847 he sold his racing stable. But in 1850 Aumont was back again – with a new trainer, Tom Jamings. In *La Clotme* he immediately found another champion horse, who won 70,000 francs in two years.

And then he introduced *Hervine* to the race-track; she was to be become one of the greatest racing fillies of France. In her second race, as a two-year-old, she collected the Prix de Chantilly. As a three-year-old she remained unbeaten in all eight races. As a four-year-old she won six out of seven races,

Victot is without doubt one of Normandy's most precious treasures, and is the home of one of the finest stud-farms in the world. It was built around 1575 and is a wonderful example of the architecture of the Pays d'Auge. Natural stone and bricks are used in a chequered pattern. Caen is not far away, so it is not surprising that its style is evident in the beautiful dormer

windows ornamented with stone carvings. The rounded tiles from the Pré d'Auge gleam in many colours. The same material is used for the terminating members of the roofs, called *Epis de Pré d'Auge*. The site is surrounded by deep moats, fed from the river Dorette. They enhance the charm of the whole edifice, which is mirrored in them.

The enormous courtyard was created around 1700 by the Seigneur de Boutin. The long stable buildings, with the half-timbered façades typical of Normandy, surround the yard on three sides; they contain fifty loose-boxes.

and as a five-year-old she managed two further victories and in the Goodwood Cup was beaten by a head by the famous *Jouvence*. Aumont's successes in 1852 were almost unbelievable; with six of his horses he won no fewer than twenty-four races.

After another successful year, in 1854 his luck turned. The three-year-old *Blason* gave away the Prix du Jockey Club, bolting a few yards before the winning-post. After winning a race, *Fitz Gladiator* was being prepared for the important Goodwood Cup, but shortly beforehand he showed himself to be in poor condition. The great *Hervine* went lame before the Cambridgeshire, and the usually excellent *Aguila* failed similarly in two important English races.

In the autumn of the same year Alexandre entered a two-year-old named *Monarque* in the Grand Critérium. He was beaten. But the same *Monarque* was later to become not only possibly the handsomest but also the greatest stallion in the history of French bloodstock breeding. After more than twenty victories at the age of three, four and five, he went on to win the Goodwood Cup as a six-year-old, carrying 55 kg (8 stone 9 lb or 121 pounds). At stud he produced many top-class horses including *Gladiateur*, who challenged his

sire for recognition as France's greatest horse.

In 1856 Aumont sold his stable for the second time, but by 1859 his colours had reappeared at the races. He was not to enjoy his new successes for long, however: he died suddenly two years later.

His son Paul's good luck with bloodstock breeding equalled that of Alexandre. *Gladiateur*, son of *Monarque*, was outstandingly successful at stud. In 12 years his descendants won 400 races and 3,000,000 francs. Until his death in 1904 he was the most notable figure on the French Turf. Paul's son, another Alexandre, carried on the Aumont tradition until 1933.

René, the last Aumont, was primarily a breeder. His colours were seldom seen at the races. Nevertheless Victot still produced favourites who won great victories in other colours. *Cousine*, for example, won 620,000 francs, and *Samaritain*, after an astonishing racing career, was sold to the State for 3,500,000 francs. In the 1946 Grand Prix de Paris three Victot horses were among the first four.

After the death of René Aumont the stud-farm was leased to M. Wildenstein, who is continuing the breeding activity in great style and has already introduced some notable winners to the racing scene.

The château was formerly enclosed by forbidding walls. Although a cheerful, brightly coloured residence has been created here, it was impossible to neglect the military aspect entirely; the moats, drawbridges, embrasures and ramparts were made necessary by the wars of religion. The walls, however, were partly pulled down by the last owners, and nothing now interferes with the view of this magnificent establishment.

After nearly 150 years, during which successive generations of the Aumont family had bred racehorses here, the stud-farm was leased to M. Wildenstein. Thus Victot continues its long tradition of breeding activity in the hands of another brilliant personality of the French Turf. Mme René Aumont still lives in the castle.

Germany

In Germany the stud-farm system was started by the Knights of the Teutonic Order, and developed to such an extent that for over two hundred years from 1732 the Prussian Stud Administration was able to run it as a prosperous concern. Since 1945 the individual Federal States in the West and the states of Mecklenburg (Redefin), Brandenburg (Neustadt a.d. Dosse), Saxony (Moritzburg, Kreuz) and Thuringia (having no stud-farm of its own) in the East have carried on the administration of the German stud system. Important horse breeding regions such as East and West Prussia with their famous stud-farms at Trakehnen, Georgenburg, Zwion, Rastenburg, Braunsberg and Marienwerder were brought under Russian or Polish administration, as were Further Pomerania with Labes, and Silesia with Leubus and Cosel (later known as Fürstenstein).

The Prussian Stud Administration was located in Berlin, at the Ministry of Agriculture and Forestry, and managed all the stud-farms of the Prussian states, to which, within what later became the Reich, only Mecklenburg, Brunswick and the South German States did not belong; these states had their own stud administrations.

In 1939 the state-owned stud-farms were located as follows:

Prussia
East Prussia:
  Trakehnen (Central)
  Georgenburg
  Rastenburg
  Braunsberg
  Zwion (Stallion Testing Station)
West Prussia:
  Marienwerder
Pomerania:
  Labes
Holstein:
  Traventhal
Hanover:
  Celle
  Osnabrück
  Westercelle (Stallion Testing Station)
Brandenburg:
  Neustadt (Central)
  Graditz (Central)
  Kreuz
  Moritzburg
Silesia:
  Cosel (Fürstenstein)
  Leubus
Westphalia:
  Warendorf
Rhineland:
  Wickrath
Hesse:
  Dillenburg

Mecklenburg
  Redefin

Brunswick
  Harzburg

South Germany
Württemberg:
  Marbach (Central and Regional)

(Left) This illustration, dating from the fifteenth century, shows the preparations for a German tournament. Originally, in the tenth century, these tournaments were bloody contests organized in advance between two numerically equal groups of mounted knights. In the eleventh century this method of fighting began to develop into a contest between two individuals, with fixed rules, which was however still far from bloodless. Not until about two centuries later were blunted weapons introduced into these combats, which meant that an opponent could be forced out of the saddle but, if possible, not killed.

Gustav Rau (1880–1954), whose fame as a horse expert spread far beyond the frontiers of Germany. He was a journalist and author, gave many lectures, and was well-known as an organizer, particularly in the realm of horse breeding. For a long time Regional Stud Director, he was also extremely successful with his campaign for country riding-clubs. His far reaching activity did much to enhance respect for the German horse in other countries.

Bavaria:
    Schwaiganger (Central)
    Landshut
    Ansbach
Palatinate:
    Zweibrücken (Central and Regional)

The central stud at Beberbeck (Hesse) and the regional stud at Gudwallen (East Prussia) were sacrificed in the cause of economy in 1929, and the Thoroughbred stud-farm at Altefeld was moved back to Graditz.

In all the German States, horse breeding is still based mainly on the basis of farming. The state-owned stud-farms provide the sires for the covering stations throughout the state, the central studs being above all responsible for ensuring the supply of a proportion of the stallion requirements from specially selected stallions and mares.

Thus the regional horse breeding service in East Prussia, through its Trakehnen source, supplied primarily riding-horses and cavalry remounts. Hanover and its breeding regions Mecklenburg, Brandenburg, Pomerania and Westphalia provided mainly artillery remounts, while Oldenburg and East Friesland with the breeding regions of Silesia, Saxony, Bavaria, Württemberg and Hesse raised the very heaviest warm-bloods. Requirements of agriculture and industry were taken care of automatically by all the above-mentioned breeding centres, whose production was made up of an average of 50 per cent of cold-bloods.

Nowadays the interest everywhere is concentrated almost exclusively on breeding horses for riding and sport. The number of state-owned stud-farms was further reduced after 1945. Thus in the Federal Republic Wickrath and Traventhal no longer exist. In the Rhineland warm-bloods are now bred, and Warendorf has taken over from Wickrath in the breeding of stallions. In Holstein the breeders' association at Elmshorn has taken over from Traventhal responsibility for the production of stallions, with state assistance. The East Friesland breeding area has been transferred to the Hanover Breeders' Association and the Celle regional stud. The Osnabrück and Harzburg regional stud districts are also taken care of by Celle. In accordance with tradition, the private stallion station at Oldenburg comes under state supervision. In Bavaria the Ansbach regional stud has been closed down.

After 1945, the precious remnants of the East Prussian regional stock of horses of Trakehnen descent were distributed over the whole of the Federal Republic. Redeveloped as a pure stock they constitute, as a special breed, a permanent element in German horse breeding, though to a much smaller extent than formerly in their home territory.

According to the new Animal Breeding Law breeders are required to make a selection of the colts intended for breeding. Every State has its own Selection Commission which must include a representative of the Government, usually the appropriate 'Landstallmeister', as director of a state-owned stud-farm. The selected stallions in private ownership must have a covering permit from the appropriate breeders' association. It is no longer necessary to castrate rejected stallions. All stallions used or intended to be used as sires have to pass an individual performance test at the age of three and a half. Not until these requirements are satisfied (after appropriate preparation) is the permit for breeding use finally granted.

German brand-marks for different breeds

1 Marbach Württemberger
2 Württemberger warm-blood
3 Zweibrücken
4 Achselschwang
5 Schwaiganger
6 Dülmener
7 East Prussian
8 East Prussian. Foal of East Prussian descent on one side
9 Trakehnen (up to 1944)
10 Holstein
11 North-German and West-German ponies and small horses
12 Schleswig cold-blood
13 Lower Saxony cold-blood, Stud Book mark
14 Lower Saxony cold-blood, National Stud Book mark
15 Westphalia, warm-blood
16 Westphalia, warm-blood, National Stud Book registration mark
17 Oldenburger warm-blood
18 Hanoverian warm-blood, National Stud Book mark
19 Hanoverian, Vorbuch mark
20 Hanoverian, Stud Book mark
21 East Friesland, warm-blood, mark for selected mares and stallions
22 East Friesland, foal mark
23 Electorate of Hesse, warm-blood
24 Hesse-Nassau, warm-blood
25 Baden, cold-blood
26 Rhineland, cold-blood, National Stud Book mark
27 Rhineland, cold-blood, Stud Book mark
28 Haflinger
29 Saarland, Stud Book mark
30 Bavaria, South-German cold-blood
31 Bavarian warm-blood
32 South Germany, small horses

Trakehnen

(Below) Coming from the railway station at Trakehnen (the last station on the eastern railway before the Russian frontier station at Eydkuhnen), and soon after passing the Bajorgallen farm with the odd-coloured herds, the visitor would turn into a high wrought-iron gateway to reach the central farm of the largest Prussian Central Stud.

Six hundred soldiers from Memel had laboured for six years to clear and drain the marshes between Gumbinnen and Stallupönen when in 1732 Frederick William I of Prussia established the Royal Trakehnen Stud Administration here and stocked it as the Court stud-farm with 1100 horses, including 500 brood mares.

By the middle of the eighteenth century Trakehnen horses were already setting new distance records and had cut the standard times for the Berlin–Königsberg stage by twenty-four hours. Tough, fast horses were thus being reared in this extreme eastern part of the kingdom.

These horses were, however, not quite up to standard as regards dimensions, limbs and conformation. When loaded with heavy cavalry baggage, and when used in agriculture which was becoming increasingly intensive, they proved deficient. This became particularly clear when in 1786, after the death of Frederick II, his stud-farm became the property of the state.

From then on breeding was directed to re-modelling the Trakehnen horse, which took over a hundred years to attain its pure type, later so much admired and never afterwards lost. Two protracted evacuations, involving heavy losses, had made the work of breeding more difficult and slowed up progress: in 1806–07 there was the flight to Russia from Napoleon and in 1812–13 there was the flight to Silesia. The province of East Prussia lost 179,000 horses at that time.

For more than two hundred years the main task of the Trakehnen station was to supply stallions for the regional horse breeding industry. After the First World War the first fundamental change took place. Army and agriculture explicitly demanded a horse standing over more ground, altogether more substantial and better set up. The rather square shape was to give way to a more elongated rectangular one. Type, class and intrinsic characteristics were to remain unchanged.

Valuable porcelain plates and vases have been preserved from the time of the Trakehnen stud director von Burgsdorff (1814–40); these provide us with a picture of the Prussian Central Stud around the middle of the nineteenth century. These rare and precious pieces were painted by Litfas and are in private collections. There is no better panorama of Trakehnen at this period, nor are there any comparable representations of particular top-rank sires and brood-mares from this era.

(Left) Thanks to the artistic skill of Countess Melissa von Sponeck (née von Oettingen), the Visitors' Book of the Trakehnen stud directors von Oettingen (1895–1912) and Count von Sponeck (1912–22) has preserved many impressions from that period. This reproduction shows how, in 1905, the Countess visualized the evolution of the stream of visitors in 1950.

in the herds of black, chestnut, brown and odd-coloured brood-mares, were sent to the hunting stables and, usually after a one-year training, were auctioned at the spring or autumn public sales.

Trakehnen has become better known than most other stud-farms in the world on account of its breeding for performance. Its auction sales set the pattern for those at Verden, which are now the leading international sales: they have the longest possible time for testing and comparison,

Trakehnen managed to do this while still retaining the racial type and individuality of the Trakehnen horse. Count Siegfried von Lehndorff and Dr Ehlert, successive stud directors, deserve the credit for this achievement.

The main farm and the fifteen other farms at Trakehnen together covered 24,000 acres. There were 15 km (nearly 10 miles) of roads and paths. Two district towns shared the administration of the area. Food for the people, horses and cattle was provided from their own fields and pastures. Stud directors ran the breeding farms and two veterinary surgeons took care of the health of the large stock. Horses and carts provided communications throughout the area. During the winter, 400 draught horses brought wood through the ice and snow from the royal hunting-grounds at Rominten for building and heating.

Colts which were not selected to become sires, and fillies which were not registered

public demonstrations, a fair system of bidding and impartial advisory services for buyers.

The number of brood-mares at Trakehnen fluctuated to a certain extent, the average number being about 300, of which 10 per cent were replaced each year, while twenty to forty stallions from each year's production went to the central and regional stocks of sires. Thus some 50 per cent of each year's production went into the breeding stock. The remaining horses

(Above) The Trakehnen Schloss was the official residence of the stud director.

(Left) The Hotel Elch was used to accommodate visitors, and together with the hospital, the school, the Post Office and other public establishments, formed part of the complex of facilities providing for all aspects of life at the vast stud-farm.

found their way to the Trakehnen sales; many were successful in competitive events or joined the farm teams at Trakehnen itself.

In addition, every year several mares were provided for the use of private breeders in East Prussia. The regional stud-farms at Georgenburg (including the former Gudwallen Stud), Braunsberg, Rastenburg and Marienwerder received the major share of the young Trakehnen stallions, while in the Posen (Poznan) area Stargard, Zirke and Gnesen were cared for and the Prussian stud-farms west of the Oder were also allocated a few Trakehnen sires.

From 1926 onwards all the three-year-old stallions together with their counterparts from the East Prussian regional production were given a year's training, culminating in a test of performance at stud. Success in this was a condition of acceptance for breeding. The training establishment was located at Zwion/Insterburg (Chernyakovsk), and for

a while also at Trakehnen, with a capacity of about 100 stallions.

At 5 a.m. on 17 October 1944, Trakehnen received from the Stallupönen District Council Office, faced with the Russian armed forces at their gates, the order for complete evacuation of the central stud-farm and the other eleven stud-farms; simultaneously the neighbouring Gumbinnen District Council Office issued a strict instruction prohibiting evacuation of the four Trakehnen stud-farms within this district.

The Stud Director, Dr Ehlert, nevertheless proceeded to evacuate all the farms, but was unable to prevent the forcible retention of the Gumbinnen horses, which were thus nearly all caught up by the Russian tanks. The greater part of all the original Trakehnen stock fell sooner or later into Russian or Polish hands. By 1945 there were only twenty-seven Trakehnen-born mares, and none of the leading sires, to form the basic stock in West Germany, together with a few East Prussian mares of

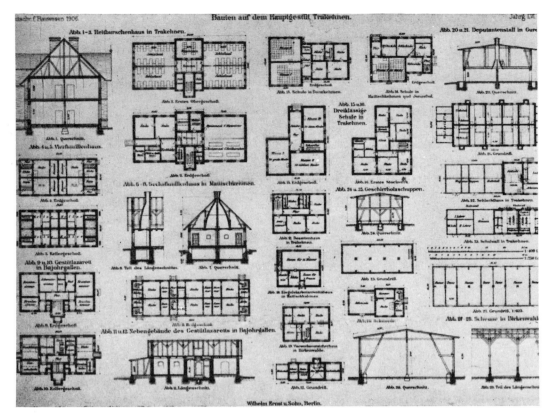

(Left) The Trakehnen organization owned hundreds of buildings. Technical drawings of some of them can still be found in the *Zeitschrift für Bauwesen* of 1906. Many of the buildings were destroyed in the First World War.

(Below) Among the buildings ruined in the First World War was the great loose-box stable which housed the hunters.

Trakehnen descent, the basic stock for preserving the Trakehnen breed, which is now flourishing once more.

In former East Prussia and in the Posen region Trakehnen stud-farms are maintained by the Polish Stud Administration, especially at Liski/Bartenstein.

The Hanover region did particularly well with the Trakehnen breed, above all with the sires *Abglanz*, *Semper idem*, *Lateran* and *Cyklon*, which were evacuated from Trakehnen to Hunnesrück in good time, mostly as yearlings.

The last living original Trakehnen horse (born in Trakehnen) was the sire *Keith* (born on 20 December 1941), by *Pythagoras* out of *Kätzerin*, by *Ararat*. He died in November 1976 at Hans Steinbrück's farm at Gilten (Lower Saxony), shortly before his thirty-fifth birthday.

(Above) The new yard comprised only a small section of the ground covered by the Trakehnen Central Farm. This photograph was taken around 1905 from the roof of the stud director's residence. This area was redeveloped by von Oettingen, and was in itself a large and impressive installation, although only a relatively small one within the whole farm organization; it was restored by Count Sponeck after the First World War.

(Left) Through long experience, the co-ordination of the stud-farm was almost perfect. Thus both at the new farm and at the old farm (where the herd of chestnut mares was kept), there were paddocks to permit free movement during the months when the horses were stabled. There were similar arrangements at all the farms; the illustration shows that at the new farm.

Neustadt

An hour's drive north-west from Berlin, and to the south of the little town of Neuruppin in the fertile meadows of the Dosse near Neustadt, are the Frederick William Central Stud and the Lindenau Regional Stud, which were started up in 1788 and 1789 under Frederick William II of Prussia. Their management was entrusted to Count Lindenau.

As at Beberbeck, Graditz and Trakehnen, the central stud-farm was used to produce sires for the Prussian regional stud-farms, while the stallion centre at Lindenau was responsible for stocking the covering stations in the Brandenburg province. At first, Oriental stallions were used as primary sires, then sires of Trakehnen descent, and later still Hanoverian stallions. The prototype of the Brandenburg stallion around 1940 was the mighty chestnut *Mailand*, who had numerous descendants in the region.

Both of these stud-farms are at present in full operation and supply the breeding establishments in the GDR. The breeding industry is carried on mainly by selection, since the importation of breeding stock from Hanover has long been discontinued. Occasionally horses of Trakehnen blood are brought in from Poland in order to overcome difficulties in carrying on the breed.

(Top, left) The central stud-farm at Neustadt, photographed from the air; in the background are the buildings of the Lindenau regional stud-farm.

(Top, right) The residence of the stud director; the primary sires are stabled in the wing on the left.

(Above) *Turcmainatti*, born in 1784, was brought to Neustadt from the East in 1791, as a gift from Prince Kaunitz; he had a notable career as a sire here until he was stolen during the war in 1806.

(Right) Stallions descended from *Turcmainatti*.

52

Georgenburg

The castle of Georgenburg, 3 km (about 2 miles) north of Insterburg, was established as the stud-farm of the episcopate of Samland around 1400. Some 550 years later, fleeing from the Russian army, 310 Trakehnen sires and 130 cold-blood stallions from the Georgenburg regional stud-farm (Prussian since 1839) abandoned the three great stables of the castle of the Teutonic Order; after them, on 17 October 1944, came a further 674 horses from Trakehnen, which had reached Georgenburg as the first stage of their evacuation, after a 60-km (37-mile) night trek, passing through burning Gumbinnen.

Georgenburg – run from 1828 to 1899 as a private stud-farm belonging to the von Simpson family (see the novel *Die Barings*) – supplied the districts of Insterburg, Niedrung, Tilsit-Ragnit, Schlossberg (Pillkallen), Stallupönen (Ebenrode), Gumbinnen, Angerapp (Darkehmen) and Goldap with regional sires. As the largest of the East Prussian regional stud-farms it controlled the stallion performance testing station at Zwion, 6 km (about 4 miles) west of Georgenburg, with a capacity for training and testing about a hundred stallions a year. Half the candidates for testing came from Trakehnen, and the other half from private breeders in East Prussia.

Within the domain of the Georgenburg stud-farm the majority of Germany's military remounts were bred. Among the most successful of the sires to become famous were: *Helm*, by *Held*, 259 remounts; *Pirol*, by *J. Pilot*, 258 remounts; *Salut*, by *Jagdheld*, 251 remounts; *Erzengel*, by *Pommerysee*, 238 remounts; *Bulgarenzar*, by *Habakuk*, 225 remounts; *Draufgänger*, by *Diebitsch*, 224 remounts.

The largest private stud-farm, with a hundred brood-mares, was the Weedern estate in the Angerapp (Darkehmen) district, run by the von Zitzewitz family. Six to eight specially selected Georgenburg stallions were stationed here during the covering season.

(Top) The Trakehnen *Hanno*, regional sire at Georgenburg and sire of 180 remounts.

(Top, left) The principal yard of the vast Georgenburg stud establishment was also the show-ground for stallion parades.

(Left and above) The chapter house of the castle of the Teutonic Order, and a larger portion of the side facing onto the road to Gillischken, showing the façade visible from the outside; the stud-farm grounds extend for about 400 m (440 yards) behind this façade and over a width of about 250 m (275 yards).

Redefin

(Below and bottom) At the top end of the great courtyard, opposite the entrance, is the riding-hall. On each side are the stables for the stallions, to the left is the paymaster's house, further to the front that of the stud director. To the right, in the middle, is the house of the veterinary surgeon and in front of that the former stable for the mares, later used as stallion testing institute.

(Centre) A four-in-hand, c. 1938, with the stud groom Emil Köhn.

In a document dating from 1710–11, one of the Dukes of Mecklenburg is recorded as having bought Redefin for the purpose of setting up a stud-farm. There are regular records of the stock of horses from 1721 onwards.

In 1832 Redefin was incorporated under the name 'Redefin and Paetow Combined Central and Regional Stud'. In 1848, however, the central stud-farm was closed down.

The regional stud-farm is still operating

for the Mecklenburg covering stations. In 1934 the sires from the Neustrelitz stud-farm were also brought to Redefin, and in 1950 the sires of the former Further Pomerania district from the Ferdinandshof Stud, which was closed down.

Redefin lies 20 km (12½ miles) to the west of Ludwigslust on the Hamburg–Berlin main road. The railway station is Hagenow-Land, 10 km (6¼ miles) by local roads through the hunting grounds, in sandy country which is suitable for training stallions (stallion testing station). The stud-farm is one of the very largest and finest horse breeding estates. All the pasturage has a park-like character. The soil is permeable, always dry, elastic and free from stones. Nearly all the 180 stallions run unshod.

In the first quarter of this century the stallions were almost all bought from Hanover, mostly as very young foals for rearing. From 1935 onwards the annual stallion selections and markets took place at Güstrow; in 1944 400 stallions born in 1942 were sold. Nowadays re-stocking of

stallions is accomplished out of the stud-farm's own product. No Hanoverian horses have been imported from across the Elbe for a long time.

Graditz

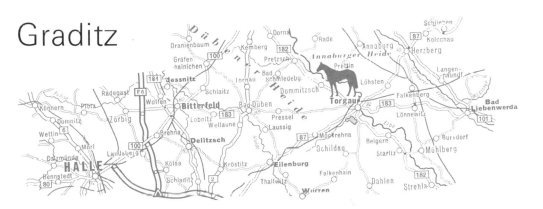

The name Graditz is closely linked with the national bloodstock industry in Germany, although over a certain period in the 1920s the Graditz Thoroughbreds were housed at Altefeld. The planning of the Prussian central stud-farm at Graditz near Torgau a.d. Elbe and the details of the buildings on its five farms can be traced back to the ideas of Augustus the Strong, Elector of Saxony in the early eighteenth century. Graditz was taken over by the Prussian Government in 1815.

The principal task of the great stud-farm on the Elbe was the production of Thoroughbred sires for breeding. For this purpose Graditz maintained its own racing stable, so as to be able to assess its products continuously in the light of their racing performance. In addition, the primary sires were made available to private owners of mares, so that at the same time the general level of German bloodstock could be improved.

Up to 1945, the black-and-white colours

of Graditz were kept to the fore above all by *Herold*, *Ferro*, *Abendfrieden* and *Alchimist*, who supplied other stud-farms with a considerable number of high-quality sires. The Graditz Thoroughbreds always combined performance and faultless external points with outstanding beauty.

Since 1945 Graditz has continued to function as the national Thoroughbred stud-farm of the GDR. In 1947, at Dröschkau (Saxony), the long-serving Graditz stud-mare *Bramouse* produced the famous *Birkhahn XX* (by *Alchimist*) who as a three-year-old won the Hamburg Derby and later, at Schlenderhan, became one of the leading sires in German bloodstock breeding. His skeleton can be seen in the German Horse Museum at Verden.

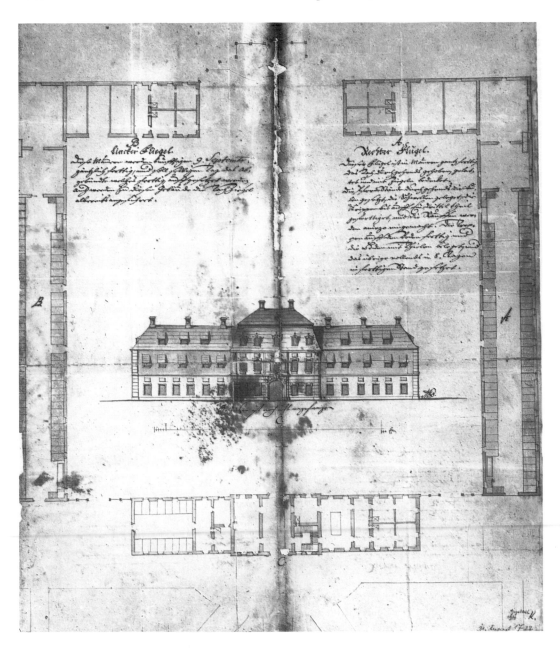

(Top) The Thoroughbred *Alchimist*, primary sire at Graditz, was fifteen years old when he fell a victim to soldiers of the occupation.

(Above) As well as such great stallions as *Alchimist* and *Dark Ronald*, the French horse *Charmant* performed outstandingly at Graditz and elsewhere.

(Left) It was in accordance with this drawing and hand-written notes by Pöppelmann that Schloss Graditz, later to become the residence of the regional stud director, was built in 1723.

Landshut

(Below) The stud-horse *Garant*, born in 1946. As breeding once again turned towards pure-bred riding-horses, the earlier Rottaler, which was more of a farm type, disappeared.

(Below, left) The stallion *Vulkanismus* lived during the hey-day of the cold-blood horse. As recently as fifteen years ago they were still leading the field at over 80 per cent; nowadays only 20 per cent of sires are cold-bloods.

(Bottom) The buildings of the regional stud-farm at Landshut were put up between 1860 and 1900.

The beginnings of the regional stud-farm at Landshut in Saxony reach back to the year 1750, when thirty foals were sent from Schleissheim to Landshut to be reared. Their first lodging was the ducal residence. From 1768, thirty-eight of the Elector's *Etalonen* (from the French *étalon*, stud-horse, stallion) stood in Lower Bavaria. The word *Hofstaller* ('court-horse'), used not so long ago for state-owned stallions, may be attributed to their accommodation in the ducal palace stables.

In 1838 a stable for sires was started at Landshut with five stallions. With the expansion of the state stallion establishment, the amount of accommodation at the ducal residence had become inadequate.

In 1859 the construction of a fully fledged regional stud-farm was ordered by ministerial decree. The construction work was started in 1860 over an area of 5 hectares (nearly 12½ acres), but was not completed until the close of the century. The accommodation was thus increased at first to 100 and later to 144 stallions. The clinic was not added until 1904. In 1937 the stud-farm was re-organized to include a riding- and driving-school with regular training courses held outside the covering season.

The Rottaler warm-blood breed flourished for a long time, based on Oldenburger stock. These horses were more suitable for farm work, and had to be improved by the introduction of Thoroughbreds, Hanoverians and

Trakehnens, in order to keep in line with modern riding breeds.

Thus there are nowadays no longer any old-type Rottalers at Landshut, and scarcely even any cold-bloods, which as recently as fifteen years ago led the field at 80.7 per cent. The stock consists of some forty pure-bred warm-blood sires, including several Haflingers.

The younger generation of stallions come from the Schwaiganger central stud-farm in Bavaria.

Lopshorn

In antiquity the kingdom of the Senones extended over the wide stretches of heath which covered the southern slopes of the Teutoburg forest and whose surviving remnants between Paderborn and Bielefeld still bear the name Senne. The horses of the old Cheruscans grazed in this wilderness long ago. A document dating from 1160 records that the Bishop of Paderborn gave a third of his wild mares on the Senne to the Hardehausen Monastery near Warburg.

In the succeeding centuries the Lords of Lippe acquired extensive properties on both sides of the Teutoburg forest. At the end of the seventeenth century they built their hunting lodge at Lopshorn and installed the stud-farm and breeding industry which supplied the princely stables with saddle and carriage horses and provided sires for horse breeding in the region.

The pasturage for the brood-mares and their young was 60 square km (23 square miles) of fenced-in woodland. In summer this afforded food in abundance for horses and game. English Thoroughbred stallions

became the primary sires, and thus in the course of generations the Senne horse became characterized by long body lines and brown colour, clearly showing the Thoroughbred influence. In addition to its responsibilities for supplying the prince's stables and the regional sires, Lopshorn also had to provide a number of remounts every year for the Paderborn Hussars.

(Above) The Thoroughbred sire *George IV*, born in 1844, by *Cadet*.

(Right) The sire *Diamant*, born in 1851, by *Malcolm*. After lithographs by Gustav Quentell.

(Top) One hundred years ago – Princess Elisabeth zur Lippe on *Kastor*, born in 1857 at Lopshorn, by *Florival*.

(Centre) The manor house at the Lopshorn Stud near Detmold, built at the end of the seventeenth century.

(Above) A Senne brood-mare, after a painting by Gustav Quentell dated 1852.

Wickrath

Wickrath is among the most beautiful of Germany's stud establishments. For this reason alone its closure is greatly to be regretted. From 1746 to 1772 Otto Friedrich von Quadt, later Count Wickrath, was engaged in laying out the symmetrical twin palace which formed the heart of the estate from 1839 onwards. The Wickrath sires were paraded annually and also took part in displays elsewhere, as illustrated in the photograph below left, taken at the 19th Provincial Horse Show in Cologne in 1936.

The Wickrath regional stud was established by a cabinet decree in 1839, in the interests of horse breeding in the Rhineland. It was not until 1876 that the stock of stallions acquired the famous reputation, which was maintained for eighty years, by producing the first of its Rhenish-Belgian cold-blood sires of extraordinary weight and strength of character.

Up to that time the stock of about forty-eight state-owned sires had comprised a motley collection of French half-breds,

Hanoverians, Brunswicks, Graditzers, Saxons, Westphalians, Holsteins, Mecklenburgers, East Friesians, Oldenburgers, Pinzgauers, Belgians, Suffolks and Clydesdales, predominantly warm-blood stallions. By contrast, the stallion register for 1912 shows 211 cold-bloods including 123 Belgians, 84 Rhenish-German cold-bloods, 1 Trakehnen, 1 Thoroughbred and 2 Oldenburgers.

In 1925, 567 cold-bloods in private ownership were selected for breeding, as against 110 regional sires at Wickrath. As well as the Rhine province the Saar region was also supplied. According to a contemporary report by Wickrath's director, Baron von Stenglin (father of the present director at Celle), from 1925 onwards private owners and societies kept on trying to 'cut the throat of their troublesome competitor'. In 1956 they succeeded. Wickrath was closed down. The area was taken over by the Warendorf regional stud-farm.

Dillenburg

The Court Stud of Hesse-Nassau was erected in the Wilhelmstrasse, Dillenburg, during the period 1768–72, by order of William V; around 1807, after the French occupation, the buildings were restored and in 1871 the establishment was renamed the Royal Prussian Hesse-Nassau State Stud at Dillenburg. Here the stocks of the Regional Studs were gathered together: from Weilburg (1811), Kassel (1818) and Korbach (founded at Arolsen in 1811 and relocated at Korbach in 1852), which were closed down. The Prince's House became the residence of the stud director. The Regional Stud at Kassel was later revived for a time, but was finally absorbed by Dillenburg again in 1957. Dillenburg has since then supplied the Hesse provinces (now the Federal State of Hesse) with state-owned sires.

For many years Hesse had a strong leaning towards the Oldenburger breed, but around 1960 it changed over from breeding farm types to the production of riding-horses, and systematically stood Hanoverians and Trakehnens at Dillenburg. After their first covering season, all four-year-old stallions are sent for three months to the Adelheidsdorf stallion testing station in Lower Saxony, where they can qualify, by individual performance tests (under the Animal Breeding Law) for a further career as sires.

Among the leading sires at Dillenburg are *Lotse* and *Lützow*, sons of the Hanoverian *Lugano I*, as well as the Trakehnens *Kosmos* and *Thor*.

(Top right) Interior of the late Baroque riding-hall built in 1769.

(Centre) The Orangery, situated in the old castle garden, was probably constructed in the time of Prince Christian (1724–39). Behind it, on the left, is the Prince's House, and in the background to the right is the castle tower, the landmark of Dillenburg.

(Above, left) The Trakehnen stallion *Kosmos*.

(Above) The illustrious sire *Adlerhorst*.

(Left) *Lotse*, son of the Hanoverian *Lugano I*. In succession to the line of working Oldenburgers, Trakehnen and Hanoverian riding-horse stallions have been used since about 1960.

(Overleaf) Holsteins and Hanoverians are among the world's best show-jumpers. An unusual snapshot: just as the photograph was being taken the horse lost a shoe.

59

Zweibrücken

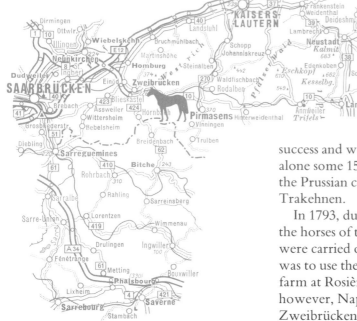

The monasteries of Hornbach and Wörschweiler in the Zweibrücken region had already been running establishments similar to stud-farms since the sixteenth century when, in 1755, Duke Christian IV decreed the creation of the regional stud-farm at Zweibrücken. The headquarters were the ducal stables.

In those days, stallions of Arab and Turkish descent were mated with English mares. Thus originated the Zweibrücken breed, which quickly became a great success and was much sought after. In 1783 alone some 150 stallions were acquired for the Prussian central stud-farm at Trakehnen.

In 1793, during the French Revolution, the horses of the Zweibrücken stud-farm were carried off to France. The intention was to use them to build up a French stud-farm at Rosières-aux-Salines. In 1806, however, Napoleon ordered the Zweibrücken stud-farm to be restored, as he was personally interested in this breed. His famous grey stallion *Fayoum* was sent as sire to Zweibrücken in 1811. The establishment was upgraded to State Stud-farm, First Class, and was officially named 'Haras Impérial de Deux-Ponts'. The Birkhausen and Eichelscheiderhof stud-farms, as well as others, belonged to the State Stud-farm. At that time about 200 stallions were standing there. As well as the horses brought back from Rosières, there were stallions from the Rheinhard forest, from Hungary and from Spain.

In 1814, the stud-farm was forced to move to France. A great many horses fell into the hands of Austrian hussars at that time, including the stallion *Nonius* who later, in Hungary, was to become founder of the Nonius breed.

By 1816 the Zweibrücken stud-farm was functioning again, and until 1890 operated as an establishment of the Palatinate district. Subsequently, it became a Royal Bavarian regional stud-farm. The product was a high-class hard-working half-bred suitable for riding, carriage and military purposes.

Around 1900 there were some sixty sires standing at Zweibrücken, the most important being *Gidran* (Arab), *Miller* (Hanoverian) and *Fabago* (Norman). The stud-farm's own mares, numbering about sixty at that period, were rich in Arab blood. They were stabled at Birkhausen, while foals were reared at Eichelscheiderhof.

After the First World War the direction of breeding was changed. Agriculture and industry, becoming increasingly intensive, demanded heavier horses. To obtain weight, cold-blood stallions were brought in.

(Top, right) The coat of arms of the Dukes of Zweibrücken over the entrance gate to the old Eichelscheid foundation stud-farm commemorates the founder.

(Above) The Arab stallion *Djebel 5878*, born in 1935, by *Obajan VII* out of *Shagya XXII*, bred in Hungary As primary sire he brought nobility, beauty and performance to the Zweibrücken breed. He served until 1956.

(Above) The central building of the Zweibrücken stud-farm with the stables for visiting mares and for Riding-Club horses. The offices and residential accommodation are in the middle section.

(Left) The Hanoverian stallion *Waldjäger 6004*, born in 1972, by *Waldfrieden*. The grandsire of this stallion was the Thoroughbred *Waldspecht*. *Waldjäger* became regional sire at Zweibrücken in 1975.

(Left) Warm-bloods at the 1951 Stallion Parade at Zweibrücken. In the background can be seen the buildings ruined in the war.

(Below) The date of this photograph is not known. It was probably taken around the turn of the century, and shows stud-grooms on warm-blood stallions in front of a stable-block at Zweibrücken.

(Bottom) Farm buildings of the former Eichelscheid bloodstock stud-farm. To the left in the inner horse-shoe yard are the stables for the horses; to the right, those for the cows.

At the beginning of the Second World War the entire stock was evacuated to Achselschwang and Schwaiganger in Bavaria. It came back in 1940, but had to be evacuated again in 1944.

In March 1945 the establishment was largely destroyed by bombing; by 1946, however, it was possible to bring back most of the horses to the Palatinate. Stables, residential accommodation and a riding-hall were erected on the existing site.

Until 1950, Zweibrücken flourished anew. Sixty regional sires, including fifteen cold-bloods, covered up to 4000 mares. After 1950 the requirements for horses for agriculture fell rapidly. The lowest figure was reached in 1960, with only 235 coverings. The Birkhausen branch was leased to the Trakehnen Society, and Eichelscheiderhof was sold. Brood-mares and offspring were also sold, and the stock of stallions was reduced. Since 1960 there have been just twenty-two stallions standing at the stud-farm.

The breeding system was adapted to suit the rising demand for riding-horses, and accordingly the covering figures again rose continuously. In 1974 the number of mares covered was 1400. In 1971 the last cold-blood stallion left the stud-farm.

Warendorf

After seeing how extremely effective state-owned stud-farms in the Prussian provinces, in Hanover and in some South German regions had been in improving horse breeding in the second half of the eighteenth century, Westphalian breeders at the beginning of the nineteenth century also wished to have their own regional stud-farms; this was founded at Warendorf in 1826.

(Below) The stud director's house.

(Bottom) The stables. The buildings on the present site were erected around 1878.

The Warendorf stud-farm was founded in 1826, fulfilling a request which the breeders of Westphalia and the Rhine province had made to the Prussian stud director, von Jagow, in 1815.

On 1 February 1826, 13 East Prussian stallions stood ready, and 943 mares were sent to them in that first year. The heavy demands on the state-owned sires necessitated continual increases of the stock. By 1830 the number of stallions had risen to 50, and by 1839 to 70. In that year the Wickrath regional stud was established for the Rhine province, and Warendorf became the Westphalian regional stud.

Nevertheless the stock continued to increase, and by 1878 a hundred stallions were stood there. The accommodation became too crowded, and the stud-farm was moved to its present site on the right bank of the Ems. In the early years Warendorf bred only warm-bloods. Pure-bred stallions improved the original local types. But the attempt to include Westphalia in the group of provinces supplying military remounts did not succeed, because the remount sales did not arouse sufficient interest.

On the other hand, the farmers wanted heavier and heavier horses. Consequently the number of high-bred stallions was cut drastically and heavy warm-bloods were brought in. But the breed could not yet be described as consolidated.

In 1894 the Provincial Association decided to introduce bloodstock breeding

(Far left) The stallion *Grünspecht*, born in 1944, by *Gründer I* out of *Alpenrose*, by *Abendsport*.

(Left) The Thoroughbred stallion *Sinus*, born in 1949, by *Ticino* out of *Smyrna*, by *Magnat*.

(Below) *Radetzky*, born in 1951, by *Ramzes* out of *Malta*, by *Oxyd*. This stallion whose sire, the Anglo-Arab *Ramzes*, came from Poland, gave the Westphalian warm-blood breed a new look. He is shown with Stud Director Kukuk in the saddle.

(Below, left) The 'Jacobowski Quadrille' at the Warendorf Stallion Parade.

'in the Oldenburg manner'. But it was then found that breeding Oldenburgers and East Friesians was not practicable with the available forage. Further trials were made with Hanoverians and Anglo-Norman horses, and finally even with trotter stallions. In 1920 there were 88 pure-bred stallions standing at the stud.

Meanwhile, alongside these not very successful warm-bloods, the cold-bloods were flourishing. They had been introduced in 1881 with the importation of two Belgian stallions, and proved a great success.

In 1920 the direction of warm-blood breeding took a decisive turn, with a return to Hanoverians. Only a few Thoroughbreds, East Prussians, Beberbeckers and Graditzers were retained.

Between the two World Wars the aim was to breed 'a powerful, broad, well-built and lively horse for work, for riding and for driving'. Numerically, however, cold-bloods still made up two-thirds of the stock.

In the 1950s the demand for cold-bloods fell, and in 1976, the stud-farm's Jubilee Year, there were only ten cold-blood stallions left. In the meantime, warm-blood breeding had been switched to a 'high-performance multi-purpose horse, with a good character and temperament', with good results.

The numerous and varied displays at the Warendorf Stallion Parade attract thousands of visitors every year.

(Above) Among the star turns at the show is driving from the saddle.

(Left) The trotter shown in this photograph is the impressive cold-blood stallion *Anatus*; he is accompanied at the gallop by the warm-blood stallion *Feldspatz*.

Celle

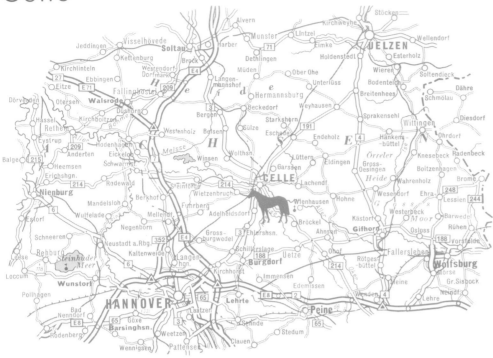

so as to be able to sell remounts to the army. By about 1800 the Celle Stud owned 100 stallions, which were sent to some 50 covering stations every year, principally in the present administrative districts of Stade, Lüneburg and Hanover. The mares sired by state-owned stallions were entered in stud registers right from the start. Around 1790 the stud-farm began to record pedigrees for the progeny of its stallions and registered mares, thus laying the foundation for an independent, planned Hanoverian breed whose origins can today be traced back 150 years to its tap-root dams.

The Regional Stud at Celle in Lower Saxony was founded on 27 July 1735 by George II, Elector of Hanover and King of Great Britain. The object of this enterprise was to make good stallions available to farmer-breeders at low cost, for covering their mares.

In the winter of 1735–36 the first thirteen stallions were acquired, from Holstein; they were mainly of Neapolitan–Andalusian strains. The stock of stallions increased steadily in the succeeding years,

and up to 1770 comprised only Holsteins, apart from a few Danes, East Prussians and Andalusians. However, in order to improve the Hanoverian breed and make it more homogeneous, in the following years more and more stallions of English origin were used, especially pure Thoroughbreds. From reports sent to George II by the stud management it appears that even at that period breeders wished to combine in their horses the calibre required for agricultural work with high class, toughness and spirit,

After the Napoleonic Wars, during which the stud-farm suffered heavily, with only thirty of the stallions evacuated to Mecklenburg later returning, in 1816 a start was made on rebuilding the horse breeding industry. Stallions were obtained mainly from Mecklenburg and England, but also to some extent from the local supply. Some 35 per cent of the stock at that time was Thoroughbreds. It was, however, quickly recognized that, in contrast to other types

(Above) In 1935 the Celle Stud celebrated its 200th anniversary. Behind the parade ground can be seen the north pavilion of the 'Spörckenstall' and the canteen.

(Right) Architectural designs for the 'Spörckenstall' building, which was, however, not constructed in this form. It was erected in 1836, from other plans.

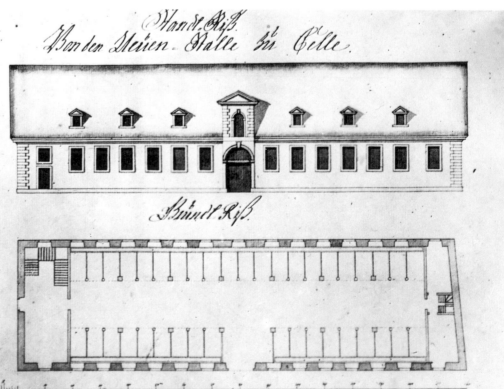

of pure-bred horse, it was dangerous to use Thoroughbreds too much, and the proportion of Thoroughbred stallions was very soon reduced.

Registration and selection of mares was taken over in 1893 by the Hanoverian Stud-Book Society which had been founded in 1888 and which continued on the strict lines set up by the regional stud-farm long before. The close collaboration of the stud-farm with the Stud-Book Society, which in 1922 was incorporated

(Top) The horses leave the 'Grabenstall' for their regular morning exercise.
(Above) *Gotthard*, born in 1949, by *Goldfisch II* out of *Ampa*. The most successful sire of riding-horses in West Germany.
(Above, right) *Galipolis*, son of *Gotthard*, Gert Wildfang's highly successful horse; painting by I. Koblischek.
(Left) *Duft II*, born in 1958, by *Duellant* out of *Gotensage*. Champion stallion in the pure-bred warm-blood group, 1964.
(Right) *Grande*, born in 1958, by *Graf* out of *Duellfast*. Three of his sons took part in the Montreal Olympics, 1976.

with the Hanoverian Warm-Blood Breeders' Association, has been maintained up to the present day. By the start of the First World War the stock of stallions had increased to 350, and in 1924 numbered 500. To provide more space, therefore, another regional stud was established at Osnabrück-Eversburg in 1925, when 100 stallions and 30 attendants were transferred there. From then on the Celle stud-farm was responsible for the districts of Lüneburg, Stade and the Hamburg region while the Osnabrück stud-farm dealt with Hanover, Osnabrück and Hildesheim.

In 1921 the stud administration took over, as stallion-rearing station, the Hunnesrück-im-Solling estate, of some 600 hectares (1500 acres); it was thus able to buy about half the breeding stallions it required as foals, and rear them itself.

In 1927 a station for testing the individual performance of stallions was established at Westercelle, after the pattern of the East Prussian testing station at Zwion. Its importance as an effective instrument for selective breeding, especially at the present time, cannot be overstated.

Towards the end of the 1920s the number of stallions in the regional stud-farms did indeed fall again, but after the Second World War it rose to reach a new peak with 380 stallions at Celle and 180 at Osnabrück. In 1946, after the break-up of the Prussian State, the Celle and Osnabrück stud-farms were brought under the jurisdiction of the Lower Saxony Ministry of Food, Agriculture and Forestry. They were joined, on the incorporation of the state of Brunswick, by the Harzburg-Bündheim regional stud-farm. As a result of the sad destruction of the old East Prussian breeding industry in the Second World War, a large number of Trakehnen stallions arrived at Celle, where they had an important influence on the breeding of Hanoverian warm-bloods.

However, technical developments and mechanization in agriculture led to a severe recession in horse breeding in the following

(Above) The stallion yard at Hunnesrück-im-Solling, which came under the Celle administration in 1921, with about 600 hectares (1500 acres) of pastureland. The estate had previously been a remount station.

(Right) The international show-jumper, the sire *Domspatz*.

(p. 69) Roman chariot at a Celle stallion parade. The photograph probably dates from about 1939. Stallion parades have been held at Celle every autumn for about seventy years. They provide an overall picture of the stallion stock and the state of Hanoverian warm-blood breeding.

One of the most important pre-requisites for progress in breeding is a rigorous selection of sires. Celle has had a stallion testing station since 1927. As the old establishment at Westercelle was no longer able to fulfil its functions properly, a new one was created at Adelheidsdorf, to the south of Celle; this was opened in 1975. It is constructed on the most up-to-date lines, and its conception is altogether unique, serving as a model for the whole of the Federal Republic.

years, and this of course had its effect on the number of stallions kept. As a result of this continuing recession the Osnabrück and Harzburg stud-farms were closed down in 1960–61, the staff and stock being taken over by Celle. In 1960 the number of mares covered by 179 stud stallions was 4238, the lowest figure ever to be reached. From the breeding point of view this great reduction in numbers had an advantage in that it enabled the change-over to the production of riding-horses to be made very quickly,

the old type of breeding material being completely cleared out.

The present stock of stallions on the 7 hectares or so of land in the town of Celle comprises some 210; they covered about 13,000 mares in 1976. The proportion of English Thoroughbreds is about 11 per cent and that of Trakehnen stallions about 1 per cent. In addition there are some 30 colts at the Adelheidsdorf (formerly Westercelle) testing station and 70 probationer stallions at the Hunnesrück stud-farm.

Marbach

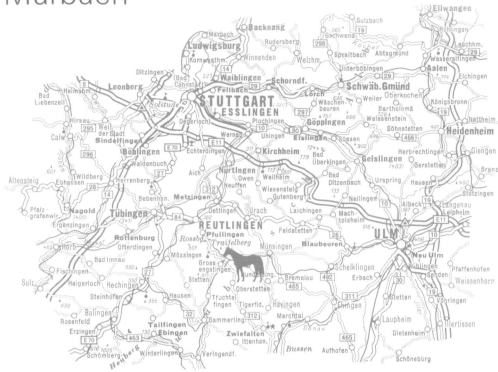

clear that horse breeding flourished in Marbach at that period, for in 1554 Christoph had a yard for foals installed at the farm of the former Carthusian monastery at Güterstein. The ducal horses became widely known, as shown by the following memorandum dated 1568: 'Not only did Duke Christoph establish a regional stud-farm (*Landgestüt*); he also had a private stud-farm and stables with horses of such high repute that foreign princes borrowed them for court festivals and revels.'

In those days it was chiefly Holsteins, Bohemians, Siebenbürgers, Hungarian and Turkish horses that were bred at Marbach. Among the stallions from Linz there were probably also Norikers, at that time favoured as riding-horses and now used for heavy work; some splendid specimens of this breed are still to be found at the St Johann stud-farm.

However, this first golden age of the Marbach stud-farm soon came to an end. Christoph died in December 1568. He was

Marbach in Württemberg is the oldest of the German state-owned stud-farms. With its herd of about fifty warm-blood mares and twenty pure-bred Arab mares it is at present also the only *Hauptgestüt* or central stud-farm in operation. Its exact age is not known.

In August 1552 Duke Christoph von Wirtemberg, while on a visit to Linz on the Danube, bought some stallions which he stood at his court stud-farm at Marbach to cover the mares of the province. And it is

(Top, right) Running parallel with the road at Marbach are the 'English stables', erected in 1840. Close to them, on the right, is the administration building, dating from the seventeenth century, with the residence of the stud director.

(Above) Between 1560 and 1563 Duke Christoph converted Grafeneck into a hunting lodge. The von Grafeneck family was closely connected with Marbach.

(Right) Marbach's trade mark is the horse-trough in the middle of the inner courtyard, erected in 1844. The figurine was cast at Wasseralfingen.

(Right) The extensive mountain pasturage, the nature of the soil and the climate provide the best conditions for the young Württembergers and Arabs.

(Far right) The special pride of Marbach is the herd of pure-bred Arab mares.

(Below and below, right) The East Prussian stallion *Julmond*, foundation sire of the breed of Württemberger saddle horses. He is commemorated by an inscribed tablet.

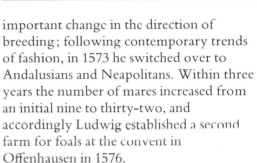

important change in the direction of breeding; following contemporary trends of fashion, in 1573 he switched over to Andalusians and Neapolitans. Within three years the number of mares increased from an initial nine to thirty-two, and accordingly Ludwig established a second farm for foals at the convent in Offenhausen in 1576.

During the Thirty Years War the entire stock of horses in Württemberg was destroyed. In 1634 Duke Eberhard III fled

succeeded by his son Ludwig, who until a few years ago was thought to have been the founder of the stud-farm. As a result of this error the 400th anniversary of the stud-farm was celebrated in 1973. This Ludwig was in fact a weak character and an alcoholic. He was interested in art, and his principal aim was to spread the Protestant doctrine; but he concerned himself little with the welfare of the country, and possibly even less with horse breeding. Nevertheless he brought about an

(Above) The riding-hall at Marbach, built between 1854 and 1860.

(Centre column) The three horses shown are Württemberger warm-blood stallions. This breed is distinguished by good action, conformation, style and points as a riding-horse, spirit and faultless disposition.

(Above) Two pure-bred Arab stallions. The grey *Saher*, by *Ghazal* out of *Sahmet*, perfectly embodies the high breeding and type of the Arab. The black Arab stallion *Gharib* was imported from Egypt in 1970. He is proving his worth as sire with Arab and selected warm-blood mares.

(Left) Horse's head over the stable entrance at the St Johann stud-farm.

to Strasbourg. Villages and estates were pillaged, many being burnt down. Practically no horses or oxen were left, so the few remaining cows were harnessed to ploughs and wagons.

In the last quarter of the seventeenth century horse breeding in Württemberg prospered anew. Baron von Kniestedt, the stud director, realized that the soil and climate on the mountainside called for an undemanding type of horse, and that horses from fertile marsh regions failed here. Spanish and Barb stallions were brought to Marbach, as well as some East Friesian stallions and heavy mares.

The eighteenth century brought new troubles, until Frederick II came to power in 1797. He set up an army, increased his lands and greatly intensified the breeding of horses. In 1811 Württemberg possessed a huge stock of 81,390 horses. In 1812 there were 190 state-owned sires, available to 36 covering stations. In that same year the Württemberg army of 15,800 men marched on Russia, with their ally

Napoleon. Five hundred of these soldiers returned, and tens of thousands of horses were left on the battle-fields. The breeding industry took a very long time to recover from this blow.

From 1860 onwards consolidation took place, primarily through the importation of Anglo-Norman stallions and East Prussian mares. Home-bred mares with a great deal of Oriental blood were also brought in. Thus, by the turn of the century the Württemberger warm-blood was fully

developed. Until after the Second World War the aim was to breed a working horse for agricultural, industrial and military purposes. This was followed, as everywhere else, by the switch to the breeding of horses for sport. To improve the breed, East Prussian stallions were introduced; some of these were of pure Arab or English blood. Enormous success was achieved with *Julmond*, who came to Marbach in 1960 and is recognized as the foundation sire of the modern Baden-Württemberg breed of

(Above) The Noriker sire *Wirt's Diamant* is a particularly impressive representative of this ancient breed. He is standing at St Johann, together with other cold-bloods. In the middle ages Norikers, originally from Roman Noricum, were in great demand as tournament and battle horses. Later they proved equally useful in agriculture.

(Above and left) The St Johann stud-farm received its name from a former hermitage with a chapel, later converted into a ducal hunting-lodge, and finally turned over to Marbach.

(Right and below) Some of the colts are reared at Güterstein. This stud-farm, with its historic half-timbered buildings, was constructed in 1819–20. Güterstein was originally a Cistercian monastery, and was sometimes used as a burial place by the ducal house of Württemberg.

riding-horses. The change-over at the stud-farm is now more or less complete. In selecting for breeding, great importance is attached to spirit and disposition as well as conformation, size and action.

Especially valued is the Marbach Arab breed. From 1814 to 1818 William I introduced Oriental mares and stallions into the Royal Stud at Weil and bred them pure. One of this breed was *Amurath 1881*. He was sold at the age of fourteen to the Prussian Government Stud at Radautz, and

had a considerable influence on many warm-blood breeds in Europe. In 1932 the pure-bred Arab stud-farm housed at Weil found a new home at Marbach.

The two stallions *Jasir* and *Hadban Enzahi* exercised a lasting effect on the breed. Brought from Egypt in 1955, *Hadban Enzahi* died in 1975 at Marbach. His descendants are to be found all over the world today. In 1970 the black stallion *Gharib* was acquired from Egypt. He is a worthy successor.

(Above) Residence on the Güterstein farm.

(Left and far left) The buildings of the Dominican convent founded in the twelfth century are still to be seen in the farmland at Offenhausen. The central point of the farm is the Early Gothic convent church, built in 1161.

Schlenderhan

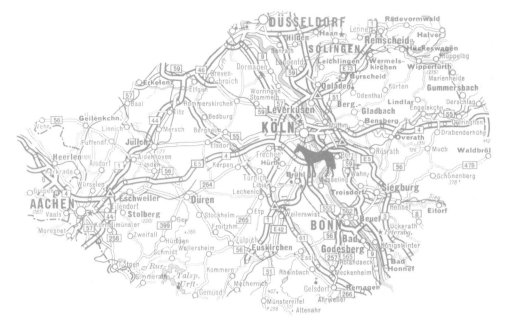

This establishment, the oldest by far of private German Thoroughbred stud-farms, was founded in 1869. It is exactly the same age as the German Derby, and the list of winners in this great and testing race includes no fewer than sixteen Schlenderhan horses. Such successes raise this stud-farm to a position of the highest eminence in Germany.

Throughout its history Schlenderhan has remained in the ownership of the Oppenheim family. The founder, Baron Eduard von Oppenheim, had the stud-farm

grounds laid out around Schloss Schlenderhan, his father's summer residence. After Eduard's death, the breeding concern was run by his son, Simon Alfred (up to 1932), and daughter-in-law, Baroness Florence von Oppenheim (up to 1935). Her son, Baron Waldemar von Oppenheim, faced the formidable task of steering the stud-farm, as well as the family-owned banking business in Cologne, through the war years and then building them up again out of the wreckage. The strain finally proved too

much for him; he died, prematurely, in December 1952. His wife, Baroness Gabrielle, continued to run the stud-farm with great skill, impressively demonstrated by her outstanding successes (for example, eight out of twenty-seven owner championships and ten out of thirty-three breeder championships within twenty-five years).

The high quality of the Schlenderhan horses is attributable partly to the excellent soil, but also to the Oppenheim family's expertise at breeding. After the successful establishment of the brood-mare herd, home-bred stock was increasingly valued. But while great care was taken in pure line-breeding, the importance of renewing the blood was not forgotten. For this purpose mares of well-proved lines, both German and foreign, were acquired, and top-class stallions were obtained from other countries. Another fact of undoubted significance is that during its 110 years of existence Schlenderhan has had only three directors. The first director was the Englishman, George Castle. He was

PRIAMOS
in Schlenderhan 1976

coincided with the centenary celebrations of Schlenderhan and the German Derby), *Alpenkönig* and *Stuyvesant*.

Schlenderhan has exercised an enormous influence on the whole German bloodstock industry and on racing. In other countries too, it continues to enjoy high esteem, both on account of victories won in its own colours, as for example in England and France, and for the high quality of the progeny of its stallions, headed by the great *Oleander*. *Oleander* got successful sons in England, France, Italy, South America and elsewhere; probably the most important of all the Schlenderhan horses, he was champion sire of the year in Germany no fewer than nine times, and was there for several decades the idol of the Turf.

Ever since its foundation, Schlenderhan has had particularly close relations with horse breeding in England. At the present time the famous *Lombard* is standing at Banstead Manor Stud, Newmarket.

Not only did Schlenderhan acquire mares from abroad, it also sold them to internationally known foreign breeders, for example to François Dupré the owner of the Haras d'Ouilly, and to Daniel Wildenstein, who now keeps his horses at the Haras de Victot, near Deauville. A few years ago Wildenstein acquired the double classic winning mare *Schönbrunn*, who went on to win the Grand Prix de Deauville in his colours.

In 1977 the stallions *Alpenkönig* and *Priamos* were standing at the stud-farm. Four more Schlenderhan stallions are standing at other establishments or are leased out.

followed by Count Kurt Sponeck who, in a partnership with trainer George Arnull lasting several decades, scored great successes. Since 1953 Ewald Meyer zu Düte has been director of the stud-farm. The above-mentioned eight owner championships and ten breeder championships, won since he took over, speak for themselves. Trainers have been changed only when absolutely unavoidable.

The number of top-class horses bred at Schlenderhan runs into hundreds. Some eighty classic winners have come out of their own racing stables in Berlin-Hoppegarten and Cologne. As mentioned above, sixteen of them won the German Derby. The winners in this, the most important of German races, were (in chronological order): *Sieger*, *Ariel*, *Marmor*, *Mah Jong*, *Alba*, *Sturmvogel*, *Orgelton*, *Wehr Dich*, the 'wonder mare' *Schwarzgold*, *Magnat*, *Allgäu*, *Asterblüte*, *Allasch*, *Don Giovanni* (whose victory at Horner Moor

Röttgen

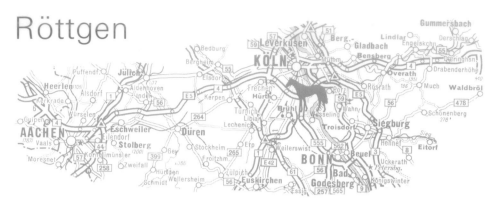

In 1975 *Star Appeal* won the hardest and the greatest race in the world, the Prix de l'Arc de Triomphe. He was the first victor to come from a German stable. In the same year he was three times victorious in the most important European races in Group I, in England, France and Italy: another record for a German horse.

As a two- and three-year-old, *Star Appeal* ran in the Röttgen colours, at four and five years in those of the Moritzberg stable. He was trained for his races by Theo Grieper at the Röttgen training grounds. By the end of his career his winnings totalled DM1,538,836, an amount never previously reached in Germany. After winning the titles 'Federal Republic Galloper of the Year, 1975' and 'Europa Champion, 1975', he is now standing at the English National Stud at Newmarket.

The Röttgen stud-farm lies to the south-east of Cologne, at the edge of the Königsforst. With an area of 240 hectares (593 acres) it is the largest as well as one of the most successful, and certainly the most beautiful, of the German bloodstock studs. Its history begins in the year 1904 when Peter Mühlens, proprietor of the 4711 Eau de Cologne company, acquired Röttgen Castle and the adjoining Maarhausen estate. In the course of time stud buildings in the Renaissance style were erected, and, following the Irish model, the grounds were enclosed with a wall 2 m (over 6 feet) high and 7 km (4 miles) long. A model industry was created, operating effectively and harmoniously. The various stable blocks are widely separated, to minimize the risk of infection. Roads and paths are bordered by hedges. In 1927 the small Durchhäuserhof estate was acquired; its special feature is the half-timbered buildings enclosing a square courtyard. A year later the Leidenhausen estate was also purchased, but this was afterwards transferred to the City of Cologne. The stud-farm was actually established in 1924, when the first Thoroughbreds moved into the stables. During the period preceding the Second World War, the racing stable was

The Maarhausen estate, part of the Röttgen establishment, is also the home of a herd of dairy cows with their calves, which have frequently been admired; they also complement the horses from the point of view of grazing.

(Above) Exterior view of the brood-mare stables. Close by is the residence of the stud director. In the paddock a herd of weaned foals.

located in the former stronghold of German racing, in Berlin-Hoppegarten. The stable colours are turquoise jacket, gold sleeves and red cap – the colours of the 4711 company. The stallion *Palastpage* wore these colours in 1932 when he won the first Derby victory for the relatively new stable.

During the war Peter Mühlens died. His daughter Maria, a successful dressage rider, took over the management of the stud-farm, which was in need of re-stocking, as most of the valuable horses had been lost.

From 1945 to 1953, Schloss Röttgen was the residence of the British Military Governor, and it was here that the negotiations between the three Western occupation powers and Konrad Adenauer concerning the German treaty were conducted. During this time Maria Mühlens made her home at the racing stables, and from that base pursued the rebuilding of the stud-farm with characteristic energy.

The training centre was at Hoppegarten, now in the Eastern sector. The Röttgen racing stable therefore moved to the trainer Schlaefke at Dortmund, where it remained until 1952 when the establishment's own training track at the Leidenhausen estate became ready for use.

Maria married Consul Rudi Mehl, who encouraged her enthusiasm for horse breeding in every possible way. Personalities such as Count Manfred Lehndorff-Preye, Adrian von Borcke and Heinz Hasler collaborated energetically as stud directors and trainers to make the stable successful.

Röttgen's numerous great horses include *Uomo*, Derby winner in 1959, *Prince Ippi*, victor in the 1972 Europa Grand Prix and the 1973 Italian Grand Prix; and *Lord Udo*, who ran second in the 1975 German Derby. *Prince Ippi* and *Lord Udo* are now standing at Röttgen. Top mares in various years were: *Königswiese*, *Stammesart*, *Wacholdis*, *Santa Cruz* and *Widschi*.

The present stud director is Dr Jens Baron von Lepel.

(Above) *Star Appeal*, the dream stallion bred at Röttgen, whose performance on the racecourse beat all other German Thoroughbreds. He is now standing at the English National Stud at Newmarket. The picture is by the internationally famous painter of horses, Ingo Koblischek.

(Left) The eighteen-year-old *Princess Addi*, dam of *Prince Ippi*, with colt at foot.

Vornholz

In the period just before the Second World War, Baron Clemens von Nagel-Doornick began to make arrangements for establishing a private stud-farm at Vornholz. The war, however, interrupted this activity. The baron, who was descended from a family of provincial stud directors, served during the war, until 1944, in the eastern region stud administration, and was director of the central stud at Razot in the Posen (Poznan) area.

When he arrived at Razot, the baron found many horses which he had known very well in his youth. This of course was because when the Prussian central stud-farm at Beberbeck was closed down in 1929 many of the brood-mares were sold to Razot.

In 1938 Baron von Nagel had brought the former Rastenburg regional sire *Oxyd* to Vornholz. *Oxyd*, then aged fourteen, had been sired by the Trakehnen *Irrlehrer*, sired in turn by the celebrated Thoroughbred stallion *Perfectionist*. The grand-sire on the female side, *Metellus*, was also a Thoroughbred. *Irrlehrer* sired numerous Beberbeck mares who went to Razot.

Oxyd proved to be a brilliant sire, producing such notable dressage horses as *Adular*, *Afrika* and *Cyrenaica* for the equestrian sports which were being revived. Meanwhile the baron secured for his stud-farm the great master Otto Lörke and his pupil Willi Schultheis. For the 1952 Olympic Games the Vornholz stud-farm provided the horses for the successful

German dressage team. *Adular* was ridden by Heinz Pollay and *Afrika* by Baroness Ida von Nagel. The Thoroughbred *Chronist*, also bred at Vornholz, had Fritz Thiedemann in the saddle.

Four years later, at Stockholm, *Adular*, with Liselott Linsenhoff, and *Afrika* were in the team which won the Silver Medal. The East Prussian *Perkunos*, carrying Hannelore Weygand, completed the German dressage team.

Immediately after the war Baron Clemens von Nagel also exerted himself to make valuable international contacts, turning his private sports meetings to advantage in promoting top German riders as well as making sporting and general contacts with riders and highly placed personalities of the occupation powers.

The Vornholz stud director performed a great service in sending to stud the superb sire *Ramzes X*, a grey Anglo-Arab from Poland, whose descendants figured largely in international jumping events. The activities of his sons as sires in Westphalia and Schleswig-Holstein ensure that the genetic heritage is carried on through grandsons and great-grandsons. His most famous son, *Radetzky*, was bred at Vornholz, out of *Malta*, by *Oxyd* (Beberbecker) on a Hanoverian foundation, as was the Olympic horse *Adular*, by *Oxyd*.

(Above) *Krowalcza* (out of the celebrated Polish jumper mare *Warschawianka*), used by the Baron to sire show-jumpers.

(Above, right) View of one of the beautiful tiled stables with a daughter of *Ramzes*.

(Right) Brood-mares and foals in a paddock.

Ravensberg

Paul Niemöller's name appeared in the German General Stud Book for the first time in 1907. This enterprising rider had acquired *Humoreske*, daughter of *Cazabat*, in the previous year, thus laying the foundation for the Ravensberg stud-farm, an establishment which, though only of medium size (with an average stock of fifteen brood-mares) nevertheless ranks as one of Germany's greatest bloodstock stud-farms, thanks to its tremendous successes in breeding and in racing.

Other brood-mares came to join *Humoreske*, but only one of those working at the stud-farm up to 1940 became the founder of a family still flourishing today: this was *Glatz* by *Glasshampton*, imported from England in 1901. Her last foal was *Grund*, who produced many good horses of whom the foremost was the Union winner and sire, *Grenzbock*.

Paul Niemöller died in 1946, but his grandson Reinhard Delius proved an enthusiastic successor. After a few years under the new proprietor the stud-farm attained a leading position in statistics, which it still maintains. This was largely as a result of the acquisition in 1940 of several mares with excellent breeding qualities, including *Copia*, *Treibjagd* and *Waldrun*. *Treibjagd* became the dam, or taproot-dam, of the classic stallions *Tannenhäher*, *Tannenberg*, *Tannenbruch*, *Tannenhorst* and *Tajo*. *Waldrun* produced the splendid mares *Windstille*, *Wildbahn* and *Witterung* and the champion stallions *Windfang*, *Wilderer*, *Waidwerk* and *Waidmannsheil*, *Windbruch* and *Windwurf*.

Since 1946 Ravensberg has supplied twenty sires, some of which have gone to Brazil, Holland, Czechoslovakia and the Soviet Union.

Up to 1976 Ravensberg produced eight classic winners, including the Derby winners *Waidwerk* and *Wilderer*. In addition (mentioning only the most important races), there were two winners of the Union, one of the Baden Grand Prix, four of the North-Rhine-Westphalia Grand Prix, four of the Aral-Pokal and three of the Europa Prize.

Ravensberg's most important sires include: *Georgios* (1923–39), *Onkel Ludwig* (1925–33), who was descended from the famous *Kincsem*, *Aventin* (1934–40), *Ansitz* (1947–63), *Neckar* (1947–54), *Waidmann* (1964–76), sire of *Tajo*, now also at stud, and finally, since 1969, *Kaiseradler*.

It was in 1906 that the first Thoroughbred brood-mare arrived at Ravensberg, but not until the 1920s was there any considerable building development at the stud-farm. In 1921 a house was erected, in 1923 the foal stable, a little later a brood-mare stable 60 m (about 66 yards) long, with twenty-five loose-boxes, and in 1926 an English-type open-plan stable with nineteen boxes for the racehorses. In the 1960s a large riding-hall was built, completing the horse-shoe arrangement of the complex. Attached to the stud-farm is an excellent training establishment.

(Left) *Neckar*, born in 1948, by *Ticino* out of *Nixe*. He stood at Ravensberg for twenty years, was on many occasions champion German sire and top sire of successful brood-mares. He sired a number of German Derby winners and the Italian Derby winner *Hogarth*, as well as the top-class mare *Tadolina*, who became internationally famous. *Neckar* died in 1974.

Altefeld

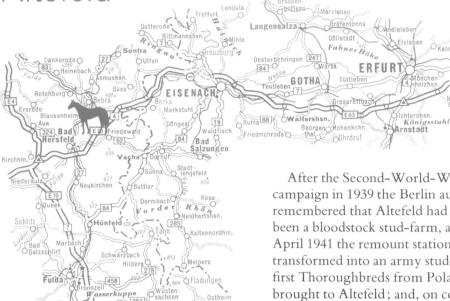

Altefeld was founded in 1913, the last of the Prussian state-owned stud-farms. Between 1914 and 1920 all the stables needed for bloodstock breeding and the accommodation for the staff were built.

In the period following the First World War the authorities in Berlin began to introduce economies, and the Altefeld stud-farm was closed down. On 1 April 1935 the Altefeld Remount Farm was established. Altefeld now supplied the military remount department, and so had horses once again.

After the Second-World-War Polish campaign in 1939 the Berlin authorities remembered that Altefeld had formerly been a bloodstock stud-farm, and on 1 April 1941 the remount station was transformed into an army stud-farm. The first Thoroughbreds from Poland were brought to Altefeld; and, on conclusion of the campaign in France, French Thoroughbreds followed. When the first products of the new Altefeld stud-farm were ready to show their ability on the German racecourses, the Second World War came to an end – and with it the breeding of Thoroughbreds. The Americans occupied Altefeld, and all the horses were taken as spoils of war. Many of the horses which had been brought in were returned to their owners in France, others were sent off to the United States.

On 1 March 1947 the State of Hesse leased Altefeld to the Hesse Stud Book Association at Kassel, and a small part of it to the Commission for Thoroughbred Breeding in Hesse.

In 1957 the whole of the Altefeld property was taken over by the Federal Republic and was run as a large agricultural enterprise by a tenant who kept up to 140 dairy cows there.

On 1 August 1962 the agreement with the tenant was terminated. About 135 hectares (334 acres) of land together with the stables and staff accommodation, the St Georg Hotel and the forage manager's house, were sold to the Waldfried stud-farm. A great deal of money had to be

(Top) The former stable of the yearling mares at Altefeld, the last of the Prussian stud-farms, founded in 1913 for breeding Thoroughbreds; the Thoroughbreds from Graditz were installed here.

(Above) Two of the sires of the Waldfried Stud, now established at Altefeld. *Norfolk*, born in 1964, by *Masetto* out of *Namedy*; *Marullus*, born in 1966, by *Waidmann* out of *Meraviglia*.

(Left) The 'Church' stable, where brood-mares are kept.

(Right) The 'Forest' stables, where the yearlings are kept.

(Below) In the foreground, the covering-hall for visiting mares; behind it, the stallion stable, with four boxes. Behind the stallion stable, and not visible in the photograph, is a second covering-hall for the stud-farm's own mares. These buildings, erected in 1914, were designed on the most up-to-date lines; they are now, however, no longer in use.

(Bottom) The farm buildings, erected at the beginning of the First World War, are also now disused.

invested, and it took the whole of Frau Alexandra Scherping's fortune to organize Altefeld for Thoroughbreds again. With its famous horses, its splendid stables and extensive pastures, the Waldfried stud-farm is now, as was the former Prussian State Stud, the ornament of the Altefeld municipality; but it is also well known among horse connoisseurs far beyond the confines of the Federal Republic.

One Altefeld horse, *Elviro*, was victorious in the German Derby at Hamburg-Horn, and is now standing at the stud-farm. Several other winners in famous races have proved the quality of their birthplace.

Denmark

After the Second World War horse breeding in Denmark, as in the rest of Western Europe, rapidly declined. Whereas in 1945 there was still a relatively large stock of 650,000 horses, by 1960 there were fewer than 40,000. It was not necessary to be a pessimist to agree with the prediction that in a few decades horses would be found only in zoos. However, the very mechanization which caused the disappearance of these animals from agriculture and transport brought them renewed popularity as a result of rising prosperity and urbanization. Within fifteen years their numbers almost doubled.

As a consequence of the new purposes for which they are bred, the relative numbers of the different breeds and types of horses have naturally changed. Cold-bloods, latterly common, are now found only in small numbers. Warm-bloods for sport, Norwegian Fjord horses and Iceland ponies for leisure riding, and English ponies for children now dominate the scene.

It would be an exaggeration to say that horse breeding in Denmark has European significance. But there is no doubt that the country breeds good horses and hard-working ponies, a result of the fact that many breeders have not been too proud to make use of experience gained in other countries. Not only have modern horses been imported, but advice and experts have been obtained, in particular from Sweden and North Germany.

On the other hand, Denmark can look back on a glorious past. In his *World Chronicle*, written around 1200, the German monk Arnold von Lübeck relates that the richest sources of revenue in Denmark are the herring fisheries in Öresund and the many good horses reared on the fertile pastures. A quarter of a century later it was recorded that 50 chargers and 50 team-horses had to be paid as ransom for the Danish King Waldemar Sejr. And shortly afterwards, according to the Royal Archives, 8400 horses were exported from the marshlands of Ribe in South Jutland alone. This was always an important region for horse breeding, with considerable exports, and it is still an

important centre for the breeding of Danish warm-bloods. Most of the horses exported in the twelfth and thirteenth centuries naturally went to Germany. But the fame of the peerless Danish horses spread much further, to France as well as other countries. It is known, for example, that in the middle of the thirteenth century Abbot Stephen of Paris sent a trusty friend to procure for him a 'brilliant' Danish riding-horse, for which 'no equal was to be found' in France at that time. At the English court, too, there were Danish riding-horses.

For the next few hundred years historical records relating to Denmark's horses are fairly scant. Systematic horse breeding was not started until about 1500. But it appears that at that time the élite horses came mainly from northern Germany and from Friesland, which in those days still lay within the borders of the Danish kingdom. Horses were in fact already being bred for certain purposes on the royal farms and the estates of the nobles and of the Church, but there were no proper stud-farms until after about 1550.

The Reformation and wars of religion affected not only the life of the Church but also the whole economic and social structure of the country. The vast domains of the Church, together with stables and horses, passed into the possession of the king. When Frederick II came to the throne in 1559, the enormous, powerful chargers, which had to carry the heavy armour and equipment of the knights, were going out of fashion: the invention of gunpowder had made them redundant. Purer-bred horses were more to the taste of the court, where they were better suited to the prevailing display of pomp and luxury. Spanish horses were most in demand all over Europe and hence also in Denmark. Innumerable horses were bought from Spain and Italy for the Danish court. Royal stud-farms, of varying sizes, were established throughout the country, and the first stud director of the kingdom was appointed. In fact, Frederick II was his own chief stud director, as is shown by documents and by legends.

The story of the royal stud-farm at Frederiksborg is related in detail in the following section.

When Frederiksborg was closed down in 1871, many of the horses went to neighbouring farms. Proud of the ancient breed of horses, the new owners did not concern themselves with trends of fashion, but remained firmly faithful to the old Frederiksborg strains. In recent decades, however, even these breeders have had to change their ways in order to continue selling their horses. The Frederiksborgs, which had been useful as farm horses, became less and less popular. Switching over to a multi-purpose riding-horse inevitably introduced problems. Steeply sloped shoulders and rounded baroque shapes are not easy to breed out, particularly when these have been features of the race for nearly three hundred years.

About ten years ago it was thought that the final disappearance of the old type of Frederiksborg was only a few years away. But it appears that since then the breed has

(P. 84) One of the most famous equestrian statues in Europe shows Frederick V on horseback. Its creation occupied the great French sculptor Joseph Saly for over twenty years, and its final cost was more than twice that of building the four palaces which today form the royal residence in Copenhagen, the Amalienborg. Saly worked from the dimensions of six horses, and created an exact representation of the Frederiksborg breed as it looked around 1760.

been given another chance. By the cautious introduction of foreign blood, enthusiastic breeders are now trying to preserve the old type of Danish horse.

Breeding in Denmark is of course not just concentrated round the former royal stud-farm, even though this is the only horse breeding centre that achieved fame outside the country for 250 years. Among the Danish breeds there are still also to be found the original farm horse, which was first bred in Jutland and is hence called a Jutlander. This is a medium-sized, powerful, heavy working horse, often chestnut, with a light-coloured mane and tail and luxuriant feathers. Naturally, the Jutlanders in particular were largely driven out by the mechanization of farming, and there are now barely 500 registered specimens in the country. In spite of this, some 50 two- and three-year-olds are shown every year at the big agricultural fair in Jutland, as representatives of the breed. When it becomes necessary to reinvigorate the blood, the breeders can turn to Schleswig-Holstein for replenishments. The present-day Schleswiger is a descendant of the Jutlander from the period before 1864, when Schleswig still belonged to Denmark.

Around the turn of the century two breeds of horses which soon attained great importance were introduced into the country. By the late 1930s the mighty Belgian had become the commonest breed. As cold-bloods have gone out of fashion, this breed has almost disappeared again, and only a few breeders still keep Belgians.

The Frederiksborg Castle collection includes the famous book by Gebauer which was created around 1820 and contains fifteen colour lithographs depicting horses from the Frederiksborg stud-farm. At that time the baroque ceremonial horse was already going out of fashion, and in 1840 the royal stud-farm switched over to breeding Thoroughbreds, though with little success. In 1871 it was closed down.

The Oldenburger became a serious competitor to the light Danish horse, the Frederiksborg, which it supplanted in many districts, especially between the two world wars.

In order to get back to the general European standard after the extremely critical post-war years, a breeders' union was founded. Horses for breeding were brought in from Sweden, Holstein and Hanover as well as Trakehnens from West Germany and Poland.

In Denmark today there are about 70,000 horses of many different breeds and nearly as many colours as in the golden age of the Frederiksborg stud-farm.

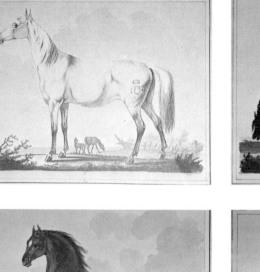

Frederiksborg

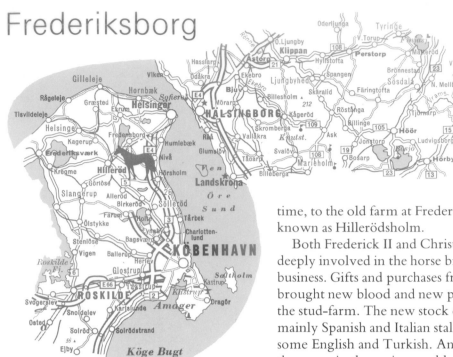

The Reformation in Denmark in 1536 was of decisive significance for the creation of the Royal Stud at Frederiksborg; it brought about an enormous increase in the power and wealth of the king. The Renaissance life-style spread to Denmark also. Horse breeding became an important activity, partly for the entertainment of the courtiers and partly to provide rapid communication both within the country and abroad.

As well as his residence in Copenhagen, Frederick II had other castles built, including Frederiksborg in densely forested North Zealand. As soon as the construction of the castle was started in 1560, a horse breeding establishment was organized in the nearby former monastery at Esrom. In 1620 the royal breeding horses were taken to Sparepenge. Extensive stables were installed at this country seat just north of Frederiksborg, which had been built by Christian IV. In 1720 Sparepenge had to make way for a large new pleasure-ground, and the stud-farm was moved, for the last

time, to the old farm at Frederiksborg, known as Hillerödsholm.

Both Frederick II and Christian IV were deeply involved in the horse breeding business. Gifts and purchases from abroad brought new blood and new possibilities to the stud-farm. The new stock comprised mainly Spanish and Italian stallions, but also some English and Turkish. An inventory of the mares in the various paddocks, dating from the time of Christian IV, indicates how much the King enjoyed experimenting (not only in the sphere of breeding). He introduced a system of brand-marking and started an annual breeding record, so it is possible to trace which mares were covered by which stallions in the years between 1611 and 1623. After the institution of the absolute monarchy in 1660, even greater importance was attached to pomp and splendour in court ceremonies. The Marshal of the Horse was assigned more official duties than ever before. At consecrations and coronations, at weddings, princely visits and receptions, at hunts and equestrian displays (including the

tournament or Carousel), individual horses of different colours and teams with matching colours played an ever greater part.

Under Christian IV the rather casual method of cross-breeding gave way to pure breeding to colour. The aim now was to produce as many horses as possible having unusual and distinctive colours as individuals and for teams.

Stud director Anton Wolf, Baron von Haxthausen, brought to the development of the stud-farm a degree of planning and order previously unknown. It is as a result of his work that the Frederiksborg horse – the 'Dane', as it was usually called – achieved European renown.

In the eighteenth century further strides were made in the development of the stud-farm, as regards both breeding activity and the expansion and renovation of the building. The number of horses at that time was about 700, and 50 to 100 foals were produced annually.

The year 1720 was the most important in the history of the Frederiksborg stud-farm.

In the second half of the sixteenth century, thanks to the enormous increase of his wealth as a consequence of the Reformation, Frederick II of Denmark was able to build more palaces in addition to his old castle in Copenhagen. Thus, in the second half of the 16th century, the palace of Frederiksborg was built at the entrance to the Kronborg Sound, 40 km (25 miles) north of Copenhagen where the Royal Stud was also installed.

(Right) The palace of Frederiksborg, seen from the little town of Hilleröd.

(Below) This is how the painter L. Baralta saw Frederiksborg in 1652. To the right of the palace are the stables where the stud-farm was housed from 1620 to 1720. The horseman in the foreground, left, is Frederick III.

(Overleaf) Frederiksborg.

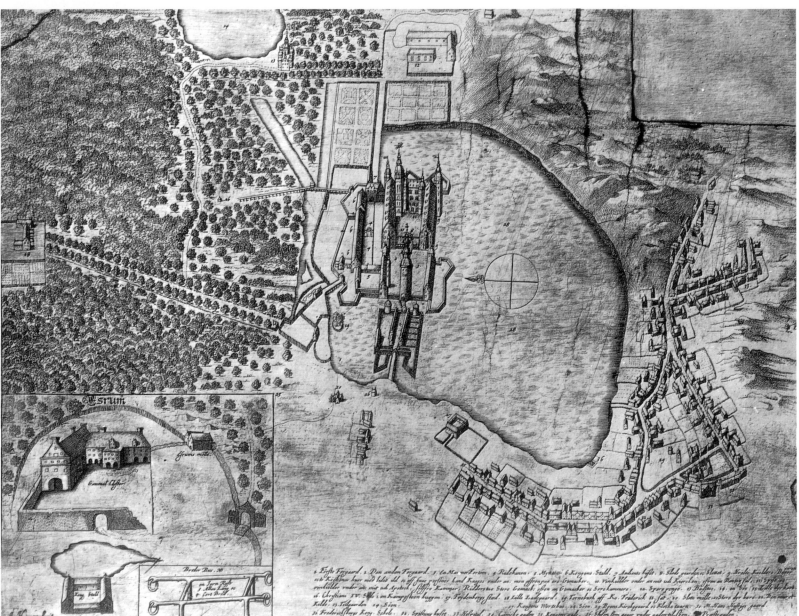

(P. 90, above) At the Rosenborg Castle in Copenhagen there are several paintings of scenes from the Royal Danish Riding-School around 1690.
(Left) Christian V riding in a carousel.
(Centre) Behind the unknown horseman stands Frederiksborg Castle.
(Right) Prince Jörgen with Vordingborg Castle, South Zealand, in the background. There was a small royal stud-farm at Vordingborg also.

As already mentioned, it was then that the horses from Sparepenge were brought to Hillerödsholm. The vast woodland pastures here were divided up by stone walls. From that time onward regular yearly reports were made, giving the fullest details of the breeding activities.

With the passage of time the Hillerödsholm establishment had to be enlarged and improved. The oldest parts dated from its foundation around 1570. In 1742 the construction of a large new stable was started, to take more than 300 horses. The planning and management of the building operation were in the hands of one of the best Danish architects of the period, L. Thurah. He arranged the new complex of buildings around a courtyard measuring 70 m (230 feet) square. Thus an imposing establishment was created in a typical baroque style, outstanding both for its size and clear layout and for the excellent balance of the large buildings and the smaller connecting sections. In 1817 the east wing was converted into a large riding-school in the classical style, with a magnificent wooden vaulted roof. With the passing of the feudal system, the basis for maintaining the costly court stud-farm disappeared. Retrenchment began in 1771 when Christian VII's minister, Struensee, introduced reforms which ultimately led to the bankruptcy of the country in 1813 and a protracted crisis in the economy of Denmark.

Attempts were nevertheless made to keep the stud-farm going. The breeding of English Thoroughbreds, which was rapidly spreading throughout Europe, found its way into Denmark also. In 1840 the Frederiksborg stud-farm was transformed into a breeding centre for Thoroughbreds. But the expected results failed to materialize. In 1871 the national stud-farm was closed down. The two farms at Frederiksborg were turned over to agriculture and leased out. The Hillerödsholm stud establishment was pulled down, and ordinary houses now stand on this ground rich in tradition.

(P. 90, below) This copper engraving dates from around 1670. The oldest of the Frederiksborg buildings can be seen (centre top). To the left, at the end of the avenue, is the later stud establishment, Hillerödsholm. In the bottom left-hand corner is a sketch of the medieval stables at the Esrum monastery.

(Above) The only building of the once-famous Frederiksborg stud-farm at Hillerödsholm which is still standing is the riding-school. This was also dismantled, together with the entire stud establishment, towards the end of the 1930s, but was bought by the Hörsholm Riding Club and re-erected at Hörsholm in North Zealand.

(Right) Frederiksborg horses, as they appear today. During recent decades the breeding system has changed, and modern-type sporting horses are now produced.

Sweden

In 1920 the number of horses in Sweden reached its peak at 720,000. Of these, 80 per cent were draught horses. By 1942 the stock had fallen to 600,000 and, continuing to diminish rapidly, passed the 200,000 mark in 1960 and reached its lowest figure (82,000) in 1970. Since then breeding levels have started to rise again and in 1976 there were some 110,000 horses in the country.

Generally speaking, the standard of horse breeding in Sweden today is high. This is largely the result of the following legislative measures:

1 The state premium: this was laid down in 1884.

2 The Stallion Inspection Law, which lays down that mares may be sent only to stallions selected by a commission.

3 In order to be selected for breeding, a mare must be able to show at least three, and a stallion at least four, recognized generations on the maternal side. In addition, both stallions and mares must pass a performance test. (Thoroughbreds and trotters are exceptions to this rule. On the other hand, they have to perform very well on the racetrack before they are allowed to be used for breeding.)

4 The selection procedure includes a rigorous veterinary examination (eyes, respiratory system, genital organs, hoofs, skin, general constitution).

5 The selection commission also makes an exacting assessment of type, conformation and action.

The different breeds in Sweden

The breeding of modern-type Arabs did not start until 1960, the foundation stock being imported from Poland and England. By far the biggest proportion came from Poland. In that country, which has an outstanding reputation for breeding Arabs, all the horses of this breed have to prove themselves on the racetrack, whereas in England breeders rely more on bloodlines and handsome conformation. About 50 stallions at stud in Sweden serve some 350 pure-bred Arab mares as well as a great many riding-pony

mares. The Swedish Arab breed already has a good international reputation. The major stud-farms (Blommeröd, Claerstorp, Indingstad and Möllebacken) have already exported a large number of Arabs, all of Polish descent, to the USA at high prices. Races are also held for Arabs.

For English Thoroughbreds there are three racecourses: Täby, at Stockholm; Aby, at Gothenburg; and Jägersro, at Malmö. The classic races are open only to horses bred in Scandinavia.

Norwegian Fjord horses have been recognized for breeding in Sweden since 1961. In 1962, 6 stallions and 62 mares were imported from Norway, and 3 stallions and 125 mares from Denmark; the quality of those from Norway was better. Breeding is carried on mainly in south and central Sweden. In 1976 the stock consisted of 63 stallions and 1475 mares. In 1874 the first Ardennais were imported from Belgium; they settled down here better than other cold-bloods and soon made tremendous progress. In 1940, 60,000 Swedish-Ardennais mares were covered; in 1976, however, this figure fell to 1700.

Around 1920 some 90 mares were being used for breeding, in 1970 about 450. Today the number of Thoroughbred mares has fallen to about 225. The expenses faced by the owners of racing stables are rising faster than the prize money. Because of this many Thoroughbred mares are now being covered by warm-blood stallions since there is a better market for riding-horses.

Warm-bloods are the most successful breeds in Sweden, and about 5700 mares are covered, about 3500 of them by 42 state-owned stallions, and the remainder by 73 stallions in private ownership. The type of animal aimed at is a riding-horse which is easy to manage and which can be used for various purposes, with a pleasant temperament and easy, generous paces.

The best and genetically most reliable maternal lines are numbered; there are 45 altogether. Of these 10 are Trakehnens, 12 Hanoverians and 23 old Swedish warm-bloods. Breeding is based at the central stud-farm at Flyinge where the young stallions are reared and selected. Many of the Swedish warm-bloods which have been exported have acquired excellent reputations in dressage.

In 1923 the Swedish parliament approved the introduction of the totalisator in horse racing. Since then trotting has shown a considerable increase. There were 4 stallions and 13 mares in 1920, 26 stallions and 300 mares in 1930, and 191 stallions and 4325 mares in 1975. Up to 1950 the breeding stock was all imported from the USA; later on horses were also brought from France and Russia. Crosses of French and American Trotters often gave excellent results. At the present time the breeding level is high, as is evidenced by the large numbers of exports to Finland and Germany.

In 1961 a Regulation was issued on the selective breeding of Fjord horses, thus conferring official recognition on this breed in Sweden. Fjord horses are not classed as ponies here; in earlier times they were used as draught animals, but nowadays about half of them – numbering some 750 – are ridden.

The old native race is the North Swede, a

(Below) The Gotland Pony, believed to have been roaming the forests in the island of Gotland for over a thousand years, a herd of about seventy are still maintained, running wild. During recent decades this type of pony has become very popular for children, and is much used for equestrian sports, jumping and trotter driving. Since 1966 their numbers have risen from 58 stallions to 121 and from 780 mares to 1750. Gotland Ponies are also being exported in increasing numbers, and there is already a special Breeders' Association for them in the USA.

powerful working horse highly prized by lumbermen. In former times the forest folk amused themselves on Sundays by organizing trotting races with these horses. Fast mares were often crossed with Norwegian Döle stallions, producing faster but also lighter offspring. At the present time two stud books are kept for this breed, one with about 1300 mares for working horses and one with about 1100 mares for trotters.

The Gotland Pony is the ancient local breed which has inhabited the island of Gotland for many hundreds of years. The Breeders' Association still maintains a herd of some 60 wild ponies in a 450-hectare (1100-acre) forest; they are left to fend for themselves the whole year round. Only in very severe winters are they given a little hay. These ponies do of course exhibit the defects of conformation common to the wild races – somewhat larger head, short neck, long slack back and sloping croup – but on the other hand they have robust health, endurance and amazing performance; their sinews, joints and hoofs are remarkable. Standing no more than 130 cm (13 hands) they are nowadays often ridden by children at events; in jumping they clear 150 cm (5 feet) without any trouble, and the fastest Gotlander trotted the kilometre (five furlongs) in 1 min 45.5 seconds. In 1976, 121 stallions covered 1750 mares.

Recognized British ponies include Shetlands, Welsh (three types), New Forest and Connemara. Of the Shetlands there are now about 1500, of the Welsh about 1000,

New Forest 1500 and Connemara 450. Just as in the rest of Europe, there is now a great interest in pony breeding.

Flyinge

In 1658, on conclusion of the Peace of Roskilde between Denmark and Sweden, Charles X of Sweden ordered that a stud-farm should be established at Flyinge, situated in the province of Skåne, which had previously belonged to Denmark. Horse breeding had of course been carried on here much earlier, on a large scale. Archbishop Absalon (1128–1202) apparently did not rely exclusively on the help of the heavenly powers; he had at his command an imposing troop of cavalry.

The main task of the Royal Stud was to produce horses for the royal stables and the cavalry. The stock consisted of a strange mixture of breeds; there were Frederiksborgs from Denmark; Holsteins, Hanoverians and East Prussians from Germany; as well as horses from Russia, Hungary, Spain, Turkey, France and England.

The duties of the central stud-farm at the present time were laid down by Parliament in 1923.

The production of Swedish half-breeds is

(Above) The entrance to the central stud-farm at Flyinge, over 300 years old; the tower is a special feature.

(Left) *Drabant*, an influential stallion. His son *Wald*, carrying Gustav Fischer, won the dressage Silver Medal in Rome. He also sired Mrs Becher's *Silver Dream* and over a hundred high-performance horses in Sweden. Among the Trakehnens who came to Flyinge in the 1920s, *Sonnensänger*, *Kyffhäuser* and *Humanist* were especially distinguished. *Humanist* founded the most important stallion line still flourishing today, the line to which *Drabant* also belongs.

(Right) Preparing for the stallion parade. Head groom Yngve Viebke is riding *Piaff*, the Munich Gold Medal dressage horse, and driving the grey *Immer* and *Gaspari*, sire of *Piaff*, in tandem. Flyinge's dressage horses are much in demand; among the best-known are Frau Linsenhoff's *Piaff*, Frau Becher's *Silver Dream* and

Elektron, Herbert Rehbein's *Mars* and *Magnus II*, W. W. Haug's *Glenn* and C. Schumacher's *Flyinge* in Germany; Henri Chammartin's *Wöhler*, *Woermann* and *Woldietrich* and Gustav Fischer's *Wald* in Switzerland; Sarah Withmore's *Junker* and D. Lawrence's *San Fernando* in England.

based on old Swedish, Hanoverian and East Prussian female lines. Between 1920 and 1930 the stallions came for the most part from Hanover, but some also from East Prussia. The most noticeable influences were exerted by the three Hanoverian stallions *Schwabliso*, *Tribun* and *Hamlet*. Their names are still often found in pedigrees. The aim of the breeders was to produce a versatile riding- and carriage horse.

From 1932 until the end of the Second World War few horses were imported

for breeding. After the war, the East Prussians *Heristal 224*, *Heinfried 206* and *Anno 282* arrived at Flyinge. *Hyperion*'s descendant *Heristal* produced 15 sires and 44 Stud Book mares. These stallions, together with *Polarstern 319*, the German reserve horse at Helsinki in 1952, exercised a great influence in reviving the blood.

Until after the war, the major customer was the army. Subsequently breeding was switched to an easy and versatile riding-horse. Most of the horses produced are

intended for the average rider and find a good market. But among the horses sold there are always some animals suitable for top-class riders.

Every autumn private breeders put forward some 150 colts, from which about 15 are selected as probationer stallions. Together with five or so foals born in Flyinge, these are all put through a very tough schooling. At the age of one-and-a-half years they are inspected; those falling below the high standard set are gelded and sold at the autumn shows. By the age of two they are broken in, and at two-and-a-half they are inspected again. They are now broken to saddle, and at three-and-a-half they are tested for performance.

All the stallions are ridden or driven every day. They are also used as riding-horses for the school for stable-workers. The mares are driven pulling the sulky.

(Above) The colts are reared under harsh conditions.

(Right) The Gotland Pony mare *Sonnett*, a particularly beautiful example of this Swedish breed, a favourite especially in the USA.

As well as the high-class Swedish warm-blood and the Gotland Pony, other types are bred at Flyinge, for example, Swedish-Ardennais, North-Swedish cold-bloods and English Thoroughbreds. The stock in January 1977 comprised 55 stallions, 20 mares and 49 foals.

(Above) The Thoroughbred stallion *Hampelmann* contributed greatly to the improvement of the Swedish half-breed in the 1920s. At present (January 1977) Flyinge has four Thoroughbred stallions, five Thoroughbred mares and three yearlings. Three of these stallions are used mainly for breeding Thoroughbreds. Flyinge's yearlings are sold at auction. A chestnut filly, *Alicante*, born in 1975, by *Montal* out of *Altamira*, by *Carnastie*, was sold, at an auction in October 1976, for 81,000 Swedish crowns.

England

There is no doubt that England has exerted a greater influence on modern horse breeding than any other country in the world. The English Thoroughbred dominates the racecourses of every continent. But, more importantly, it is impossible to imagine the production of any high-performance warm-bloods without this breed.

However, alongside this pinnacle of horse breeding, whose quality and influence are only to be compared with those of the Arab, several other English breeds have played an important part in other continents. The Cleveland Bay and the Yorkshire Coach Horse were in demand in many countries as elegant carriage horses. The Norfolk Trotter played a decisive part in the genesis of many breeds, and produced in conjunction with Thoroughbreds and native ponies the once-famous Hackney: this is a spirited carriage horse with an extremely high knee action, and is still a great favourite on show-grounds, especially in Holland, Germany and the USA.

(Above, right) *Godolphin Barb*, the stallion with the thick neck who drew a water-cart in Paris and was discovered there by an Englishman who brought him to Derbyshire. However, it was not until he had twice changed hands, and then only by chance, that he was sent to stud, and became one of the three foundation sires of the Thoroughbred stock.

(Above) *Pretty Polly*, a brilliant racing mare, who later produced only four winners. In later years, however, her descendants included such great horses as *Donatello II*, *Premonition*, *Supreme Court*, *Vienna* and *St Paddy*.

English cold-bloods – the heavy, thick-set Suffolk Punch and the powerful Shire – also found friends in various parts of the world and have been instrumental in improving a great many cold-blood breeds.

And finally, not less than five types of ponies – usually much underrated – originated in England: the Exmoor, Dartmoor, New Forest, Dale and Fell types.

In addition there is the famous Welsh Mountain Pony, of which various types, including a cob, are now being bred. Ponies, which have existed in the British Isles for thousands of years, did in fact provide the foundation stock and thus exerted a decisive influence on the evolution of all the indigenous breeds of horse – including even the noble Thoroughbred. There is at present a great increase in the production of pure-bred ponies; their undemanding, lovable nature and resilient good health make them ideal for leisure riding, which continues to increase in popularity.

Roman chariot races and Galloways

England possesses many breeds of horse, though the larger breeding establishments are all dominated by the Thoroughbred. While the three great ancestral sires of this breed arrived in England less than 300 years ago, the history of the breed goes back much further.

Horse races were held in England many centuries ago. Indeed, it is more than likely that the Romans organized chariot races at Epsom, site of the racecourse with the richest tradition in the world.

Galloway racing was then a favourite pastime. Galloways were ponies, mostly standing far less than 140 cm (14 hands). On occasion Arab blood was introduced to increase the speed and endurance of the ponies. As well as the Galloways, which originated from the Scottish county of that name, other ponies were also used for racing and were improved by crossing with Oriental types.

Some 30 of these better quality pony mares, tried and tested over many

generations for speed and endurance, constituted the foundation for the Thoroughbred. Many of these mares had been bred in Royal Studs and had already been largely interbred with Oriental stock.

Byerley Turk, Darley Arabian and Godolphin Barb

Captain Byerley rode his Turkish stallion in William III's Irish wars. According to the legend, it was the speed of his horse which saved him from capture at the Battle of the Boyne. In 1691 the stallion was sent to stud in Yorkshire and was given the name *Byerley Turk*.

A racing enthusiast by the name of Richard Darley had a brother who travelled to the Middle East on business. He procured for his brother an Arab stallion who was brought to England in 1704 and who was to become famous as the *Darley Arabian*. This horse showed no particular aptitude for racing and was therefore at first only used for covering medium-class mares. In 1715 *Betty Leeds*, a mare owned by a Mr Childers, was sent to the stallion. The foal was named *Bartlett's Childers* or – because he was often afflicted by burst blood vessels in the nostrils – *Bleeding Childers*. This horse sired *Squirt*, who in turn got *Marske*; and *Marske* became the sire of the phenomenal *Eclipse*. At the present time some 90 per cent of racehorses running in England can be traced back through the male line to *Eclipse*.

Godolphin Barb, also known as *Godolphin Arabian*, had a chequered history. Sent to the stables of Louis XV of France as a gift from the Bey of Tunis, he did not find much favour there; he had a strong thick neck. He was either sold or given away, and came into the hands of a water-seller, whose cart he pulled through the streets of Paris. A certain Edward Coke, from Derbyshire, saw him thus occupied and bought him – for reasons which are not known, but certainly without appreciating the horse's special qualities. When Coke died four years later the stallion was inherited by Roger Williams, owner of a coffee-house, who sold him to Lord

(Below) Three great Thoroughbreds (from the top downwards): *Diamond Jubilee, Sceptre* and *Eclipse*.
Diamond Jubilee, a son of the unbeaten *St Simon*, won the Triple Crown in 1900.
Sceptre is rated as possibly the best racing mare of all time. Although completely untrained, she won five of the most difficult races.
Eclipse, great-great-grandson of *Darley Arabian*, ran about twenty races and left all his competitors far behind. As a progenitor he is almost unmatched.

Godolphin, into whose breeding establishment he was taken on trial. It was only after repeated refusals by a mare that the ugly stallion from Tunis managed to mate. The results were so promising that he was mated with other mares, and his descendants were soon to be found in the forefront of the racetracks. This stallion, who became famous as *Godolphin Barb*, had an iron constitution and lived to the age of twenty-nine.

Together with the thirty or so mares mentioned above, these three stallions became the foundation of the breed of Thoroughbreds, all of whose details have been recorded in the General Stud Book since 1793.

In less than 200 years the Thoroughbred has spread all over the world. At the end of the eighteenth century there were 600 of these horses in England; today the total number of Thoroughbreds in the world far exceeds a quarter of a million.

Around 1800 there was a marked trend towards breeding racehorses for speed rather than endurance. A result of this was the development of the colt. *Eclipse* did not appear on a racetrack until he was five years old, which was usual at that period; but by the second decade of the nineteenth century races for two-year-olds had been introduced. Nowadays a Thoroughbred is at his peak at three years and many are sent to stud after the second racing season.

The National Stud

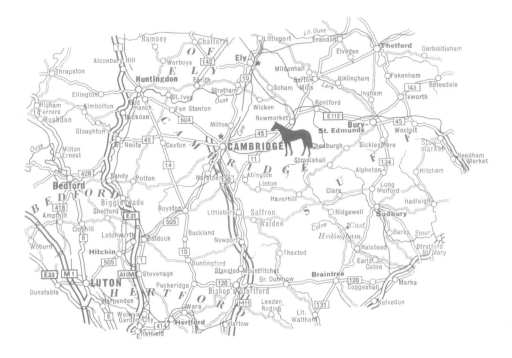

The ultra-modern National Stud at Newmarket, with its distinctive round buildings, was built for the most part between 1965 and 1969. The National Stud itself, however, had been in existence since 1915.

In the autumn of that year Colonel William Hall Walker, renowned throughout the world for his services to horse-racing, offered his bloodstock to the British Government on condition that it be used for founding a National Stud. This gift consisted of 6 stallions, 43 brood-mares, 10 two-year-olds and 19 yearlings, together with over 300 head of cattle. The significance of the gift lay in the fact that the horses came from the Tully stud-farm, on the edge of the Curragh racecourse in Ireland, one of the most famous establishments in the world, which had already produced an impressive series of winners. At the same time, the stud-farm was offered for sale to the Government and was acquired by them at their own valuation of £47,625.

The most outstanding horse bred at Tully in the first decades of the National Stud was *Blandford*, who sired the four Derby winners *Trigo*, *Blenheim*, *Windsor Lad* and *Bahram*. Other top-class horses bred at the National Stud during this era included *Stardust*, *Myrobella* and *Challenger* (leading sire in the USA in 1939), and classic winners *Royal Lancer* (1922 St Leger), *Big Game* (1942 Two Thousand Guineas), *Sun Chariot* (1942 One Thousand Guineas, Oaks and St Leger) and *Chamossaire* (1945 St Leger).

During the Second World War Tully was sold to the Irish Government, who established their own National Stud there, while the British National Stud moved to Gillingham in Dorset, where it had purchased the Sandley stud-farm. This, however, was less than half as large as Tully. Soon after the war a further 243 hectares (600 acres) of land at West Grinstead was leased.

Up to 1963 the National Stud was controlled by the Ministry of Agriculture, but in that year the management was transferred to the Horse Race Betting Levy

(Top) The stallion unit has six boxes, arranged on either side of the covering hall.

(Above) One of the five circular stable blocks for mares. Two of these are reserved for mares with foals and give access to a covered yard. Mares covered at the National Stud are brought back the following year for foaling, and stay on a few weeks afterwards.

(Right) The thatched cottage at the Bunbury stud-farm; famous horses were reared here as far back as 200 years ago. They include *Diomed*, winner of the first Derby in 1780.

Board. From that time the stud-farm received no further financial support from the Government, but operated as a self-supporting enterprise, 'national' in name only. One of the consequent changes was that brood-mares were no longer kept at the stud-farm, only stallions.

Not long afterwards the stud-farm was moved to Newmarket, the centre of bloodstock breeding in England. A 999-year lease of the Bunbury stud-farm was obtained from the Jockey Club. Peter Burrell, who

had been Director of the National Stud since 1937 (and was to hold that post for 33 years altogether), planned the new establishment on the most up-to-date lines, with the buildings widely dispersed over an area of 202 hectares (500 acres). In the autumn of 1966 the first stallions, *Never Say Die* and *Tudor Melody*, moved into their brand-new boxes.

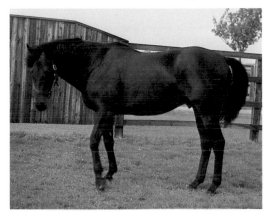

(Above) The grey stallion *Habat*, born in 1971, by *Habitat* out of *Atrevida*. Leading English two-year-old of 1973 and winner of the Two Thousand Guineas Trial Stakes at Ascot as a three-year-old.

(Right) *Star Appeal*, born in 1970, reared at Röttgen, by *Appiani II* out of *Sterna*. As two-, three-, four- and five-year old won a total of £261,806. Winner of eleven races in 1975.

(Top) The foaling unit. The symbolic weathervane features a stork with a foal in its beak. There are twelve boxes in the unit, together with a small laboratory for the veterinary surgeon and watch-room for the grooms.

(Centre) Portrait of the chestnut *Grundy*, born in 1972, by *Great Nephew* out of *Word from Lundy*. Unbeaten in his four races as a two-year-old, winner of five races as a three-year-old.

(Centre, right) Portrait of *Mill Reef*, 1968, by *Never Bend* out of *Milan Mill*. After winning a number of races as a two-year-old and three-year-old, he remained unbeaten as a four-year-old. Both these portraits are by the well-known artist Ingo Koblischek, who has kindly allowed them to be reproduced here.

(Above) *Blakeney*, born in 1966, by *Hethersett* out of *Windmill Girl*. A winner as a two-, three- and four-year-old, his greatest victory was the 1969 Epsom Derby.

Stanley and Woodlands

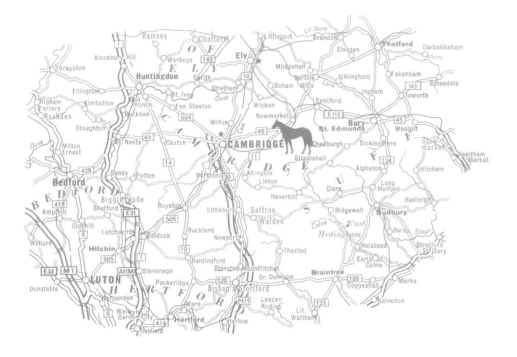

(Below) *High Top*, born in 1969, by *Derring-Do* out of *Camanae*, by *Vimy*. In 1976 *High Top* and *Lyphard* were the winning firstling stallions.

(Bottom) Part of the stud-farm and extensive racing stables built by the 16th Earl of Derby about the turn of the century on his newly-acquired estate at Newmarket.

Woodlands stud-farm was founded in 1894 by the 16th Earl of Derby. Out of the property left by the Duchess of Montrose he purchased an agricultural estate at Newmarket and developed it into a racing stable and stud-farm, thereby reviving the great racing tradition of his family.

On the advice of the Duchess's stud groom, the Earl also brought in a mare, *Canterbury Pilgrim*, who then won the 1896 Oaks and at the end of her racing career was used as a brood-mare. In due course she

produced the champion sires *Swynford* and *Chaucer*, thus becoming the foundation dam of Stanley and Woodlands. *Chaucer* got *Selene*, a filly who was considered not big enough for classic races and was therefore not named. This was undoubtedly a mistaken decision, for in two years she won 16 races and £14,386. Thus in spite of having no classic successes, she was rated as the best mare of her year; and she was no less successful at breeding. Her first three sons were top-class racers. Then she was sent to

Gainsborough, the 1918 Triple Crown winner. But when, on Good Friday 1930, she foaled a puny little colt, there was no great joy in the establishment. However, since people had originally been disappointed in his undersized dam, the poor little thing was reared in spite of all misgivings. Turning to Greek mythology, they named him *Hyperion*. But at that time nobody dreamt that the bearer of this name was to become one of the most important Thoroughbreds of all time. His successes as racer and sire are so splendid and far-reaching that it is only possible to mention them briefly here, without doing them full justice. For example, he won the Derby easily, although Lord Derby himself – a notoriously bad tipster – had scarcely given him a chance. And he also won the St Leger in spite of the hard ground, a condition not generally relished by descendants of *Gainsborough*.

Hyperion was sent to stud at five years. He was champion sire six times. His dominating role is perhaps shown most clearly by the following victories: in 1946 *Hyperion*'s

descendants took the second, third, fourth and fifth places in the Two Thousand Guineas, the first and third places in the One Thousand Guineas, the second and third places in the Derby and the second place in the Oaks.

Stetchworth Park

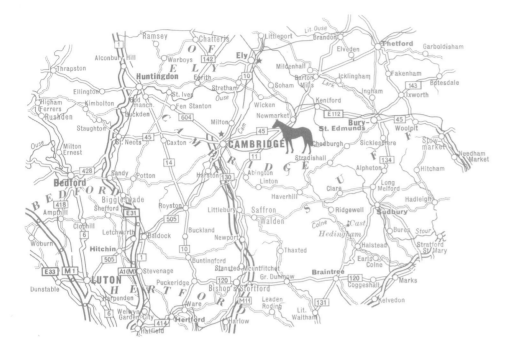

champion *Hyperion*. In 1926 another outstanding horse was foaled here: *Tiffin*, unbeaten in 1928 and 1929.

No stallions are kept here at the present time. In 1960 the stud-farm was leased by Colonel and Mrs Douglas Grey. It is one of the smallest breeding establishments in the Newmarket area, but its collection of mares is nevertheless exceptional. Mares, foals and yearlings are boarded here, some belonging to English, and some to foreign, owners.

Visitors to the Stetchworth Park stud-farm near Newmarket will certainly be impressed first of all by the wonderful park itself, containing ten large paddocks, all surrounded by hedges, set about with brushwood and shaded by giant trees, some of them more than 200 years old.

To the north, the estate is bounded by a most remarkable defence works: the Devil's Dyke, an ancient earthwork with steep sides, believed to have been constructed by Queen Boadicea about 1900 years ago.

The stud-farm was founded in 1883 by Lord Ellesmere. At the present time the whole estate belongs to the Duke of Sutherland, grandson of the founder. The Duke's mother lives in the Georgian manor house, close to the stables.

The foundation stallion, *Hampton*, bought by Lord Ellesmere nearly 100 years ago, also became the most famous horse in the history of the establishment. During his ten-year stay at Stetchworth Park he founded the famous line of stallions bearing his name. Among his direct descendants is the great

(Left) The entrance to the stable block, built in 1883.

(Above) The splendid ivy-covered manor house belonging to the stud-farm is the residence of Lady Ellesmere. Her son, the Duke of Sutherland, is the present owner of the estate. The stud-farm, with its ten extensive paddocks, has been on lease to Colonel and Mrs Douglas Grey since 1960.

The mares remain here all the year round and produce their foals here. At the yearling stage the foals are either sold or sent into training. Most of the mares are covered by the best stallions at Newmarket, such as *Mill Reef*, *Grundy* and *Brigadier Gerard*.

Over the years many excellent horses have been foaled and reared here, but as they did not race in Stetchworth Park colours their connection with this establishment is not generally known.

(Above) *Hampton*, purchased nearly 100 years ago by the founder of the stud-farm, became his most famous horse; he was a direct ancestor of *Hyperion*. The painting, by A. C. Havell, and *Hampton*'s tail, carefully preserved (above right), hang as souvenirs in the office.

(Left) *Sweetstone*, Mrs Douglas Grey's personal mare, was bred and reared at Stetchworth. Her most important descendant was *Sinthesis*, who won the Italian One Thousand Guineas.

(Overleaf) Young Arabs. Hundreds of years before the foundation of the English Thoroughbred, native English types were improved by interbreeding with Oriental horses.

Someries

Horse breeding at Someries was started in 1927 with the purchase, by Captain C. Boyd-Rochfort acting for Lady Zia Wernher, of a yearling chestnut mare, *Double Life*, by *Bachelor's Double* out of *Saint Joan*. She proved to be a very good runner, with six wins, but also an outstanding brood mare. Her most important sons were *Precipitation*, *Persian Gulf* and *Casanova*; after successful racing careers they were sent to stud and got winners in eight classic races. The total amount won by all her progeny was over £900,000. And *Double Life*'s daughters were quite up to her standard; *Doubleton* and *Fairly* founded families which included winners such as *Meld*, *Charlottown*, *Judicate*, *Astraeus* and *Double Eclipse*.

The stud-farm itself was bought in 1937 by Lady Zia and Sir Harold Wernher. It is situated near Newmarket and comprises stables with 75 boxes and 27 paddocks, the total area being nearly 200 acres.

Typical of Someries' products, and founders of the establishment's high reputation, are *Precipitation* and *Meld*.

Precipitation was a son of the St Leger winner *Hurry On*, and Someries' first sire. Though he won no classics, he nevertheless distinguished himself in competition with the best in the land as a first-class stayer in a number of long-distance races. Out of ten races he won seven, including the Ascot Gold Cup. His performance as sire is even more impressive; his descendants won over 500 races and more than £333,000. His most important sons were *Airborne*, *Premonition* and *Chamossaire*.

Someries' most famous mare, *Meld*, a daughter of *Alycidon*, can be traced back on the maternal side to *Double Life*. Her pedigree thus includes some great names. She won the One Thousand Guineas, the Oaks and the St Leger; the most important of her notable descendants was *Charlottown*.

(Top) The tombstones of the great mare, *Double Life*, and her son, *Precipitation*.

(Centre) The boxes for the mares and foals.

(Above) The boxes for the stallions.

(Left) *Charlottown*, son of the Aga Khan's *Charlottesville*. As a two-, three- and four-year-old he ran eleven races altogether and won seven of them, with prizes totalling £116,863. In 1966 he won the Epsom Derby and came second in the Irish Derby and in the St Leger. Up to 1976 his descendants had won more than 100 races and £150,000. In that year he was sold into Australian ownership.

Dalham Hall

Great Nephew, Dalham's only sire, was best stallion of the year in 1975. In England he came second in the two Thousand Guineas and third in the Royal Ascot; in France he won the Prix Dollar and the Prix du Moulin as well as other races. At stud he got, in the first five years, winners of 222 races. His most successful son up to the present is *Grundy*, now standing at the National Stud.

(Bottom) The foaling unit at Dalham Hall, where there are seventy-two boxes for mares, foals and yearlings as well as isolation units.

In 1975 Dalham Hall was the home of the leading sire, collected the largest total amount of cash at the Houghton Sales, fetched the highest average price and finally, with winnings of nearly £40,000, found a place among the 20 best stud-farms. The average price of 52,714 guineas obtained for its seven yearlings beat every existing record east of the Atlantic.

Dalham Hall operates systematically according to the old maxim: mate the best only with the best. Only two of the seven brood-mares have not been winners, although they have been placed. J. R. Philipps, the owner, owns an impressive dozen shares in leading sires, including champion horses such as *Mill Reef*, *Brigadier Gerard*, *Habitat* and *Run the Gauntlet*, as well as three shares in *Great Nephew*, the establishment's own sire. In 1976 none of the mares travelled further than Ireland to be covered, although Mr Philipps had in previous years sent mares to the USA to find the 'right' stallion for them, such as *Sir Ivor* or *Nijinsky*.

Dalham Hall was founded at Gazeley in 1928 by Mr Philipps' father, Lord Milford; and *Flamingo*, winner of the Two Thousand Guineas, was installed there as stud horse. The present stud-farm was originally part of Sir Alec Black's huge establishment between Newmarket and Cheveley. In 1970 Mr Philipps sold the Gazeley property and acquired Derisley, which was re-named Dalham Hall.

Flamingo was succeeded by the sires *Horus*, *Flyon*, *Honeyway*, *Romulus*, *Indiana* and *Tin King*. *Honeyway*, whose offspring won 965 races, was the most outstanding. His best son, *Great Nephew*, came as sire to Dalham Hall in 1968 after a brilliant racing career, and ushered in a new era. *Great Nephew* is a horse of great fertility; all the mares covered by him in 1973 conceived.

Nearly half of the seventeen brood-mares at Dalham are descended from the old lines, the best known of these goes back to *Honeyway*'s dam, *Honey Buzzard*, whose daughter *Rum Honey* produced ten foals, all of them winners.

Three of the mares which were not bred at Dalham come from English stud-farms: *Tudor Melody*'s daughter *Pilgrim Soul*, *Pall Mall*'s daughter *Grey Shoes* and *Victorian Era*. But American influence at Dalham is also very considerable, with the mares *Oh So Fair*, *Little Firefly*, *Goosie* and *Oulanova*.

Childwickbury

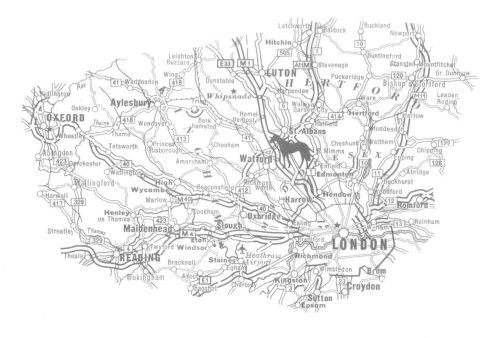

The first owner of the Childwickbury stud-farm was Sir Blundell Maple. After his death the property was acquired in 1907 by J. B. Joel, and it is now run by his son, H. J. Joel. It is one of the most beautiful and best equipped establishments in England. Since it was taken over by J. B. Joel it has developed into a centre which has steadily produced top-class champions.

J. B. Joel's first important acquisition for Childwickbury was *Sundridge*, by *Amphion* out of *Sierra*, by *Springfield*; he bought this horse as a four-year-old for 1450 guineas at the Newmarket December Sales.

Sundridge's pedigree included classic medium distance runners, but he was a genuine sprinter. His poor staying power was most probably due to respiratory trouble. *Sundridge* was an outstandingly successful sire, exerting a world-wide influence; one of his most noteworthy descendants was the Two Thousand Guineas and Derby winner *Sunstar*.

Childwickbury was consistently successful in the classic races. *Our Lassie* won the Oaks in 1903, as did *Glass Doll* in 1907, while *Sunstar* marked 1911 by carrying off the Two Thousand Guineas and the Derby. In 1912 *Jest* won the One Thousand Guineas and the Oaks, a double victory which was repeated in the following year by *Princess Dorrie*. Likewise, in 1913 *Black Jester* triumphed in the St Leger. *Humorist* won the Derby in 1921.

Towards the end of J. B. Joel's life Childwickbury went into decline. The stallions *Black Jester*, *Prince Palatine*, *Diomedes* and *Thunderer* turned out to be failures as sires, while the good female lines gradually died out. After his death in 1940, his son H. J. Joel made a great effort to revive the establishment. He retained only the very best mares and acquired from the second Viscount Astor the Two Thousand Guineas winner *Court Martial*, a first-class sire; he was also extremely selective in his breeding activities. Gradually Childwickbury won back the high esteem which it had enjoyed before the First World War.

This renewed success relied principally on the revival of the *Absurdity* line, from which *Black Jester* and *Jest* were descended. *Absurdity*'s daughter *Gesture*, by *Sunstar*, foaled *Amuse*, by *Phalaris*, who in turn produced the One Thousand Guineas winner *Picture Play*, by *Donatello II*.

Childwickbury is undoubtedly one of the most beautiful stud-farms in England. As well as the breeding establishment itself there is a glorious park and a wonderful rose-garden.

(p. 110, below) The old coach-house with the former stables for the carriage horses.

(Top) Childwickbury House is protected by a magnificent iron gate. The house was restored during the reign of James II, between 1685 and 1688, and was considerably enlarged in 1854 by Henry Toolman.

The stables at Childwickbury have the typical English boxes, 300 in all.

(Overleaf) A small portion of the collection of winners' shoes. Every time a Childwickbury horse wins a race, one of his shoes is put up on the Honours Board. The collection was started in 1900 and today contains no fewer than 1 202 shoes; since 1940 alone 662 have been added.

111

(Below) *Royal Palace*, born in 1964, by *Ballymoss* out of *Crystal Palace*, leading sire at Childwickbury. He came first in nine races and won a total of £166,062: Acomb Maiden, York and Royal Lodge Stakes, Ascot, as a two-year-old; Two Thousand Guineas, Newmarket and Derby Epsom, as a three-year-old; Coronation Stakes, Sandown, Coronation Cup, Epsom, Prince of Wales Stakes, Ascot, Eclipse Stakes, Sandown and King George VI and Queen Elizabeth Stakes, Ascot, as a four-year-old.

(Left) Tombstones erected in memory of great horses; they speak for themselves.

At the present time the most important mare at Childwickbury is *Picture Play*. The first seven of her eight foals were winners, including *Promulgation*, by *Court Martial*, a top-class two-year-old, and *Red Shoes*, by *Bois Roussel*, winner of the Falmouth Stakes and dam of *West Side Story*, who was only beaten by a hair's breadth in the Oaks, ran third in the One Thousand Guineas, and triumphed in the Nell Gwyn Stakes and the Yorkshire Oaks.

(Above) The stallion stables.

(Right) The tomb of *Doris*, the greatest mare and one of the best horses ever bred at Childwickbury.

Picture Play has produced a great many outstanding racers of both sexes. The most important representative of her line is *Royal Palace*, by *Ballymoss* out of *Crystal Palace*; he was not only one of the most important Derby winners of the post-war years, but also won the Two Thousand Guineas, the King George VI and Queen Elizabeth Stakes and the Eclipse Stakes. Other victorious horses who can be traced back to *Picture Play* are *Major General* and *Red Gauntlet*, both of whom were to become successful sires in Australia, as well as *Queen of Light*, *Ancient Lights*, *Picture Light*, *Welsh Pageant*, *Father Christmas*, *Illuminous*, *Dazzling Light*, *Photo Flash*, *Chandelier* and *Moonlight Night*.

From time to time it is necessary to introduce new female lines into the stud-farm. H.J. Joel bought a number of young mares for this purpose. The best of them is *Nagaika*, by *Goya II* out of *Naim*, whom he acquired shortly before the end of her racing career and who won two races for him before being sent to stud. Up to the present *Nagaika* has produced seven winners; she is

also the dam of the outstanding racer and sire, *Connaught*.

Other families contributing to the success of Childwickbury can be traced back to *Bravour II*, *Isola d'Asti*, *Seascape*, *Rustling Waters* and *Indian Game*.

A particularly promising acquisition was the yearling mare *Rose Dubarry*, by *Klairon* out of *Pristina*, descended from *Mumtaz Mahal*; she ranked as the best two-year-old mare of her year, running third in the One Thousand Guineas. Her first offspring, *Scented Air*, was victorious in 1976, in his first race.

Cheveley Park

Cheveley Park is situated in the heart of the world-famous bloodstock breeding district around Newmarket. The thousand-acre estate, with its buildings dating from different periods, is one of the most beautiful stud-farms in England. After a period of recession, Cheveley Park is now experiencing a phase of renewed and vigorous activity.

A few years ago the establishment, then somewhat run-down, was bought by Ken Mackey, a highly successful meat importer and exporter. Together with his three partners, he set about restoring Cheveley Park's old reputation, tackling the task with enormous enthusiasm and substantial capital.

Cheveley Park has a considerable history. Researches in old books and chronicles lead to the conclusion that horses may have been bred there as long ago as the tenth century.

There are, however, records which indicate that in 1673 Sir John Cotton sold the property to one Henry Jermyn, who later became Earl of St Albans. If contemporary accounts are to be believed, after the death of

Charles I he became the lover of the royal widow, Henrietta Maria.

Whether or not the younger Jermyn enjoyed the Queen's favours, it is clear that Henrietta Maria was very fond of Cheveley Park. It was her wish, for example, every year to have the first melons from the estate, and the Cheveley gardener always had to send these to her in London by the quickest route.

The jewel of the estate at that time was a small castle in the Elizabethan style. Unfortunately, this did not escape the marauding and plundering then rife; in 1688 it was largely destroyed.

One small mansion survived all these disorders. Together with the rest of the property, it passed into the ownership of the Duke of Rutland as part of a marriage settlement.

It is known for a fact that horses were bred at Cheveley at the time of the 5th Duke of Rutland. During that period *Cadland* was foaled there. He won the Epsom Derby in the colours of the ducal stable, but the race

finished as a dead heat and to clinch his victory he also had to win a toss.

Towards the end of the nineteenth century Cheveley Park was bought by Colonel Henry McCalmont, who had the old mansion pulled down in 1892. The estate was still considerably bigger at that time than it is now.

The Colonel had a house of enormous size built; it contained no less than 80 bedrooms, and the windows numbered 365, the same as the days in the year. The edifice was set off by a terrace copied from the famous one at the château of Saint-Germain.

However, the Colonel certainly had some knowledge of horse breeding, and during his time there Cheveley Park acquired an outstanding reputation. The stables which he installed for stallions and brood-mares were both handsome and practical.

The greatest horse to inhabit these stables was *Isinglass*. Although his racing career spanned four years, he was nevertheless entered in only 12 races. In 1893 he won the Triple Crown – the Derby, the Two

(Top and left) The small enclosed yard with the stallion boxes and the stud-groom's house were installed at the end of the nineteenth century by the owner, Colonel Henry McCalmont, who also built for himself a mansion with eighty bedrooms.

(Above) Cheveley Park foals grow up in scrupulously tended paddocks.

Thousand Guineas and the St Leger. His total winnings amounted to £57,455, a record which was not to be beaten for more than half a century; it was exceeded only by *Tulyar* in 1952.

In 1921 the Cheveley establishment was purchased from the McCalmont family by Robert Sherwood, a Newmarket trainer. The new owner found the upkeep of the giant mansion (which, incidentally, had been used as a hospital in the First World War) too expensive and it was pulled down in the late 1920s.

Sherwood did not manage to maintain the successes of his predecessors. After his death the property, together with the stock of horses, was inherited by Albert Stafford-Smith, who subsequently passed it on to his son Dick Stafford. But neither father nor son raced any horses whose performance measured up to the old tradition.

However, to return to the latest owner, Ken Mackey. His energy, together with the skill of his partners, gives grounds for fresh hope. A comprehensive programme of

reconstruction and expansion was executed in 1975, and Cheveley is now not only one of the most beautiful but also one of the best equipped stud-farms in the whole of Newmarket. The training centre stables have been renovated; the new brick buildings fit in splendidly with the surroundings.

Royal Studs

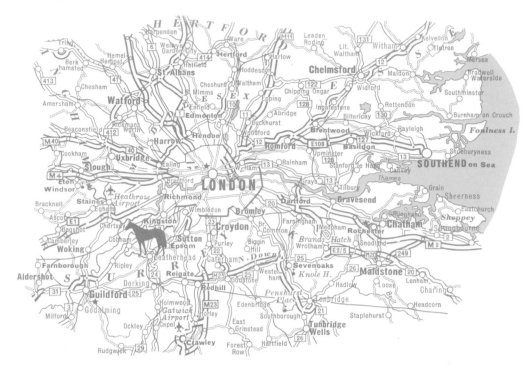

The first royal stud-farms were established in the sixteenth century. Around 1880 the Prince of Wales created the stables at Sandringham (below) and Wolferton (bottom), both in Norfolk. In 1894 the royal horses were brought to these stables from Hampton Court, and at present the Queen's twenty brood-mares are lodged here, together with one sire at each stables. There are also six mares belonging to Queen Elizabeth the Queen Mother; these are used for breeding steeplechasers. The active and highly successful group of chasers are trained at Lambourn.

Hampton Court stables were founded by Henry VIII in the sixteenth century and are thus actually older than the Thoroughbred breed. These early royal stables are still in use today, and together with those at Sandringham, Wolferton and Polehampton constitute some of the finest establishments of their kind in Britain.

While Henry VIII, James I and Charles I all took part in equestrian sports, Charles II was the first to play a leading role in encouraging racing. In 1650, under the Commonwealth, Hampton Court was closed; in due course, however, Charles II opened a new stud-farm at Tutbury. During the reign of William III and Mary II Hampton Court was re-opened and in 1713, under Anne, the establishment was enlarged. Neither George I nor George II showed any great interest in racing; however, George II's son, the Duke of Cumberland, bred one of the most renowned horses in the history of the Thoroughbred: *Eclipse*, a racehorse far superior to all his rivals.

William IV's interests were mainly in breeding and in the stud-farm at Hampton Court. After his death in 1837, however, the establishment with its stock of twenty-three mares and four stallions was broken up, and not restored until 1850. Queen Victoria did not race the products of the royal stables in her own colours; her yearlings were auctioned every year at Tattersall's. The many successful horses bred at Hampton Court during this period included *Orlando*, *St Albans*, *Prince Charlie*, *Sainfoin* and

(Left) The statue of *Persimmon*, one of the great sons of *Perdita II*, the first mare to bring fame to Sandringham. *Persimmon*, born in 1893, won the Derby, the St Leger, the Eclipse Stakes, the Ascot Gold Cup and the Jockey Club Stakes. His first son was the legendary *Sceptre*, who won all the classic races except the Derby. *Persimmon* also sired the Oaks winners *Keystone II* and *Perola* and the St Leger Winners *Prince Palatine* and *Your Majesty*. *Persimmon* died in an accident in 1908.

(Below) The first royal stables at Hampton Court, erected by Henry VIII early in the sixteenth century. It was mainly hunters that were kept here at that time, but horses were also bred for racing. Thoroughbreds had not yet been evolved. It was not until over a hundred years later that the first stallion was imported from the east, the Arab *Markham*; he, however, was not greatly effective as a progenitor. Another century passed before the Thoroughbred stock was founded by *Byerley Turk*, *Darley Arabian* and *Godolphin Barb*.

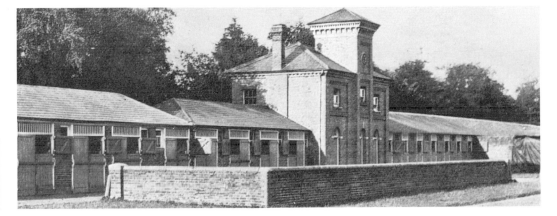

Memoir, all of whom were winners of classic races.

In 1894 Hampton Court was once again closed down. In the meantime, however, the Prince of Wales had established stud-farms at Sandringham and Wolferton, to which the breeding stock from Hampton Court had been transferred. At one of the last Hampton Court sales one of the very greatest racehorses was sold: *La Flèche*.

The first mare to bring fame to Sandringham was *Perdita II*. Mated with *St Simon*, she produced *Florizel II*, *Persimmon* and *Diamond Jubilee*. Other top-class horses from this establishment were *Friar Marcus*, born in 1912, and *Scuttle*, ten years later; both were equally successful as racers and sires. From the period of George VI's reign *Hypericum* and *Avila* must be mentioned as doing full credit to their sire, *Hyperion*.

Five days after the coronation of Queen Elizabeth II in 1953, her colt *Aureole*, also sired by *Hyperion*, came second in the Derby. In 1954 he was judged as the best European racer, and in later years was twice the best sire of the year. His success inaugurated six exceptionally good racing seasons, in which *Doutelle*, *Prétendre*, *Fighting Ship*, *Pall Mall* and *Almeira* in particular distinguished themselves. The 1960s were comparatively poor years, but the following decade opened with renewed successes, particularly with *Magna Carta*, *Albany*, *Charlton*, *Example*, *Highclere*, *Escorial* and *Joking Apart*.

(Above) *Highclere*, born in 1971, by *Queen's Hussar* out of *Highlight*, by *Borealis*; he won the One Thousand Guineas and went on to beat a high-class field in the Prix de Diane in France. *Highclere* was the first British-trained horse to win over £100,000 in a single season.

(Left) *Bustino*, now standing at Wolferton, was the best horse of his year as a three-year-old. As a four-year-old running in the Coronation Cup he broke the track record, and ran the 'race of the century' against *Grundy* in the King George VI and Queen Elizabeth Stakes, being beaten by only half a length.

Ireland

Until about 6000 years ago Ireland was still physically joined to England and the continent of Europe. It can therefore be assumed that in the course of their extensive migrations some ancestors of our present-day horses also reached this region and made their home there. However, there is no firm evidence of the presence of horses in Ireland until the fifth and fourth centuries BC, with the arrival of the Celtic tribes. It is known that they brought horses with them, and from their legends it is clear that they made use of their ponies for chariot racing and for hunting. The horse played an exceedingly large part in their lives and hence in their thinking. Thus, for example, horse-racing was among the pleasures they expected to enjoy in heaven.

The first detailed and reliable information about horse breeding in Ireland appeared in the eighth century. In the Brehon Laws, for example, it was required that everyone should be trained to deal with horses. It was also maintained that suitable pieces of land, regardless of their ownership, could be used for races without requiring any payment in compensation. Thus it is obvious that great importance was attached to racing, and in this way the foundations of the pre-eminent Irish horse breeding industry were probably laid. Fame was achieved for the first time in the late middle ages, with horses known as Hobbies. The name is probably derived from the verb 'to hobble', which was used at that time for hopping and dancing. The horses could have been so named because their type of action was rather like dancing. Hobbies are also mentioned in an account of a journey in the sixteenth century, in which the Italian Raphael Maffeus Volaternus recorded that Ireland possessed nothing worthy of note apart from corn and excellent horses.

The sixteenth century also saw the first exports of horses from Ireland; most were sold to Italy and England.

This was also the period when breeding for special purposes, such as racing, hunting and agriculture, was started, especially in England. The conditions for such a development in Ireland were rather special. As an island, the country was obviously isolated; there were practically no imports, and the Hobby constituted the sole foundation for all the different breeds of horse. However, in later years it appears that this did not adversely affect developments.

Thoroughbreds

Right from the start, bloodstock breeding in Ireland modelled itself on the English system. Aristocratic and wealthy Englishmen and Irishmen imported Oriental stallions and tested their offspring on the racetrack. But while bloodstock breeding in England was able to develop unimpeded, horse breeding in Ireland suffered greatly in the early centuries under the political yoke of England. Not until the end of the eighteenth century and the beginning of the nineteenth did the Irish bloodstock industry as a whole see better times. Continental Europe was ravaged by the Napoleonic wars and was therefore forced to turn to imports. This also provided encouragement for the bloodstock industry, which was able to develop significantly by the latter part of the nineteenth century. Horses were produced which were good enough to win classic races in England. Until then Ireland had been famous only for its excellent hurdlers and hunters. The breeding of horses for flat racing has become more and more important during this century; it was very badly

'It is sweeter to hear the cry of hounds than to seek mercy.' These are the words with which a native is said to have responded to St Patrick, missionary and later patron saint of Ireland, in the year 432. Whether or not this is true, it is certainly a good story, and shows clearly that hunting was already an important activity for the Irish in the early middle ages. And so it is still. Even today, hunts like those enjoyed in Ireland can only be dreamed about in other countries.

(Overleaf) Ireland. Visitors often feel that here time has stood still.

affected in the 1930s by economic tension between England and Ireland, but managed to recover after the Second World War. And when, in 1969, the Government exempted the industry from income tax the position also became much more attractive for foreign breeders.

Irish Draught and Hunter

In the eighteenth century agriculture became more intensive, and required powerful

horses; but the poorer farmers were not in a position to import new stock. All they could do was select the most suitable ones from among their own horses; these were mostly descended from the Hobbies, and had good qualities as riding-horses. They were called Irish Draught; and are famous particularly as, when crossed with Thoroughbreds, these working horses produce the outstanding Irish hunters. The heavy hunter is normally produced by mating an Irish Draught mare with a Thoroughbred stallion, and the light hunter by mating a hunter mare with a Thoroughbred stallion. These horses, originally bred for hunting, are now the most successful in the world for show-jumping and military purposes. The successes of this type of cross may be explained by the fact that both types of hunter have common ancestors in the Hobbies of the middle ages.

The breeding of the Irish Draught and the hunter is carried on almost exclusively by private breeders, supported by a highly effective system of state subsidies.

Connemara Ponies

Connemara is a region of rocks and hills in the west of Ireland which, on account of its inhospitable nature, has remained almost untouched up to the present day. Just as the Celtic culture and the Irish language have been preserved, the horses still closely resemble the Celtic ponies of former times. Connemara Ponies were bred pure until the middle ages, when rich merchants from Galway crossed them with Barbs and Andalusians. But since then there has been no mixed breeding, apart from a small number of insignificant crossings. Since 1923, breeding has been controlled by the Connemara Pony Breeders' Society, whose strict supervision has led to successful results.

The Irish National Stud

(P. 127) The new stallion stables with ten boxes. Although their design may be controversial, technically they are almost perfect.

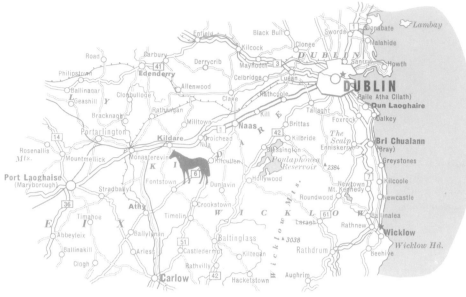

The fascinating history of the Irish National Stud begins at the turn of the century, when James Fay sold his stud-farm at Tully to Colonel William Hall-Walker, son of a Scottish brewing family and later to become Lord Wavertree. Contrary to his father's wishes, Hall-Walker started a bloodstock breeding enterprise at Tully. This was successful right from the start, and the successes increased from year to year; between 1904 and 1914 Tully recorded no fewer than seven classic victories. These results are all the more remarkable since Hall-Walker appears to have used quite unusual breeding methods. His views were widely regarded as grotesque and eccentric, and it was often asserted that he was a firm believer in astrology. The story goes that he matched mares and stallions according to their zodiac signs and had a horoscope cast for every foal; if this turned out to be unfavourable the foal had to be sold, no matter what good qualities it might have. This was supposedly the reason for selling *Prince Palatine*, the outstanding racehorse

Eriskay, with a foal by *Tudor Music*. Small breeders are permitted to bring mares to the National Stud when they are about to foal; here the birth of the foal and the first days of its life can be watched over, under very favourable financial conditions.

who subsequently won the St Leger and the Ascot Gold Cup, the latter on two occasions. His critics were not slow to remind him of this action, but they usually overlooked the fact that he was nevertheless among the four most successful breeders in the British Isles eleven times in fifteen years.

Hall-Walker was of service to horse breeding in many ways. His greatest service was undoubtedly the offer of his stud-farm to the United Kingdom Government in 1915. In addition to the buildings and

grounds, the establishment included at that time 6 stallions, 43 brood-mares, 10 two-year-olds, 19 yearlings and some 300 head of cattle. After long consideration the government accepted this magnificent gift; in this way Tully in Ireland became the first British National Stud. Captain Henry Greer, who had formerly been the Aga Khan's stud manager, was appointed director. Tully continued to produce outstanding horses, such as *Blandford* (sire of four Derby winners), *Big Game* (winner of the Two Thousand Guineas) and *Sun Chariot* (winner of the One Thousand Guineas, the Oaks and the St Leger).

In 1943 the ownership of Tully was transferred to the Government of the Republic of Ireland and two years later the Irish National Stud Company was founded; its functions were to improve Irish bloodstock breeding and to guard and promote its interests. The existing arrangements were continued, and included the acquisition of top-class stallions whose services are available to Irish breeders on

very favourable terms. The most important of the National Stud stallions up to the present are *Preciptic, Vimy, Panaslipper, Miralgo, Tulyar, Blackrock, Whitehall, Eudaemon, Khalkis, Whistling Wind* and *Sallust*.

The activities of the Irish National Stud have expanded enormously since its foundation. For example, work is conducted in the field of veterinary medicine and breeding research; improved methods are developed for grooming and feeding horses,

and for stud management and accounting; there is a library and a first-class information service for breeders; and training courses are run for stud workers. All in all, it is an outstanding achievement. As a result, Tully ranks as one of the most important stud-farms in the world, thanks largely to the efforts of the present manager, Michael Osborne.

Five famous stallions:

(Top) *Sallust*, born in 1969, by *Pall Mall* out of *Bandarilla*. He won seven races, setting up new track records at Goodwood and Longchamp. Total winnings were £62,234.

(Above) *Lord Gayle*, born in 1965, by *Sir Gaylord* out of *Sticky Case*. He won £23,655 in six races.

(Above, centre) *Tudor Music*, born in 1966, by *Tudor Melody* out of *Fran*. He won £27,353 in six races.

(Above) *Linacre*, born in 1960, by *Rockefella* out of *True Picture*. He won six races and came second in the Champion Stakes at Newmarket in 1963 and 1964. Total winnings were £26,933.

(Left) *African Sky*, by *Sing Sing* out of *Sweet Caroline*, by *Nimbus*.

Ardenode

(Below) *Hardicanute*, born in 1962, by *Hard Ridden* out of *Harvest Maid*, by *Umidwar*. Bought as a yearling by Paddy Prendergast for the Mullions, he was one of Ardenode's most successful sires. Unbeaten in his three races, he was sent to stud in 1966. In 1972 he was Europe's most successful sire, with his son *Hard to Beat* winning the Prix du Jockey Club. He is now owned by a syndicate and is standing in France.

(Bottom) The Ragusa Stud, the new addition to Ardenode, was constructed in 1965.

In 1956, after Jim Mullion and his wife Meg had made their name as successful racing stable owners, they bought the Ardenode stud-farm. At first they ran it as a completely private establishment, breeding horses purely for their own racing stables. One of their best trainers was Paddy Prendergast, who built up their racing stock by astute purchases. Among his bargains was *Ragusa*, a yearling stallion by *Ribot*, who was bought for £3800 at the Ballsbridge September Sales in 1961 and later won the Irish Derby and the St Leger, running in the Mullions' colours. After an extremely successful racing career he was sent to stud at Ardenode. In order to provide the necessary conditions for this an adjoining piece of land was bought, and there in 1965 the Ragusa Stud was opened as a public section of Ardenode. This brought the total area to over 600 acres, and there were now boxes for 280 horses.

Unfortunately *Ragusa*'s career at stud did not last long, because he developed a brain tumour. He was replaced by his two sons, *Ballymore* (1972 winner of the Irish Two Thousand Guineas) and *Flair Path*.

At the present time, however, the stallion *Guillaume Tell* is also standing at Ardenode, although owned by the Moyglare Stud. On the other hand, Ardenode's *Prominer* is standing in France. The Mullions send the offspring of the herd of about forty brood-mares to various trainers: Paddy Prendergast and Michael Kauntze in Ireland, Freddy Palmer, George Bridgland and André Adèle in France, and Ian Balding, Gavin Pritchard-Gordon and Ryan Price in England.

International relations are also evident in the sales policy. Every year at auctions in Ireland, England and France, horses are sold stemming from lines already represented at Ardenode. There is a great demand for these horses, which corresponds to the quality they offer.

Moyglare

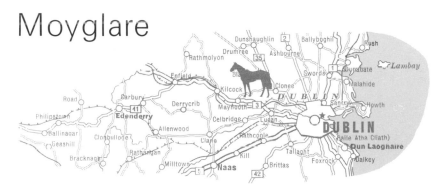

The Moyglare establishment is still very new. It was bought in 1962 by the Swiss businessman Walter Haefner. Up to that time it had been primarily an agricultural concern, and offered few possibilities for bloodstock breeding. The man appointed to plan and set up the stud-farm was Eric Miville, also from Switzerland; he became the first manager, and his work was marked by a legendary perfectionism. He was succeeded by Stan Cosgrove, who is also the owner of the greatest horse clinic in Ireland.

Nearly all great stud establishments have a tradition; Moyglare does not, but interestingly enough this is not felt to be a disadvantage. Rather, one has the impression that a virtue has been made of it; Moyglare is young and, indeed, right up to date and run exclusively on the latest lines.

Yearlings from Moyglare have repeatedly beaten records in recent sales at Keeneland, Saratoga, Kill and Deauville. The foundation for this success was created in the space of a few years by building up a first-class herd of mares. Moyglare's mares represent some of the best female lines in the world; their ancestors include classic winners, and they have bred champions such as *What a Treat*, *Aladancer*, *Miralla*, *Lagunette*, *Seximée*, *Irish Lass* and *River Lady*.

It goes without saying that such mares are mated only with top-class stallions. Though Moyglare has no resident stallion, Walter

Haefner has shares in stallions such as *Kashmir II*, *Zeddaan*, *Exbury*, *Mill Reef*, *My Swallow*, *Kalamoun*, *Nonoalco*, *Rheingold*, *Sassafras*, *Thatch*, *Nijinsky II*, *Riva Ridge*, *Foolish Pleasure*, *Secretariat*, *Bold Forbes*, *Honest Pleasure* and others; the total value of these shares is over £1,000,000.

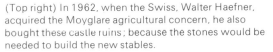

(Top right) In 1962, when the Swiss, Walter Haefner, acquired the Moyglare agricultural concern, he also bought these castle ruins; because the stones would be needed to build the new stables.

(Above) From left to right: the mares *Miralla*, *Seximée* and *Irish Lass*.
Miralla, born in 1972, by *Allangrange* out of *Miralife*, by *Miralgo*; winner of the Irish Two Thousand Guineas and two other races.
Seximée, born in 1966, by *Hasty Road* out of *Jambo*, by *Crafty Admiral*; she is *Nonoalco's* dam.
Irish Lass, born in 1962, by *Savajirao* out of *Scollata*, by *Niccolo dell' Arca*; she is *Irish Ball's* dam.

(Left) *River Lady*, born in 1963, by *Prince John* out of *Nile Lily*, by *Roman*. She is the dam of the outstanding *Riverman*, in France.

Gilltown

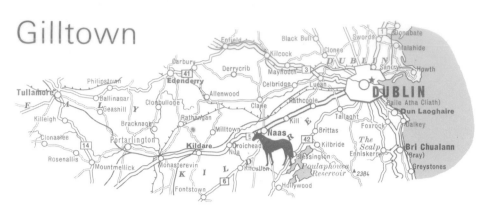

The history of Gilltown gives an accurate picture of bloodstock breeding in Ireland and illustrates its powerful local influence. The Burrowes family lived there from the seventeenth century onwards; but after the end of the First World War they sold the estate to Lord Furness, who started breeding Thoroughbreds and for this purpose erected most of the buildings still standing.

As with most of the famous stud establishments, Gilltown owes its subsequent success to one exceptionally fine mare. This was *Americus Girl*, one of Lord Furness's first mares. One of her daughters (by *Sundridge*) was *Lady Josephine*, whose racing performance was gratifying and who was later brought back to the stud-farm. On being mated with *Son-in-Law* she produced *Lady Juror*, the dam of *Fair Trial*.

In the following year *Lady Josephine* was covered by *The Tetrarch*, and this foal was named *Mumtaz Mahal*; on account of her incomparable galloping action she was nicknamed 'the Flying Filly'. *Mumtaz Mahal* ranks as one of the most influential brood-

mares in the annals of bloodstock breeding and personifies an ideal for every breeder.

On account of the economic tension between Britain and Ireland in the 1930s, Lord Furness moved to Gillingham in Dorset, England, taking his horses with him. At the start of the Second World War he decided to return to Gilltown, but he died before he could put this intention into effect. Gillingham was thereupon taken over by the British National Stud, while Gilltown was bought by the Aga Khan. This signalled the beginning of a period during which the Aga Khan played a leading part in bloodstock breeding in Ireland.

Gilltown now belongs to Mr and Mrs Bertram Firestone of Virginia, who, like a number of other American breeders, have recently become active in Ireland.

Standing at stud at Gilltown at present is *Run the Gauntlet*. He won, among other races, the Washington DC International, and in 1971 was Champion Turf Horse in the United States. The second sire, *King's Company*, was leased to Japan in 1977.

The stud-farm was established by Lord Furness after the First World War, on the 300-year-old Gilltown estate. After his death it was bought by the Aga Khan. In 1957 it was handed down to Prince Aly Khan, and after his early death to his son Karim Aga Khan. At that period it was the Gilltown horses *Stardust*, *Palestine* and *St Crespin* who made the head-lines. The present owners of Gilltown are Mr and Mrs Bertram Firestone, who also own the Catoctin stud-farm in Virginia.

Balreask

It was in 1780 that Patrick Clarke founded the Balreask Stud at Navan. At first it bred hunters, but in 1837 the great-great-grandfather of Paddy Clarke, the present owner, started to breed Thoroughbreds. Up to the turn of the century Balreask produced, as well as hunters, mainly chasers, but then turned to the systematic breeding of high-class horses for flat racing.

Balreask's first important stallion was *Coup de Lyon* (by *Winalot*, out of *Sundy*, by *Sunstar*). His finest offspring was *Etoile de Lyon*, who won the Irish St Leger. *Golden Cloud* (1952), a reliable sprinter, produced winners of over 530 races, and collected total cash winnings of about £290,000; his most noteworthy offspring are *Gallivanter*, *Skymaster*, *Precious Heather*, *Matador* and *Crimson*.

Another extremely interesting stallion was *Quorum*. As well as winners over all distances, he sired the phenomenal and unforgettable *Red Rum*, who won the Grand National three times and twice came second.

But it was with one of its mares,

Kingsworthy, that Balreask achieved special fame. Her daughter *Moment of Truth*, by *Matador*, was sold to the United States as a yearling in 1960, and after an unsuccessful racing career was sent to stud in Florida. There she produced six winners, including a filly by *Fleet Nasrullah*; this was *Convenience*, who won eleven races to the value of $451,435, including the highest-valued match race ever run in the United States. This race was run on 24 June 1972 at Hollywood Park, Los Angeles, and she won

it by a head from *Typecast*, bringing her owner the sum of $250,000.

As well as *Moment of Truth*, Brood-mare of the Year 1973, *Kingsworthy* produced another six champions. At the age of twenty-three she was withdrawn from breeding, and because of this her last foal, a filly by *Capistrano*, was kept at Balreask.

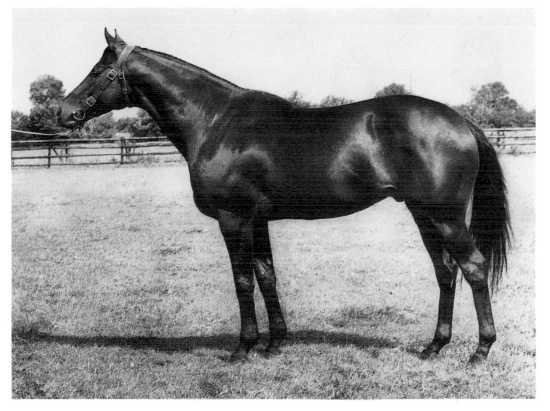

Owner of the Balreask stud-farm is Patrick Clarke whose ancestor, bearing the same name, founded the establishment 200 years ago to produce hunters. The owner's great-great-grandfather started to breed Thoroughbreds in 1837.

(Left) *Typhoon*, born in 1958, by *Honeyway* out of *Kingsworthy*. Races won by him include the Coventry Stakes, Royal Ascot, the Richmond Stakes, the Goodwood and the Barrow Plate; in addition he came second in the Prix Morny and won ten races in the USA.

Tulira Castle

(p. 133) The brilliant stallion *Tulira Mairtin*, by *Toreen Ross* out of *Glen Nelly*, an exceptional sire, whose progeny inherited the finest qualities of the Connemara Pony. One of his sons is the champion stallion of Australia.

There have always been horses at Tulira Castle. Hunters were bred there, and Hemphill Thoroughbreds are found at the sales even today. What is most unusual at Tulira, however, is the breeding of Connemara Ponies, which have become well-known far beyond the shores of Ireland during the last fifteen years.

When John Huston broke up his stud of Connemara Ponies in 1963, Lord and Lady Hemphill bought two of his mares: *Glen Nelly* and *Star of Fahy*. Both were winners of various events, for example the Clifden Championships.

On being mated with *Toreen Ross*, *Glen Nelly* produced *Tulira Mairtin*, a pony of splendid build and other excellent qualities, who has been the stud-horse at Tulira for nearly ten years now. This grey is shown on the opposite page. Altogether there are some forty ponies in the pastures at the Castle.

Many of the ponies were found in the Connemara hills. Among them was a little mare, *Noreen Grey*, who turned out to be an excellent breeder. In eleven years she produced ten foals, every one of them good; *Tulira Rocket* in particular made a name for himself. His sire was *Tulira Paddy*, a half-brother of the Castle's *Tulira Mairtin*.

Rocket was one of Ireland's most successful ponies. After being well placed at Stoneleigh, he won the Irish Pony Club Championship three years in a row with the Galway Group. He also distinguished himself as a first-class hunter. Since being sold to England he has already won various championships there.

Rocket's sister *Tulira Maria* has also had many victories in England, and his brother *Tulira Sparkler*, at the age of four, shows promise of becoming a new champion.

Patsy Fagan, the best known of all the Tulira ponies, was foaled by *Smokey*, at thirty-three probably the oldest Connemara Pony alive. Ridden by Lord and Lady Hemphill's daughter, then aged eight, *Patsy* became famous in hunting circles and won numerous events of all kinds. At the age of five *Patsy* stood half an inch too high for the largest pony class and had to compete with horses, but even in these circumstances he won a whole series of competitions.

(Above) *Tulira Mary Ann*, daughter of the young stallion *Cregmore Colum* and a winner of numerous prizes, was sold in the summer of 1976 to a buyer in France.

(Right) An auction at Tulira Castle. Ponies from this stud-farm have been sold to nine countries. The first Connemara Ponies to go to Spain came from here.

Spain

Just as the look of the Spaniard has changed in the course of the country's eventful history with the constant influx of new races (Romans, Celts, Greeks and Arabs), so too the evolution of the Spanish horse has been influenced by interbreeding with a great variety of types. Hannibal's campaign obviously introduced a multitude of horses; and it is recorded that Hasdrubal had more than 20,000 Libyan horses brought across the Straits of Gibraltar as mounts for his army. It is possible that even before the Moorish invasion, horses of Arab origin had been brought to Spain and left their influence on early breeds. The same applies to horses brought by the Goths, the Vandals and the Swabians.

The best region for breeding horses has always been the south of Spain, especially Andalusia. The fact that the Muslim dominion was stronger and lasted longer in the south explains the enduring influence of Arab and Barb horses on breeding in Andalusia. This region was not only the most important source of mares for the country, but also the point of departure for the considerable shipments of horses to the New World. It was from here that Columbus and the succeeding conquerors and settlers set out across the Atlantic, and every one of their ships carried Andalusian horses.

During the rule of Ferdinand and Isabella, horse breeding received a considerable boost from official policy, which concentrated on fully exploiting and increasing the wealth of Spain and the New World. The stock of horses was greatly increased and their suitability for riding and for use by the army was significantly improved. The reduction in price which came with the increase in the number of horses was naturally very important, since overland transport relied almost exclusively on horses.

During the middle ages it was common practice, in the Kingdom of Aragon as well as in Catalonia and Castile, to remove stallions and brood-mares to remote parts in times of trouble, so that the enemy could not get hold of them. Monasteries were particularly suitable for this purpose, as they offered excellent protection and the monks looked after the animals. As payment for services rendered, it was usual to leave them some horses; these, together with others donated by legacies, formed the basis of the monastic stud-farms.

In the Muslim-controlled region, too, horse breeding flourished, and was conducted with even greater care than in the Christian areas. As well as Arabs and Barbs, Andalusians and crosses were also bred. The stud-farm of Almanzor, the Moor, at Alhamirilla, near Córdoba, was especially renowned at that time. His huge stables were built partly into the rock.

Neapolitan and northern horses were introduced to Spain in the seventeenth century. But crossing them with the Spanish and Oriental breeds was highly contentious and was opposed by some breeders. In particular, the Hieronymite Fathers and the Carthusians already recognized the dangers of such cross-breeding at a time when it was highly fashionable all over Europe.

The broad sun-baked landscape of Andalusia has been the home of Spanish horse breeding since time immemorial. The climatic conditions, combined with the influence of the highly skilled Moors and their Oriental horses, promoted the development of animals which for centuries were the envy of the rest of Europe. Until a few decades ago each of the many isolated farms was obliged to keep a large number of horses to supply the country's needs for mule breeding and for transport purposes.

The close association with the horse is clearly demonstrated at every Andalusian festival; it is impossible to imagine any celebration without the presence of the fiery Andalusian.

The Spanish Carthusian horse was bred by the monks of Jérez de la Frontera. These horses have a very refined conformation and a straight profile, and are specially distinguished by their marvellously elegant action. The purity of their blood-lines was maintained without interruption, and their high quality has been recognized from time immemorial. They were the representatives of the highly esteemed Andalusians. In 1835 the Government dissolved the religious communities, and the Carthusian monks found themselves forced to leave their monasteries. Consequently they had to get rid of many of their horses by selling them to the state and to private breeders.

The Habsburgs and the Bourbons made great efforts to improve horse breeding in Spain. Philip IV gave the responsibility for horse breeding to the cavalry. The military organization is at present known as the Directorate of Horse Breeding and Army Remounts Service; its activities are described in detail in the following section.

As well as the state stud-farms and local stallion centres, there are now a great many private establishments where various breeds are produced. These are primarily sporting horses, bred for racing, show-jumping, bullfighting and also of course for equestrian sports and leisure riding. While the number of horses in Spain has greatly declined in recent decades, their quality has improved.

Horse racing in Spain is becoming more and more popular; races are run in Madrid, San Sebastián and Seville, and latterly also in Barcelona and Valencia. At Sanlúcar de Barrameda there are races on the sands in the summer.

Jumping competitions are held in all the provincial capitals and many other towns.

Equestrian sports are very popular, especially in Seville, Jérez de la Frontera and Santiago de Compostela. And finally polo must not be forgotten; this is popular above all in Madrid, at Jérez and at Sotogrande, near Algeciras.

Jérez

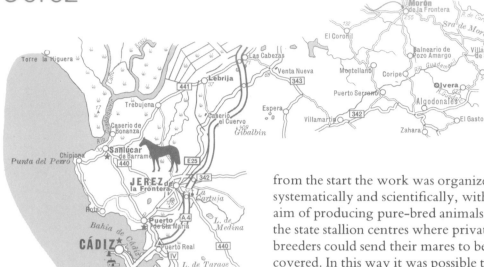

from the start the work was organized systematically and scientifically, with the aim of producing pure-bred animals for the state stallion centres where private breeders could send their mares to be covered. In this way it was possible to improve breeding throughout the country.

Various crossings were tried, but it was primarily the pure Spanish breed, the Andalusian, that was produced. Work was begun with a group of pure-bred Andalusians. It is worth noting that to maintain the breed with all its qualities is an

extremely delicate and arduous task. At first glance it might seem that there should be no difficulty in producing good pure-bred animals if the same class of stallions and mares are used. In fact, great problems in this respect immediately arose, no doubt primarily because the breeding stock came from a wide range of establishments and had received many different infusions of blood. The offspring in the early years were not uniform; but gradually it became possible to stabilize the type with its good characteristics. Andalusians are on the whole very beautiful horses, with a harmonious conformation and an equable, friendly nature; they are tough, intelligent and useful for many purposes. Thanks to these qualities, they rank as by far the best loved and most widely used breed in Spain.

The Jérez establishment has some 75 Andalusian brood-mares and another 200 or so horses of the same breed.

With the pure Arab breed they achieved success right from the start. Breeding began with a foundation stock of mares and a few

By a royal decree dated 26 June 1893 a Military Stud was founded at Córdoba. This was installed on the leased estate of Moratalla, and remained in operation until 1956. At that point the lease was terminated and the stud-farm was moved to the regimental headquarters at Jérez de la Frontera and the farms of Vicos and Garapilos near Jérez.

The influence of the Military Stud on horse breeding in Spain began to make itself felt soon after the turn of the century. Right

stallions from the Near East, mostly of excellent quality. Arabs were also kept at Moratella, near Córdoba, and a further stud group was installed at Jérez in 1912. Surplus stock was auctioned off, leading to the creation of various new private Arab stud-farms and giving the existing ones the opportunity of renewing their stock with the excellent army horses. At the end of the civil war in 1939 the Duke of Veragua made over his stock of 177 Arabs to the state; this included 47 brood-mares.

Almost all the Arabs at present standing at the military stud-farm are extremely beautiful. Their high quality is attributable not only to their noble origin, to expert selection and careful rearing, but also to the favourable ecological conditions in the south of Spain.

The Anglo-Arab unit comprises ten mares who are covered by stallions of the same breed. The stud-farm also owns a number of English Thoroughbreds, mostly kept at the Lore Toki establishment near San Sebastián.

This stud-farm, reorganized in 1941, formerly belonged to King Alfonso XIII. The basic breeding stock consisted of a number of mares which had been given by the Frenchman Edmond Veil Picard to Generalissimo Francisco Franco, who in turn passed them on to the Military Stud. The yearlings are now auctioned off every year. Most of the racing stables in Spain have horses from this establishment, where there are at present about thirty mares in production.

(p. 138, top) This engraving shows a lancer of Villaviciosa.

(Centre) Andalusia is famous for its painted tiles. This one represents the great Arab stallion *Van Dick*. Brought from Russia, he was reckoned to be the best stallion of this breed ever possessed by Spain. The picture is at the entrance to the officers' mess.

(Bottom) The yard of the training centre, with the drinking-trough.

(This page, above and left) The inner yard with the boxes for the officers' horses is shaded by vines.

(Overleaf) Mares and foals are turned out into paddocks where the shade of eucalyptus trees protects them from the heat and where feeding-troughs are provided.

(Right) The entrance to the Cortijo de Vicos, the military stud-farm, situated on the road from Jérez to Arcos.

(Below) The iron gates to the stable yard.

At Ibio, Santander, there is a unit for sporting horses; this includes Thoroughbred mares, Anglo-Arabs, hunters and other cross-breeds. Most of these horses have distinguished themselves in jumping competitions or military events, and they provide sporting horses for the Spanish forces.

Finally, at Cordovilla la Real, Palencia, there is a section for draught horses. The breeding of this type began around the turn of the century in the east of Spain, using horses of various origins. Later the industry spread to the Pyrenees, Catalonia, Huesca, Navarre and Burgos. This unit, created in 1946, also made use of various cold-bloods for breeding. However, Postier Breton stallions were preferred, since they came from a harsher environment than the other breeds and were hence able to adapt better to their surroundings.

From the beginning of the nineteenth century the business of horse breeding in Spain was subjected to many changes, but in 1864 all branches of the service were brought together in a purely military organization, the War Ministry. The royal decree related this measure to the undeniably bad state into which horse breeding had fallen at that time despite the efforts of the Ministry of Food. At this stage there were seventeen stallion centres; these were, however, predominantly concerned with horses for army units. It was not until 1875 that these centres were organized as they are at present. The original seventeen were reduced to four: Jérez, Córdoba, Baeza and Valladolid.

The Jérez centre was installed at La Cartuja, as the city administration did not have the accommodation required for the 100 stallions available. The first director was Lieutenant-Colonel Francisco Sanjuan Valero (who had been made an honorary lieutenant at the age of ten); he took over the centre in 1876.

In 1919 Alfonso XIII reorganized the administration. There was now to be one centre in each breeding zone of the country, and the original Jérez centre now became the

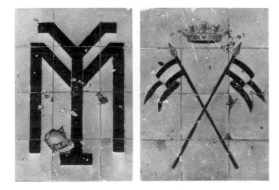

Painted floor-tiles with the brand of the military stud-farm (*Jeguada Militar*) and the lances of the cavalry surmounted by the crown decorate the entrance to the Vicos farm.

(Left) In the central square in front of the stylish officers' mess the Andalusian stallion *Jenson* (left) and the Arab stallion *Jacio* are paraded.

(Below) Five-in-hand display team in front of the officers' mess at the main entrance to the stallion centre at Jérez de la Frontera.

second most important.

After the civil war La Cartuja was, by ministerial decree, handed back to the Carthusian monastic order, to which the property had formerly belonged. In the meantime the Jérez administration had made a suitable piece of land available on the outskirts of the city, on the farm of González Hontoria. The transfer document was signed in 1941, but it was not until 1948 that the new buildings and stabling were ready for occupation.

In 1948, too, the stallions were distributed over 34 public covering stations in the provinces of Cádiz, Seville, Huelva and Málaga, and 37 stallions were placed at the disposal of private breeders. In that year 3916 mares were covered; by 1955 that number decreased by about a thousand, but it has since risen again. In 1972, 43 stallions got 3947 foals.

Important stallions from this centre who have been particularly successful are: *Hechicero* and *Destino* and their offspring *Maluso*, *Cantabro*, *Baturro*, *Bombardino* and

Juglar among the Andalusians, and *Wany Drick*, *Escanderich*, *Gandhi*, *Fueron*, *Congo*, *Tabal*, *Mayuillo* and *Zancudo* among the Arabs.

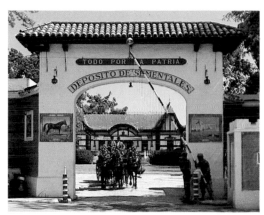

(Centre) The bay English Thoroughbred stallion *Pongo*, born in 1961, by *Tuoragua* out of *Dona Fly*, by *Tourbillon*.

(Above) *Pongo*: The grey Andalusian *Jenson*, born in 1968, by *Agente* out of *Empalar*, by *Maluso*.

(Left) The station commandant's house, decked with flowers.

Córdoba

The Spanish Seventh Stallion Centre is in the city of Córdoba. It accommodates about 150 horses and 20 or more donkey stallions. There is also a unit at Baeza, Jaén, which belongs to the Córdoba centre and houses some 60 stallions. From February to June most of them are at their covering stations.

The Royal Stables, where the stallions of the Seventh Centre are housed, are among the most magnificent and impressive in the world, as illustrated overleaf. The building was started in 1230 under Ferdinand III and completed under Philip II in the late sixteenth century. It stands on the spot where the Emir Alhakem once had the stables for his 2000 Arab horses, beside the River Guadalquivir. On the opposite bank was the palace of the emirs, erected in earlier days by the Visigoths, and later extended and elaborated by the Moors. This ancient palace now serves as the seat of the bishop. During Córdoba's greatest period, under Alhaken, who reigned in the tenth century, many other magnificent buildings were also erected, as well as the grand stables. Besides Arab horses, the Emir loved books, and he left behind him a library of some 400,000 volumes.

Unlike the library, the stables unfortunately did not survive. In 1735 a fire broke out in the straw stores, and all the buildings were burnt to the ground. Ferdinand VI ordered the stables to be rebuilt, but this was not completed until 1760, under Charles III. A shield at the great gate, carrying his armorial bearings,

(Top) The gateway to the stallion centre at Córdoba.

(Centre, from left to right) the riding-school, the entrance to it, and an exhibit in the carriage museum.

(Left) Fountain with marble horses, shaded by luxuriant vines, at the side of the inner courtyard.

(Far left) English Thoroughbred.

(Left) Andalusian.

(Below) Breton.
In 1976 the stallions standing at Córdoba were of the following types: 13 Thoroughbreds, 19 Arabs, 64 Andalusians, 11 Spanish Arabs, 37 draught horses and 22 donkeys.

(Overleaf) One of the superb stable units at Córdoba, erected in the thirteenth century and restored in the eighteenth.

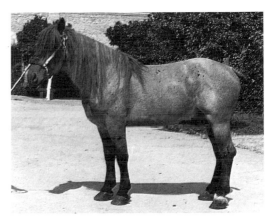

commemorates the occasion.

Towards the end of the nineteenth century the buildings were withdrawn from royal tenure and were converted into barracks with a stallion centre.

As well as the stallions which are sent to the official covering stations every year, other stallions are placed at the disposal of private breeders, on condition that they have at least twenty mares available, of whatever breed. For English Thoroughbred mares the minimum number is fixed at ten, but in that case the offspring must be made available for racing training.

Stallions stay with the breeders for about 115 days, and each of them is looked after by a soldier seconded for the purpose. The cost of the stallion's services is minimal.

Ecija

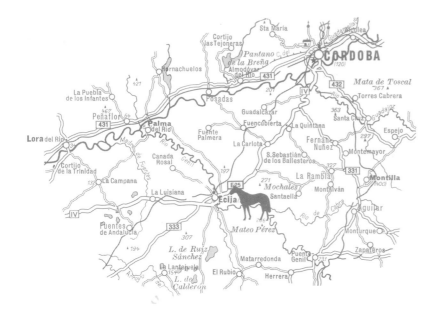

This centre was originally known as No. 3 Remount Establishment, Extremadura. It was then situated at Morón de la Frontera near Seville. From there it was moved in 1906 to Ecija, some 45 km (28 miles) to the west of Córdoba. Following a further decree, it was reorganized and on 4 December 1919 was renamed 'Rearing and Training Centre of the First Breeding Zone'. Finally, in 1926, it was given its present designation: 'Rearing and Training Centre, Ecija'.

As indicated by its name, the main function of this centre is to rear and train the foals acquired during the course of the year by the Purchasing Commission. This Commission is composed of the management personnel of the centre, and is responsible to the Directorate of Horse Breeding and Cavalry Remounts.

The foals, which are mostly bought from the local breeders as yearlings, are first taken to the Las Islas estate. Here they are inoculated and become accustomed to

running out in the paddocks and to stable feeding. In the autumn they are moved to the Las Turquillas estate, where they spend the winter. After a second summer, again spent at Las Islas, they arrive at the main centre in October. A start is now made with training, which lasts until mid-May. They are then ready for use, and are handed over to the various units and centres. In accomplishing these tasks the Ecija centre is able to make use of the other estates mentioned above. Here, as well as the stables

(Top right) The upper picture shows the stables for horses under training, the lower one, the saddle room.

(Above) The fountain at the entrance to the staff quarters. Like the long matching bench, it is decorated with tiles on which are depicted the brands of the Andalusian breeds.

(Left) One of the many pictures of horses on Seville wall tiles, which can be seen at Ecija.

(p. 149) A section of the wall backing the fountain.

(Below) Painted tiles depict an Arab horse.

(Left) The tiles on the risers of these steps illustrate various stable colours.

and paddocks, there is agricultural activity, which provides forage and straw for the horses. Cattle are also kept here, so that better use is made of the pasture.

The establishment is located in a region predominantly given over to agriculture and cattle breeding; there are a number of stock farms and stud-farms with well-known names. Undoubtedly the presence of the centre with its training duties and great need of foals has a stimulating effect on local horse breeding.

As well as rearing and training riding-horses, Ecija also devotes considerable attention to breaking in carriage horses. Various types of carriages are used, and teams are made up of six to eight horses of different colours. These are paraded at agricultural shows and take part in driving competitions, for example at the International Fair in Madrid or the celebrated Spring Festival at Seville.

(Right) Another horse-painting on ceramic tiles: this one shows an Andalusian.

(Above) Entrance to one of the courtyards of the Ecija centre.

Dehesa la Mocheta

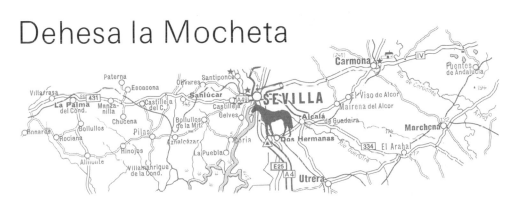

In 1940, the year of their wedding, the Duke and Duchess of Aguilar embarked on horse breeding. They had the good fortune to be able to buy twelve Arab mares from the Duke of Veragua, and these had a few foals with them.

In that lean period it was extremely difficult to obtain any sort of forage; however, a friend let them have 400 kg (880 lb) of oats, which they used for feeding the stallion from the state centre at Córdoba during the covering season. This stallion was *Cotillo*. In the next few years they used the services of *Eblis*, another horse with markedly Arab features, who suited their mares very well.

However, not wishing to concentrate exclusively on breeding pure Arabs, they made a trip to south-west France to buy a two-year-old Anglo-Arab. But they could not agree whether to take *Farfadet* or *Gargantua*, and in the end bought them both. In fact, the Duchess was right; *Farfadet*, whom she had preferred, turned out to be by far the better stallion. Later they acquired *Orvietain*, a son of *Nithard*, and *Adage*, who is at present serving with excellent results.

The mares are of medium size, nearly all dark chestnut, and very robust. They spend the whole year in the open, with only a little shed to protect the feeding-troughs from the rain. In the heat of the summer the mares and foals retire to the shade of the eucalyptus trees. At first the mares used to spend the nights in individual boxes; later on it was found not only much simpler and cheaper but also just as healthy to let the stock stay out in the open.

The Anglo-Arab brood-mares at La Mocheta stay in the open all year round. Towards the end of September the foals are weaned and moved to another farm. At the age of two-and-a-half the stallions are broken in and those considered not good enough for breeding are gelded at the age of three. Fillies are usually sold off as two-year-olds.
Stud horses who have recently proved their worth are *Adage* and *Maréchal de Logis*.

(Overleaf) In the stud yard of Cortijo de Quarto, at Dos Hermanas near Seville.

La Cascajera

The La Cascajera estate, in the vicinity of Seville, was acquired by the grandfather of the present owner around the middle of the nineteenth century. At first horses were bred there with no particular breed being decided on. However, in 1910 the establishment went over to the exclusive production of pure-bred Arabs.

The founder of the Arab stud was José de Ybarra y Gómez-Rull, father of the present owner. The stock was based on a small number of mares purchased from the military stud-farm. These first brood-mares were descended from two stallions of Egyptian origin, *Korosko* and *Sabat-el-Heir*, together with one imported from Poland, named *Van Dick*.

The most outstanding of these mares was *Babilonia*, daughter of *Korosko* and *Salambó*. She was the ancestor of the famous stallions *Mahoma* and *Babilonio*, and the dam of the champion mare *Gomaru*, by *Alfanje*, who in turn was the offspring of *Sabat-el-Heir*.

At this period of manifest breeding success, José de Ybarra bought a stallion named *Ursus*, imported from Poland by the Spanish Government. *Ursus* came to exercise a decisive influence on the breed, not only at Cascajera but throughout Spain. The mating of *Ursus* with *Gomara* produced the horse who had possibly the greatest influence of all on the Arab breed in Spain: *Gandhi*. After this magnificent stallion had served for a time at Cascajera he was acquired by the military, and in the end he left his mark on all the Arab stocks in Spain. His name will be found in the pedigrees of most Spanish Arabs.

Spurred on by his breeding successes, Don José bought a part of the Arab stock of the Guerrero stud-farm at Jérez de la Frontera, thus introducing a line descended from *Sawah the Second* into his breeding stock.

Ilustre, a descendant of *Scanderich*, was another magnificent horse standing as sire. *Scanderich* was a Sakalawy, imported from Baghdad by the government, and made a great reputation for himself in Spain. Another sire, produced at Cascajera by the mating of *Ilustre* with *Triana*, was *Congo*,

who proved to have a great influence on the breeding of Arabs throughout the country. Among his descendants the most outstanding were *Tabal* and *Zancudo*.

Tetuán, by *Gandhi* out of *Teutónica*, is also worthy of special mention among the stallions bred at Cascajera. After siring a number of splendid horses at his native stable he was taken to Uruguay, and one of his offspring later became champion at the Buenos Aires Show.

Since the death in 1964 of Don José de

Let out of the stable late in the afternoon, mares and foals slake their thirst at the fountain before charging out to the broad pastures.

(P. 154) La Cascajera, very near Seville, is a typical Andalusian country estate, where the Ybarra family have been breeding horses for over a hundred years.

(Right) *Procyon*, born in 1972, by *Saludo* out of *Casiopea*; champion two-year-old at Madrid in 1974.

(Below, left) *Mizar*, born in 1969, by *Saludo* out of *Bizancio II*, national champion at Madrid in 1975.

(Below, right) *Kiew*, born in 1967, by *Corinto* out of *Ucrania*, by *Congo* out of *Gomara*. *Kiew* was the victor at the Seville Show organized in 1972 on the occasion of the first WAHO Convention.

Ybarra, the stud-farm has been managed by his son Luis; under the new regime the following sires have been serving: *Zafiro*, by *Fabuloso* out of *Kafira*, by *Tetuán*; *Corinto*, by *Malvito* out of *Undina*; and the state-owned *Saludo*, by *Maquillo* out of *Jacobita*. *Maquilli* is a descendant of *Gandhi*.

A great number of Cascajera Arabs have already been exported – to Germany, France, Holland, Switzerland, the United States, Uruguay, Venezuela, Guatemala and the Dominican Republic. Many of these horses

have won prizes at shows in their new countries. *Hacha II*, for example, took the first prize for mares at the Paris 'Salon du Cheval'. The mares *Laga*, *Laida* and *Lira* received respectively the first, second and fourth prizes in Switzerland. *Tetuán*'s successes in South America have already been mentioned, and other horses from Cascajera have won in the United States.

The herd of mares now running through the wide pastures under the burning Andalusian sun, and the three superb sires at present in use – *Kiew*, *Mizar* and *Procyon* – show every promise of carrying on the great tradition of Cascajera.

(Above, left) In summer, bright purple bougainvillaea clothes the columns and walls of the main yard.

(Far left) Part of the stallion stables.

(Left) Mares and foals in the stable yard.

Valdehelechoso

obviously suit Arabs very well. The foals are allowed to run free up to the age of two years, under veterinary supervision, and only then are they put on the rein. The free movement encourages strong bone formation and proper development of muscles and organs.

Like his predecessors, Juan del Cid from time to time buys mares from the military stud-farm and endeavours to carry on the series of famous brood-mares. Among those acquired from the state which have already

At the beginning of this century the best Arab horses in Spain were to be found in the Córdoba district. The Military Stud was at that time still situated on the Maratalla estate and the stallion centre was right in the middle of the city of Córdoba, where it is today.

On 25 May 1912, cattle breeders Don José Maria and Don Juan del Cid attended the annual market in the city, which was once the centre of the Caliphate and which still today bears the impression left by the Moors. They were invited to look around the stallion centre, where they saw the famous stud-horse *Van Dick*, recognized as the best Arab that Spain had ever possessed.

On the following day mares from the military stud-farms were auctioned, and the Cid brothers acquired a mare named *Europa* with a bid of 800 pesetas. The other breeders at the sale were amazed: at that time 800 pesetas was a lot of money, and certainly much too much to pay for a horse in such bad condition and, to all appearances, with so many defects. However, the mare had

been covered by *Van Dick*, and it was on this that the Cid brothers placed their hopes.

On 20 January 1913 *Europa* produced a brown colt; he was named *Van Dick III*, and was destined to become the first champion at the Madrid International Show in 1922.

A year later he was sold for 12,500 pesetas to the firm of Perea in Jérez de la Frontera, on condition that he would cover the Cid mares for another two years. These events originated the Cid family's partiality for pure Arabs. The brothers bought additional mares every year at the government sales at Córdoba and later at Jérez de la Frontera, and within a few years the stud-farm achieved a world reputation. They were scrupulously careful in their selection and never acquired an animal – male or female – of uncertain origin. Indeed, they always searched out horses of the type which had made the stud-farm famous.

After the death of the two brothers Juan del Cid Galonge took over in 1964 and carried on the work. The animals thrive in the hills of Huelva under conditions which

(Left) Tiles decorated with the brand of the stud-farms, at the entrance to the establishment.

(Right) The Valdehelechoso estate, 80 km (50 miles) north-west of Seville at Aracena, close to the Portuguese frontier; the style of the building is typical of the province of Huelva. The hilly countryside, set with olive trees, has proved extremely suitable for breeding Arabs.

(P. 156, top) The entrance gates to the Valdehelechoso estate. In the background is the fortress of Aracena.

(Right) The stallion *Cicerón*, born in 1970, at the age of six. This extremely promising horse was sired by *Xamir*, an outstanding stallion from the Spanish military stud-farm.

produced first-class offspring at the Cid farm are: *Salambó, Almena, Bigerta, Bárbara, Borgia, Arábiga, Eneida, Floralia, Centa, Duquesa, Despierta, Fenicia, Húngara, Fedra, Fastuosa, Nadadura, Pajarera, Paisana, Kabarda, Laguna, Mamiña, Nácar Orbea, Odesa, Oklaoma, Rapidez* and *Ibatia.*

Various state-owned stallions are used for covering, the following having been most successful: *Korosko, Bagdad, Eco, Laberinto, Fajo, Habiente, Mosafi, Xamir* and *Maquillo.*

The most important of the stallions foaled at Valdehelechoso were *Van Dick III, Serranito, Caid, Babieca, Babieca III, Fandanguillo, Trueno IV, Serranito III, Carbonero, Cherif, Kashmir II, Xerif, Huracán, Komusté* and *Africano.*

The Spanish government bought more than a hundred horses from the Cid farm, and horses have been exported to most Latin-American republics as well as to Portugal, Morocco, France, England and Germany.

Many of the products of this stud-farm have won prizes at international Iberian and Ibero-American championship competitions, at the Concours International de France, at the Madrid and Seville shows and at the Jérez de la Frontera horse fair; and the establishment has received the Diploma of the Spanish Government.

The stallions are kept at the Valdehelechoso estate at Aracena in the Huelva province, near the Portuguese frontier. The mares have their home in the pastures of La Parilla at Cala, Huelva.

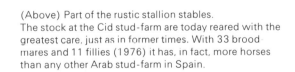

(Above) Part of the rustic stallion stables. The stock at the Cid stud-farm are today reared with the greatest care, just as in former times. With 33 brood mares and 11 fillies (1976) it has, in fact, more horses than any other Arab stud-farm in Spain.

157

Switzerland

Switzerland does not rank as a great country for horse breeding. Bloodstock breeding, only just emerging from infancy, has had to make do with half a dozen stallions, but is now making encouraging progress. The market for working horses has shrunk with the advances of mechanization, and sporting horses bred in Switzerland are hard to sell abroad. The international successes of Swiss riders at show-jumping, dressage and military events are almost all gained with imported horses, and Swiss-bred horses have triumphed at international trials only in driving events. However, the picture was not always like this.

The history of horse breeding in Switzerland can be traced back about a thousand years. At the Benedictine monastery of Einsiedeln, founded in AD 934, horses were bred right from the start. This monastery stud-farm is described in detail in the next section.

Horse breeding in Switzerland expanded considerably in the second half of the fifteenth century after 15,000 to 20,000 horses had been brought into the country during the Burgundian wars, in which the Swiss Confederation was victorious. These spoils, captured from the luckless Charles the Rash, came at a time when the country people were keeping horses more and more as domestic animals, and breeding them. The farmers had their own mares and foals, while the stallions stood in monasteries, at country seats, or in the care of priests.

It was not long before other countries discovered Switzerland as a source of horses. The Italians and French particularly became customers, their preference for Swiss horses due not so much to their handsome appearance as to their hardiness, their capacity for work and their toughness. In 1714 France imported 10,000 cavalry remounts from Switzerland, and in 1784 as many as 12,000. Freiberg and Seeland horses were used as barge horses on the rivers Rhône and Sâone. Better specimens of Swiss horses at that time were used as official post horses as far away as the Pyrenees.

This first period of prosperity for horse breeding in Switzerland came to an end in 1798, when the French invaded the country. The stock of the Einsiedeln monastery was carried off, down to 'the last foal's tail', and every farmer's stable was cleared out. The work of decades was destroyed in ten years of war.

Twenty years later horses were again being exported in great numbers; in 1830 the canton of Bern alone supplied 30,000 remounts to France. Germany and even England bought horses from Switzerland. But it was soon found that the performance and conformation of these animals left something to be desired. When the first National Horse Show was held at Aarau in 1865, the quality of the horses was generally rated as 'fair to low'.

The Einsiedeln monastery, with its acquisition of the English half-breed stallion *Bracken* in 1866, and the Jura industry, with its successful change to heavy draught animals, stood out for some time as isolated exponents of horse breeding in Switzerland. The Freiberg industry profited from a sudden increase in the requirement for draught horses at the outbreak of the First World War; but the business was badly hit by the serious crisis of 1920. This crisis, caused by the flooding of the Swiss market with cheap imports as a result of cavalry reductions in many countries, also affected the associations of horse breeders which had been founded around the turn of the century. Of the twenty associations existing in 1914, with 1200 registered animals, only seven were left in 1933, with 227 horses. As purchaser of heavy draught horses for the artillery and transport, the Swiss Army was the most important customer, especially for Freiberg horses.

A new peak was reached in the Second World War when not only food but also petrol was rationed. There was a rapid increase in the stock of horses: in 1936 the number was 140,000, and by 1945 it had risen to 152,000.

As a result of the mechanization of agriculture during the years that have passed since then, the use of horses for traction has greatly diminished; every year

There had been mounted units supporting the Swiss Confederate troops in military encounters before the Thirty Years' War; but it was only then, when cities like Bern and Zürich set up bands of horsemen, that the cavalry gained real importance. Compared with the infantry their numbers were still small, but they were incontestably élite troops with considerable striking power. In 1973 the Swiss cavalry was disbanded as it was considered that, while it might be useful, it was not essential.
(Left) This watercolour by Wilhelm Stückelberger, painted in 1897, in the possession of the Federal Military Library in Bern, depicts a sergeant-major of dragoons as standard-bearer.

(P. 159, above) General Henri Dufour (1787-1875) was the first of the four generals who were in command during the four great reorganizations putting the Swiss army on a mobile basis. Like his successors (Hans Herzog, Ulrich Wille and Henri Guisan) he always showed great understanding of the needs of the cavalry. (Below) The mounted field artillery of the Swiss army can look back on a great tradition.

(Overleaf) In recent years there has been a tremendous increase in the popularity of racing in Switzerland. The winter races on the frozen lake at St Moritz are well-known far beyond the country's borders.

their numbers fall by 5,000 to 7,000. In 1957 there were still 100,000 horses in Switzerland, in 1966 only 59,000, while in 1976 the stock was down to 42,620 animals, of which 30,280 were working horses. The disappearance of horses from the farmyard, the increasing popularity of leisure riding and the accompanying rise in the demand for sporting horses brought about big changes in horse breeding in Switzerland. Since 1960 there has been a marked recession in the production of Freibergs as a result of the

decreasing demand for working horses. On the other hand, the production of Anglo-Normans and Holsteins has doubled. An innovation in the east of Switzerland has been the concentration on breeding Haflingers. Thanks to the continual spread of interest in riding sports to wider groups of the population, there has been a veritable boom in the breeding of warm-bloods in the 1970s.

Since 1943 performance tests for warm-bloods have been held at Avenches every

spring. These tests include a veterinary component (assesssment of conformation and veterinary examination of respiration, heart action and general condition) as well as a physical part covering dressage, cross-country and kilometre drive, 15-km ($9\frac{1}{2}$-mile) run, jumping and dressage driving.

The bloodstock breeding industry in Switzerland is only five years old. Thanks to purely private initiative, however, breeding from Thoroughbreds had already started back in the 1940s, at the Rohrzelg stud-farm with *Mullingar XX* and at the Arniberg stud-farm with *Padichah XXX*; and a daughter of *Padichah XXX* won the Austrian Derby in 1950. But it was not until 1973, under the supervision of the newly established Breeding Commission of the Swiss Society for Equestrian Sport, that the first selections of Thoroughbred stallions were made and registered in the newly created Stud Book. Seven Thoroughbred stallions covered 56 mares in 1976, and in addition 7 trotter stallions covered 16 mares.

159

Einsiedeln

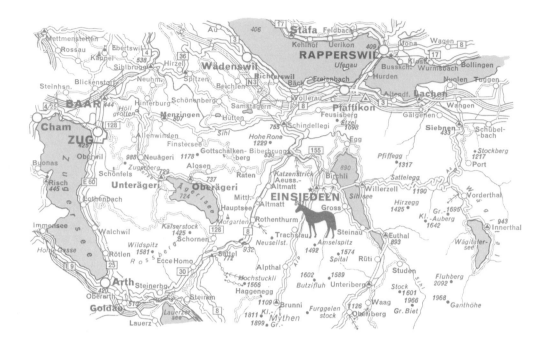

stock of 'Horses on 1 January *anno* 1655'; there were 71 horses in the monastery at that time.

The present monastery buildings, with the splendid baroque church, were erected during the years 1704–35, from the plans prepared by Brother Kaspar Moosbrugger. In the course of the work the monastery horses dragged 'a thousand heavy waggon-loads of costly sandstone blocks from the quarry by the Etzel to the building site'. The stable, put up between 1764 and 1766 under

In January AD 861 the venerable Meinrad was struck down in his hermitage (*Einsiedelei*) by two robbers. He had dwelt here alone in the 'dark forest' in the upper Sihltal for twenty-five years. In AD 934 Benno and Eberhard of Strasbourg founded the Benedictine monastery, 'Our Lady of Einsiedeln', in his memory.

In those days monks came from noble families, and brought their own saddle horses with them to the abbey.

The Einsiedeln stud-farm is mentioned for the first time in a document dating from 1064, in which the Emperor Henry IV granted the monks, among other things, the rights to secular court offices including the office of a marshal. This 'horse attendant' from the ranks of the nobility was responsible for superintending the stud-farm. Einsiedeln can thus claim to possess one of the oldest stud-farms still in operation.

On account of the increasing numbers of horses, tenants were soon obliged to pay part of their rent in the form of oats and horseshoes.

The harsh climate of the lower Alps, combined with the wholesome grass and herbage and not least the skill of the monks in breeding horses, led to the production of horses of outstanding quality and high class as well as great beauty. The monastery's horses were admired by the whole district, and as the demand for them increased, the establishment soon started to breed for sale as well as for their own requirements. Nobles and dealers came from far places. In particular, the Dukes of Milan and Mantua acquired many 'Cavalli della Madonna' and transported them through the St Gothard pass to Italy.

A period of great prosperity for horse breeding at Einsiedeln began in the sixteenth century under the abbot Konrad III, who bought back property and land which had been lost in the preceding border struggles and which was available once more for grazing horses.

Systematic breeding was started when *Statthalter* Father Josef Reider inaugurated the first stud book with an entry detailing the

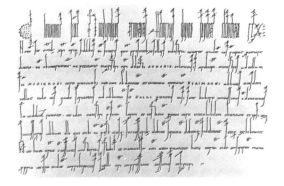

(Far left) Extract from a document dating from 1064, in which the Emperor Henry IV grants to the monks of Einsiedeln the same rights as previously enjoyed by the monastery of St Gallen. These include the right to secular court offices including the office of a marshal, a 'horse attendant'.

(Left) Extract from a stud book dating from 1856. At that period the number of horses at the stud-farm reached its peak: 150. The first stud book was started in 1655.

(P. 162, top) The stud yard, with buildings dating from 1704 to 1718.

(This page, far left) From the arch of Mark's Gate, Brother Mark gazes down on his fellow-men with a mocking expression. According to all accounts, this horse-lover's lack of beauty was compensated for by his biting wit.

(Left) The Einsiedeln stable was erected in the years 1764 to 1766. The imposing architecture with the cross-vaulting and bow windows was designed by Brother Kaspar Braun. Nowhere else in the world is there a stable built in this style.

Brother Kaspar Braun, represented a princely recognition of the work done by these horses. With its bold cross-vaulted ceiling, caught by the light streaming through the wide bow windows, its style is unique.

In the eighteenth century the stock was crossed with Spanish, Italian, Friesian and Turkish stallions. Father Isidor Moser, who in 1784 compiled a stud book revealing an astonishing knowledge of horses, recognized the loss of quality resulting from this non-selective crossing; by systematically breeding pure to the old Schwyzer stock he managed to restore the individual Einsiedler type.

A little later, however, on 3 May 1798, the monastery lost all its horses, when the French Revolutionary Army under General Schauenburg captured all the animals.

In 1801 the monks returned and immediately began to procure horses again, mainly from local farmers who paid their rent in this form. In 1811 there were 53 horses in the stables, and the stock reached peak numbers in 1841, with 154 horses.

At the Swiss Horse Show in 1865 it was recognized that animals of the Schwyzer type had various deficiencies, compared with other breeds. Until then, the monks had been using Schwyzer stallions as sires, but they now stopped using them and bought a Yorkshire stallion, *Bracken*, who, together with three of his sons, considerably improved the type.

Since 1890 the Federal Stallion Centre at Avenches, now the National Stud, has supplied stallions for the covering season; the best offspring have been produced by crossing Einsiedler mares with Anglo-Norman stallions.

The monastery's present mares are descended from lines of which two can be traced back to *Bracken*, one to a North-German mare, and one to an Anglo-Norman mare.

Just as in earlier centuries, the local farmers are continuing to collaborate with the monastery on horse breeding, and in 1906 the Einsiedeln District Horse Breeders' Society was formed; it now has about 60 members. Some 45 mares are served every year at the monastery's covering station, and every October a show is held in the monastery yard and prizes are awarded. These venerable stables at present house about 30 horses.

(Above) The view from Meinradsberg over the wide pastures to the Einsiedeln monastery. The Einsiedeln horses brought sandstone blocks for building the monastery from the stone quarry by the Etzel in 'a thousand heavy waggon-loads'.

(Left) The Anglo-Norman stallion *Il s'en va* born in 1959, by *Ibrahim hb* out of *Eglantine*. Since 1890, the Swiss Federal Stud at Avenches has been supplying stallions to Einsiedeln for the covering season.

Avenches

(Below) The amphitheatre at Avenches, once the Roman capital of Helvetia, when it was called Aventicum. In 1898 it was decided to set up a Swiss centre for stallions and foals at this picturesque little town in the Vaud canton. With the arrival of the first ten brood-mares in 1927 the centre became the Avenches Federal Stud.

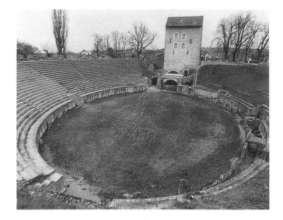

On 1 July 1898 the Federal Parliament decided to establish at Avenches a Swiss Centre for Stallions and Foals, and voted a grant of 372,000 francs for acquiring and enclosing the necessary land and building stables for the foals. This was the first really decisive step in the improvement of horse breeding in Switzerland.

Earlier efforts in this direction – in particular 'concerning the supply of horses for the army' – had been initiated in 1863, when stud-horses to the value of 30,000 francs had been purchased and stood at the military horse establishment at Thun. One year later a seven-man Federal Commission for Horse Breeding was created. During the next decade the Commission arranged for the importation of stud-horses, mainly from England, by the Federal authorities, who then sold them to the Cantons at 30 per cent below purchase price. Various societies and clubs put forward proposals for creating stud-farms or stallion centres, and in 1878 the Department of the Interior advanced a project for a State Stallion Centre, but all these proposals were turned down by the Commission. On the other hand, in 1874 a Federal Foal Centre was established at Thun for rearing probationer stud-horses, but this was closed down seven years later as no customers came forward for the stallions.

In 1887 it was decided to open a cavalry remount centre at Thun, under the control of the Government Horse Establishment. And in 1890, under this same administration, it was the first time that state-owned stallions

(Above) The yard with one of the two stable blocks accommodating altogether a hundred stallions: in the background, one of the two half-timbered houses; to the left, the riding-school.

(Above right) Interior of one of the stable blocks for warm-blood stallions.

(Right) The Avenches stallions are driven as well as ridden.

(Far right) The warm-blood probationer stallion *Sirocco*, undergoing a test in the autumn of 1976.

(Far left) The imported Hanoverian *Alfa*, born in 1970, by *Absatz 4052* out of *Wolgaheldin H 65146*.

(Left) The warm-blood stallion *Vagant*, born in 1973, by *Vagabond 433* out of *Anette 6173*. He was imported from Sweden in 1976.

(Below, left) Inside one of the stallion stables, built in 1900.

had been stood for breeding warm-bloods: they were three Thoroughbreds imported from England and France. During the mating season they were sent to Einsiedeln, Tramelan and Lausanne.

In 1899, a year after the decision to create the Centre for Stallions and Foals at Avenches, the Federal Parliament voted a further 620,000 Swiss francs for the construction of buildings for the stallion centre including administration offices, domestic accommodation and a riding track. In the same year the importation of Anglo-Normans was discontinued, as the offspring of crosses with this breed did not meet the army's requirements.

In 1901 the Thun stallions were brought to Avenches, and the first Freiberg stallions also arrived at the centre; and a year later the first donkey stallions were imported, for breeding mules.

In 1927 the first ten mares were installed at Avenches and the centre was renamed the Federal Stud.

At present (1975) the stock comprises 41 Freiberger stallions, 69 warm-blood stallions and 50 warm-blood brood-mares. The objectives are those of warm-blood breeding all over Europe. However, some 500 horses for top-class sport still have to be imported into Switzerland every year, and the position regarding leisure activities is similar, with the domestic product having to be supplemented by importing about 1500 horses.

(Right) The Anglo-Norman stallion *Filon d'Or*, born in 1971, by *Kalabaka XX* out of *Violette*. He was imported from France in 1974.

(Far right) The Freiberger stallion *James*, born in 1969, by *Judo* out of *Pâquerette 1467 VS*.
The numbers of these small, easy-going working horses decreased sharply after the Second World War, but they now remain steady at almost 12,000. The 3,000 or more prize-winning brood-mares produce about 1,800 foals annually. In addition to the forty-one state-owned stallions, there are fifty-four more available for covering purposes, either owned privately or by societies.

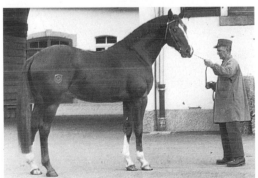

Italy

One of the first high points in the history of equitation in Europe was attained at the court of Naples in the early middle ages. It was then that the best riding-school for the equestrian education of young noblemen was created. This establishment exercised a strong influence throughout Europe (just as Saumur, Pinerolo and the Spanish Riding-School in Vienna did later) through its foreign pupils. Grisone's school must have had a lasting effect in particular on the great English horseman William Cavendish, Duke of Newcastle, whose writings, together with Grisone's original work, provided the basis for the theories of the great Frenchmen who dominated this field in later decades.

This was also the era of a first flowering of European horse breeding. The establishments of the Dukes of Mantua and of the Medici above all enjoyed a high reputation far afield. Not for nothing did Henry VIII of England send emissaries to Italy to acquire breeding stock. These animals must certainly have influenced the mares in the royal stables who, after crossing with Oriental stallions, were the foundation of the line of the English Thoroughbred.

The political divisions of Italy led to fundamentally different ideas about horse breeding. In Spanish-controlled northern Italy the greatest importance was attached to the influence of Andalusian horses, while further south at the courts of Florence and Naples, English bloodstock was used for breeding as early as the eighteenth century.

Horse breeding received a great impetus during the Napoleonic wars, which swallowed up enormous numbers of horses. The cavalry demanded a faster and more spirited animal. In view of this development the then Cisalpine Republic promoted a modern bloodstock breeding industry in northern Italy, in which English stock was of course widely used.

While the traditional Italian races after the style of the Palio di Siena – which have survived to the present day – continued to be held in the streets and large squares in the middle of the towns, the first modern grass racetracks were introduced in Turin, Milan

(Above) Anatomy of a horse, from Federico Grisone's *Gli Ordini di Cavalcare*, published in the sixteenth century and the first post-classical work on equitation.

(Left) Sketches for an equestrian monument, made by Leonardo da Vinci around 1500.

(P. 167, above) Neapolitan courser, from *The Newly Opened Riding-School* by William Cavendish, Duke of Newcastle, Grisone's most famous pupil.

and Florence at the beginning of the nineteenth century.

In 1806, also, the first modern Thoroughbred industry was created by the Prince of Butera and the Sicilian Prince Agesilao Gioeni. However, bloodstock breeding in northern Italy suffered severely under the post-Napoleonic Restoration and Austrian rule, and did not make its definitive breakthrough until the reign of Victor Emmanuel I.

The first bloodstock society was founded in Florence in 1836, to be succeeded in 1881 by the Italian Jockey Club. Since then everything connected with racing and breeding in Italy – as in most of the leading bloodstock-breeding nations of the world – has been co-ordinated and controlled by the Jockey Club.

In 1884 the first Italian Derby was run, at the Capannelle track in Rome. In this period also, steeplechasing first gained popularity, with important races for officers at Merano, Torre di Quinto, etc.

The upper classes in Italy, at that time still the owners of extensive estates, took every opportunity to introduce breeding stock. Racing, pursued in all the provinces and on more than thirty racecourses, went through a golden age. An important landmark prior to the turn of the century was the creation in 1888 of the modern racecourses at San Siro and Milan; this gave new and decisive impetus to racing in northern Italy.

Around this time also there was a great increase in riding sports among the upper

classes, and a certain Federico Tesio made a name as champion on several occasions. This same Tesio soon turned his attention to bloodstock breeding and in the succeeding decades became one of the most successful breeders of Thoroughbreds in the world with his Dormello establishment.

In the years preceding the First World War it was mainly Thoroughbred mares that were brought to Italy, and these left their mark in the stables of Tesio and his great rival de Montel, as founders of lines still

flourishing today. One of the horses to arrive in de Montel's stable, in 1916, was *Havresac II*, a son of *Rabelais*. This horse, acquired as a bargain, was destined to maintain the world-famous line of *St Simon* in Italy right up to the present day, via *Cavaliere d'Arpino*, *Bellini*, *Tenerani* and *Ribot*. With *Ribot*, born in 1952, the best racehorse of his time in the whole world, and one of the greatest sires of all time, horse breeding in Italy reached its peak.

(Left and overleaf) The first regular trotting races were held in the provinces of Bologna and Modena at the end of the nineteenth century; since then Italy has become one of the most important trotter centres. The country's brood-mares, numbering about 6000, are covered mainly by top-class stallions imported from the United States and selected in classic races in Italy. The most important trotter breeder is probably Count Orsi-Mangelli at Persicuto. Races carrying big money include the Premio Loteria in Naples, the Premio Europa in Milan and the Trotter Derby in Rome.

Besnate

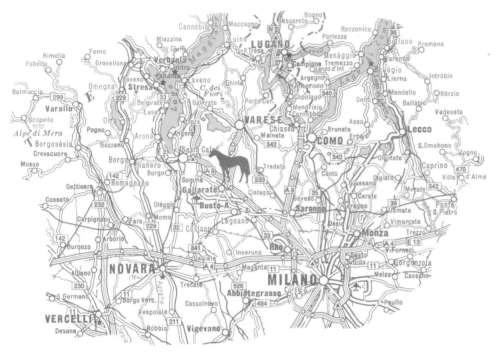

to be ideal for racing and breeding. In the period of prosperity in the 1920s the Besnate stud-farm very quickly registered great breeding successes and soon became well known.

After the death of the founders, in the post-war period, the management of the stud-farm was taken over by G. Trenta. This great and respected breeder recognized that with proper management Besnate could be made an attractive boarding stable for smaller owners.

The expansion of bloodstock breeding in Italy was remarkable from 1960 onwards, especially as a result of the growing number of private breeders without land of their own. During this time, the extremely active Milan racing club SIRE, the Society for the Encouragement of Horse Breeding, took over control of this establishment. Additional boxes were built and other necessary improvements made, and the Society has now created at Besnate one of the finest and best managed breeding complexes available to the Italian Thoroughbred

In contrast to the conditions in Tuscany and Rome, the unsettled political situation in Lombardy and Piedmont impeded the orderly development of racing and bloodstock breeding almost up to the turn of the century; at that stage, however, the finest hour arrived for 'Ippica Lombardia' also. Parallel to the economic impetus now felt in these regions, the richest in Italy, and as a result of the industrial revolution, racing and bloodstock breeding also developed under the guidance of far-seeing members of the

nobility of northern Italy and the aspiring middle classes in and around the city of Milan. It was not long before they outstripped Florence and Rome, traditionally the champion equestrians.

Also during this period the Besnate stud-farm was founded by the Bocconi brothers in Milan. They were keen sportsmen and built up considerable wealth as wholesale merchants and store owners. Besnate lies in the idyllic countryside of Brughiera, and horse-lovers in Milan soon found this region

(P. 170, above) The ochre buildings of Besnate fit in with the Brughiera landscape to make a picturesque scene. This district has long been the centre of bloodstock breeding in Italy.

(Below) The old central yard at Besnate. Originally a private establishment, it was taken over by the Milan Racing Club, and a number of additional boxes and farm buildings were provided.

(This page, left) One of the boarding stables at Besnate. Founded at the beginning of the century by the Bocconi brothers of Milan, the establishment is now run by the Milan Racing Club (SIRE) and is used mainly for rearing horses.

Novella at Malnate. Another traditional breeding district in Italy is the fertile strip of land along the Po from Parma to Bologna. There, as well as important trotter stud-farms, are found such great Thoroughbred establishments as the National Breeding Centre at Noceto (Parma) and the boarding stud-farm of the National Breeders' Association, ANAC, at Volta de Beno, Bologna, where again at least one high-class stud horse is always kept.

As part of the energetic efforts of the state to promote the animal breeding sector within the framework of agricultural planning in central and southern Italy, breeders have in recent years been offered long-term loans at cheap rates for starting new stud-farms. Together with a sharp increase in racing activity in these regions, the above measures have contributed greatly to the establishment of a number of new stud-farms in the Florence–Rome–Pisa triangle, traditionally known for the production of half-breeds.

industry. As at the Society's other boarding establishment, in the park at Monza, there are always three or four champion sires standing here. Recently they have included *Canisbay*, champion sire in 1974, *Chiese* and *Gailodges*, as well as the Dormello-Oligiata stallions *Claude*, *Viani* and *Hogarth*.

In taking these important steps the far-seeing members of SIRE have – under the guidance of leading racing personalities such as E. Locatelli and his successor V. di Capua – rendered an extremely valuable service, in

particular as regards the quantitative build-up of the domestic production of yearlings on a broader basis. Until a few years ago Italy's bloodstock industry was concentrated mainly in the region to the south of Lake Como and Lake Maggiore. As well as the stud-farms described separately in this book, it is worth mentioning in particular the Razza del Soldo at Gornate, Dr Vittadini's breeding establishment at Oriano, the successful stud-farm of Scuderia Aurora at Bedizzole on Lake Garda and the Razza la

(Above, left) There are always several top-class stud horses standing at Besnate, including stallions from Tesio's Dormello-Olgiata stud-farm.

(Left) The sire *Furibondo*, born in 1966, by *Floribunda* out of *Blue Range*.

171

Ticino

The most well-known and most remarkable building of the Ticino stud-farm is the old racing stable. This half-timbered building is situated in Milan, very close to the racecourse. It was here that many of the progeny of *Havresac II* were trained: this outstanding stallion was brought to Ticino from France in 1916 as one of a bunch of yearlings – a wonderful piece of good fortune for the Italian bloodstock industry.

The Ticino stud-farm was founded in 1915 by the Milan industrialist G. de Montel. In the space of a few years this breeder became a great rival of Federico Tesio. Only one year after announcing his stable colours, de Montel made an extraordinarily lucky purchase from France. In consequence of the difficulties occasioned by the First World War, the Marquis de Nicolay, famous breeder and owner of the Montfort stud-farm, decided to hand over all his yearlings to the young Italian racing-stable owner. They included a stallion destined to make international racing history: *Havresac II*, son of *Rabelais*. He had already made a name for himself by winning classics such as the Premio Ambrosiano and Principe Amadeo, and later he proved his worth to Italian bloodstock breeding as a champion sire. As sire of *Manistee*, and above all of the great *Cavaliere d'Arpino* (whom Federico Tesio, his breeder, described as the best racehorse ever to come out of his stable), he founded the most successful branch of the superlative *St Simon* line, especially through *Cavaliere d'Arpino*, *Bellini*, *Tenerani* and the great *Ribot*. They were to perpetuate the competitive spirit and staying-power inherited from *St Simon* (probably the most important nineteenth-century sire) more effectively than any other of his descendants.

Outstanding among many other horses bred by de Montel and later by the Ticino establishment, the descendants of two particular foundation or tap-root mares have produced a whole series of important international winners.

The first of these was *Hollebeck*, who started the famous O-line for de Montel. By beating the French champion *Kantar* and the unforgettable Schlenderhaner *Oleander* in the 1929 Prix de l'Arc de Triomphe, her descendant *Ortello* was to give the Italian bloodstock industry its first decisive international success.

The second of these outstanding mares was *Signa*, ancestor of the classic winners *Stratford*, *Salvo*, *Sedan* and, currently, *Sirlad*, unbeaten after six starts (up to the end of May 1977), including the 1977 Italian Derby.

In 1947, a few years after the death of de Montel, the whole establishment, including the renowned stud horses *Orsenigo*, by *Oleander*, and *Macherio*, by *Ortello*, was taken over by Signora B. Varga. Possibly her greatest racing success was achieved by the new owner with *Molveno*'s victory in the 1961 Prix de l'Arc de Triomphe. *Molveno* was a product of *Ribot*'s first year at stud. This imposing stallion had been working in France for several years without great success; his splendid qualities only came into evidence after he returned to his home stud. In 1975 he was the most successful sire of brood-mares, and in 1976 the champion sire of Italy.

Close to the Razza Ticino racing stables at the San Siro racecourse in Milan are the training stables of the Milan Racing Organization (TRENNO), comprising a majestic row of half-timbered buildings.

The Ticino stud-farm proper is situated in the park-land of Varesotto, above the plain of Lombardy. It was founded in the 1920s by the Milan industrialist G. de Montel who after only a few years became the great rival of the world-famous breeder Federico Tesio.

Dormello

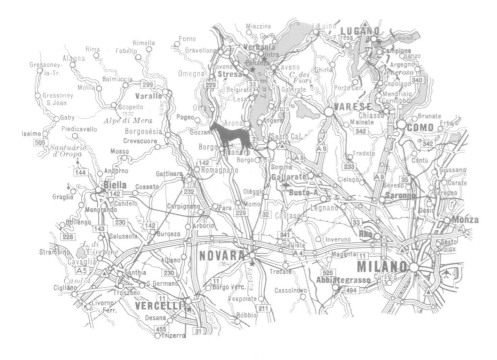

The stud-farm which has the red St Andrew's cross in its stable colours is undoubtedly the most famous in Italy. Federico Tesio, its founder, is one of the most brilliant personalities in the world of Thoroughbred racing. Not without reason did his contemporaries call him 'the magician of the Turf'. Lord Rosebery in his address to the Thoroughbred Breeders' Association at Newmarket in July 1964, demonstrated this clearly by saying: 'Together with the late Lord Derby, Signor Tesio has had more influence on the breeding of the Thoroughbred than anyone else in my time.'

Above all on account of the enormous influence exercised through the descendants of his top-class stallions *Nearco*, *Donatello*, *Tenerani* and *Ribot* in all countries where breeding is practised, this stud-farm has an enormous reputation. The influence of the *Dormello–Olgiata* stallion lines is greater today than ever before, principally through the many descendants of *Nasrullah* and *Ribot*.

It was in 1888, shortly after his marriage to Donna Lidia di Serramezzana (herself a member of a family with a rich tradition in horse breeding), that Tesio founded his stud-farm near Lake Maggiore. He acquired nearly all his horses at the Newmarket sales in England. Despite his initially rather modest budget, he turned out to be remarkably lucky with all his purchases. His greatest coup was the acquisition of *Catnip* for only 75 guineas at the war-time auction of 1915 at Newmarket. She later became his most important and internationally successful tap-root mare, and still exercises a great influence on bloodstock breeding all over the world, both through her daughter *Nogara* and her two sons, *Nearco* and *Niccolo dell'Arca*, and also through her daughter *Nella da Gubbio*, who was exported to Germany and founded the internationally successful N-line (*Neckar*, etc.) of the Erlenhof stud-farm and later of the Countess Batthyany's breeding stock.

Other outstanding acquisitions during the early phase included the *Dormello–Olgiata*

In 1888 a stud-farm was created at the south-west corner of Lake Maggiore that was to become the most famous in Italy; its stable colours, with the red St Andrew's cross, are still a force to be reckoned with, as was the founder himself, Federico Tesio, one of the most remarkable figures on the international Turf. The idyllic character of the establishment still bears witness to the magic of this extraordinary man.

- RIBOT -

line foundress *Ducia di Buonisegna* (*Donatello II*, etc.), *Chuette* (*Coronach, Cavaliere d'Arpino*, etc.), *Try Try Again* (*Tenerani, Tissot*, etc.) and *Bucolic*, who founded the line which later produced *Ribot*, the greatest racehorse of his time.

One of the basic rules of Federico Tesio's breeding theories was that his mares should never be covered by stallions he had bred himself, except in exceptional circumstances. This principle is reflected in the pedigrees of his breeding stock. Tesio spared no expense to obtain from leading establishments – after careful study – the most suitable stallions as mates for his mares.

In the 1960s, after the death of Tesio and his wife, Dornello was taken over by the Marchese Inchisa della Rochetta. Since then the excellent Dormello mares have continued to produce great winners. The tradition of the cross of St Andrew is worthily carried on by such horses as *Hogarth, Tadolina, Tierceron, Claude* and *Appiani* (sire of *Star Appeal*).

(Above) With the birth in 1952 of *Tenerani*'s son *Ribot* the history of bloodstock-breeding in Italy reached its peak. The best horse of his time in the whole world, this small colt twice beat the cream of European Thoroughbreds by winning the Prix de l'Arc de Triomphe. After his phenomenal racing career he got progeny who became champions in Europe and in the USA; the most important of them are *Graustark, Art and Letters, Rafusa, Ribero, Molvedo* and *Tom Rolfe*. The artist Ingo Koblischek painted this portrait of *Ribot* specially for the present book.

175

Yugoslavia

The grey stallions of the Spanish Riding-School in Vienna are famous all over the world. This breed of horses, in great demand for hundreds of years in all the stables of Europe, originated in a stud-farm situated in the barren Karst mountains in Yugoslavia, not far from Trieste. It was founded in 1580, by Archduke Charles of Austria; its animated history is related in the following pages.

The Lipizzaner, which was developed from crosses between hardy mares of an ancient local type and Spanish, Italian and Oriental stallions, is the best-known of all display and parade horses and is unbeaten in the classical Spanish school of equitation. What is not widely known, however, is that far greater numbers of these horses are used in farm-work (also in Hungary) and that they are excellently suited for this purpose. Similarly, it is not realized that by no means all Lipizzaners are grey: bay and black horses, more practical for working animals, are not at all uncommon.

In Yugoslavia at the present time Lippizaners are being bred not only at Lipizza but also in the State stud-farms at Lipik, Kutjevo, Fruska Gora, Prnjavor and Dobricevor.

Because the numbers exported are relatively small, it is also not widely appreciated that Yugoslavia's stock of horses is still one of the biggest among the countries of Europe, amounting to over a million, or about one horse to every twenty inhabitants.

Traces of the migrations which swept through this country at different periods are evident in the sphere of horse breeding. Illyrians, Greeks, Romans and Goths, and later Bulgarians and Romanians, have passed through here. The horses of ancient Greece (the Achaean, the Thracian and the Thessalian) must certainly have found their way into the southern parts of present-day Yugoslavia, and the blood of the diminutive Thessalians may still be flowing in the little mountain horses of Macedonia. The native

horses in the north had most probably received infusions of foreign blood from the saddle horses and chariot horses of the Romans. But it was undoubtedly the Turks who had the biggest influence; they held sway over a long period, and their Oriental horses ennobled the breed throughout the country.

Apart from the Oriental horses, the Lippizaners, the Nonius horses from Hungary and a few other, less common breeds, the top place in horse breeding in Yugoslavia goes to the Bosnian mountain type, of which there are over 400,000, making it definitely the most important breed in the country. The Macedonian mountain horse, a very similar type, is found in the southernmost part of Yugoslavia. The later influence of Oriental blood is unmistakable, and its effect on conformation and character shows up clearly in many specimens. The Bosnian – which from its height of 130–140 cm (13–14 hands) would

be regarded as a pony, but which in type is definitely a horse – has been improved by Oriental blood. This is manifest especially in the fine but thoroughly sound bone structure, in the often very handsome shape of the head with its large expressive eyes, in the temperament and in the colour, which is often white or grey. This Arab refinement, though desirable for a saddle horse and undoubtedly an advantage for the light cavalry at the time of Frederick the Great,

was more of a drawback for the farmers and woodcutters who used the little horse as a draught and pack animal. It was not until the 1930s, after a very long period of selective breeding, that a sturdier working-type animal with shorter legs was developed.

(Left) Lipizzaners are bred in Yugoslavia not only at the original stud-farm at Lipizza but also at various state stud-farms. Most of them are used as farm-horses.

(Above) Out of more than a million horses in Yugoslavia over 400,000 are of the Bosnian mountain type. These small animals, standing mostly between 130 and 140 cm (13-14 hands), are used as pack, draught and saddle horses. The Bosnian is indeed rated as one of the toughest, most robust and most undemanding of all breeds. It will be a long time before the small hill-farmers and mountain troops of Yugoslavia can do without these reliable and untiring helpers. The frequent early infusions of Oriental blood can be recognized in the fine but thoroughly sound bone structure, in the often very handsomely shaped head, in the spirit, the eagerness to learn, and the loyal nature. In recent years Bosnians and Macedonian mountain horses (a related type found further south) have proved highly suitable to leisure uses. The two-year-old Macedonian mare shown here belongs to Monique and Hans D. Dossenbach.

Lipizza

In the harsh climate and on the sterile limestone soil of the Karst region, horses of great hardiness, strength and endurance have been thriving for thousands of years. The Romans came here long ago for their riding-horses, and praised their qualities. And from sixteenth-century records it is known also that the strong, swift horses from the Karst were favoured for jousting.

These facts may have decided the Austrian Archduke Charles to create a stud-farm here in the limestone mountains near Trieste, so as

(Right) One of the newer buildings at Lipizza is the 20m × 65m (22 × 71 yards) riding-school, which is used by holiday visitors in bad weather. At other times, however, the Karst countryside (centre) offers splendid possibilities for excursions on horseback.

(Bottom) Young horses outside the stables. Lipizzaners are dark-coloured at birth; most of them turn grey by the age of six or eight, but some remain brown or black.

to have a supply of riding- and carriage horses for the court stables at Graz. In 1580, as Regent of Styria, Carinthia, Carniola and Istria, he bought Lipizza village from the Archbishop of Trieste. The first director of the stud-farm was a Slovene named Franz Jurko; after only five years he was able to inform the Archduke that the prosperity of the establishment was assured.

In the very first year horses were brought from Spain to improve the hardy Karst animals. At that time Spanish horses were very much in fashion in all the European courts, on account of their high action, their proud bearing and their refined appearance. During the next few years further breeding stock was acquired, including some animals from Polesine in Italy, which were quite similar to the Spanish horses, but much cheaper.

In the eighteenth century five family lines were started which have survived up to the present time. The *Pluto* line was bred from the grey Spanish-Danish grey stallion of that name. *Conversano* was a black stallion from

Naples. The foundation sire *Neapolitano* was a bay, also from Naples. *Favory* was a cream stallion from Kladrub in Bohemia, and from Kladrub also came the grey *Maestoso*.

The sixth ancestor of the breed which was founded at Lipizza, and which still survives, had as sire the original Arab stallion *Siglavy*, purchased in 1816. The Siglavys have very noble heads, similar to Arabs, more slender necks and a more refined conformation than the other foundation lines, but they do not have the stately action of the baroque parade horse.

For two centuries the establishment prospered without great incident, acquiring more land and new buildings from time to time; in the reign of Maria Theresa (1740–80) it possessed more than 150 brood-mares. However, Austria's war against Napoleon brought great troubles to Lipizza too, and in 1796 the stud-farm with over 300 horses was forced to seek refuge at Szekesvehervar in Hungary. Sixteen mares are said to have foaled on the way, without any losses. In 1798 the horses returned to

their original home. In November 1805 the stud-farm again had to be moved, to escape from Napoleon's advancing troops; it stayed away for 16 months, and just one foal was lost on this occasion. In 1809 there was a third exodus, when the stud-farm remained for six years at Mezöhegyes.

There followed a hundred peaceful years before Lipizza had to be evacuated once more, on Italy's entry into the First World War. Most of the horses were taken to Laxenburg, near Vienna. After the war, Italy

The vaulted principal stallion stable remains essentially in its original form, apart from a few new features. A plaque at the entrance gives 1703 as the year when it was built. Another over the door carries the names of the Emperor Leopold I and his successor Joseph I. A number of other buildings were also erected under Joseph I (1705-11). Charles VI (1711-40) extended the establishment considerably by buying the Postojna (1718) and Prestranek (1728) estates, thus ensuring abundant pasturage for the stock and their offspring. In the reign of Maria Theresa (1740-80) the Lipizzaners were recognized as first-rate saddle horses, but there was also a strong feeling that carriage horses should be developed. Accordingly, in 1768, twenty mares were brought from the Kopcany stud-farm to Lipizza; but after only three years these were withdrawn from breeding and sent back.

gained the region around Lipizza and demanded the return of the horses, but received only 107. Of the remainder, 97 went to Piber in Styria and 37 young ones remained at Kladrub, where they had been staying until then.

The heaviest blow of all for Lipizza came in the Second World War; in October 1943 the establishment was moved to Hostinec in Czechoslovakia.

Shortly before the Russians invaded, American troops took the horses to Schwarzenburg, and in May 1945 most of them were transferred from there to the Spanish Riding-School in Vienna. Ultimately, part of the herd was relinquished to Italy, and these horses became the foundation of the Fara Sabina stud-farm near Rome; the rest were again taken to Piber in Styria.

In the autumn of 1947 a mere 11 Lipizzaners returned to their original stud-farm; they included a Siglavy stallion and 3 brood-mares. In the next few years they were joined by a further 24 horses, and with this stock Lipizza began afresh the laborious task of developing systematic breeding – a task which has since been crowned with success.

Lipizza suffered greatly during the Second World War; in 1947, however, a start was made to rehabilitate the breeding industry with eleven horses, later joined by twenty-four more. The aim was to continue to breed the classical Lipizzaner type, but with the saddle-horse characteristics rather more emphasized and the overall impression more refined. Thus the Lipizzaners produced at their foundation stud-farm became somewhat larger, and they now have more prominent withers, more sloping shoulders and greater freedom of movement, with a more accentuated but not too high action. Heavy convex profiles are rarely encountered. The stallions illustrated are: (Left) *Pluto-Dubovina VI*, born in 1967;

(centre) *Favory-Dubovina II*, born in 1959; (right) *Maestoso-Bonavoja 45*, born in 1967.

(Overleaf) Lipizzaner brood-mares coming in from the paddock.

Austria

Austria was once a country of importance in the sphere of horse breeding; apart from the special case of the Lipizzaners, however, this is not the case today. The former Austro-Hungarian empire included regions and provinces known all over the world for horse breeding, together with an exemplary state breeding industry, the benefit of which is still to some extent enjoyed by the successor states. The empire stood second only to Russia for the number of its horses. When a horse-census was carried out (over a

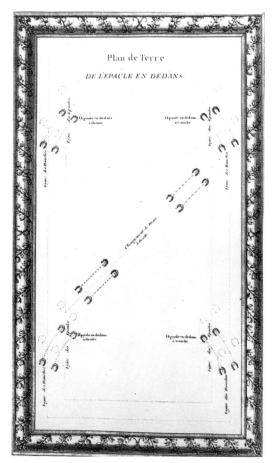

The great French riding masters of the seventeenth and eighteenth centuries exercised a direct influence on the art of equitation at the Spanish Riding-School in Vienna.
(Top) An engraving from Antoine de Pluvinel's instruction manual published in 1623; Pluvinel's most famous pupil was Louis XIII.
(Above) In 1733 there appeared another manual, *Ecole de cavalerie*, by François R. de la Guérinière; this emphasized above all the importance of side-steps, and described various exercises which are also represented choreographically, for example the 'Shoulder In', illustrated here.

span of ten years, from 1866 to 1876), the figure of 3,569,434 was recorded for Austria. In Germany there were 3,352,231 horses, in all other countries far fewer.

The most important horse-breeding regions under the old Austrian regime were Hungary, Bohemia and Moravia, southern Poland with Galicia and Croatia or Slovenia. German Austria bred a cold-blooded type, the Pinzgauer, later called Noriker, which is still in existence but has almost gone out of fashion.

'Everything of significance and value in Austria can be traced back in one way or another to the Empress Maria Theresa.' This saying, often quoted with a touch of sarcasm, applies to the creation of the state stud system. The Seven Years War with Prussia (1756–63) was a disastrous affair for the imperial cavalry. Although purchasing units were despatched as far as Russia and Turkey, a shortage of horses prevailed. In this situation the Empress issued the first edict on the use of state-owned stallions and the encouragement of the rearing of foals. Her son, Joseph II, continued these efforts with enthusiasm and founded stud-farms at Radautz, Mezöhegyes, Babolna and Piber, to name only the most important.

The Austrian state stud-farms were run on a purely military basis. The officers had to take special courses lasting for several years, some of them at the Faculty of Veterinary Medicine in Vienna. In 1869 stud activities were placed under the control of the Ministry of Agriculture for technical aspects and under the control of the War Ministry as regards military and personnel matters. Exceptions were made for the court stud-farms at Kladrub, Lipizza, Kopchan and for a short time Halbturn: these were run by court officials.

From the technical point of view, and on account of the influence it exercised, the Radautz stud was of great importance, and since it is not dealt with separately in this book, as are the other major studs of Old Austria, it is described in somewhat more detail here. The establishment was founded in 1780 at Waszkonz, and it was not until

1792 that it was moved to Radautz in Bukovina. It covered an area of about 10,000 hectares (25,000 acres) and extended 120 km (75 miles) end to end. In addition to the main station there were a number of out-stations and hill pastures on the slopes of the Carpathians. Around the turn of the century there were as many as 2,000 horses. Both light and heavy half-bloods were bred, to serve different purposes for the army. There were also some Thoroughbreds, especially among the stallions.

But the most famous were the Radautz Arabs, both pure and half-bred; in the latter class the Shagyas attained great importance. The pure Arabs from Radautz set their stamp on many of the Arabs bred in Hungary and in Poland, and in this way influenced breeding throughout Europe. *Amurath* acquired an international reputation.

Anglo-Arabs from Radautz also spread to many parts, the best known being the Gidran chestnuts.

And finally the Lipizzaner breed – systematically treated here also as a working type – became widely distributed. Even Lipizza itself acquired the occasional Lipizzaner from Radautz.

Radautz's principal responsibility was to produce stallions of all these breeds and types to stand at the numerous state-run stallion centres.

During the First World War practically the entire establishment was evacuated to German Austria. During the following decades nearly all the Radautz horses were sold, while some were handed over to farmer-breeders without payment. By the end of the Second World War they were scattered to the four winds. The very last of them, a group of some twenty brood-mares, are still to be found at Piber – they have, in the meantime, been subjected to type modification, for jumping qualities, by selection and crossing with Hanoverian stallions.

After the Second World War the stock of horses in Austria was made up of 80 per cent Pinzgauers, 12 per cent Haflingers and about 6 per cent warm-bloods. In 1950 there were

(Right) The stallion boxes of the state stud-farm at Radautz, which was dispersed during the First World War.

(Below) The hall of the Spanish Riding-School is one of the most magnificent examples of baroque architecture. Built between 1729 and 1735 by Josef E. Fisher von Erlach, it is 55m (180 feet) long, 18m (59 feet) wide and 17m (56feet) high, and the gallery is supported by 46 columns. At this institute, the only one where classical equitation is still pursued in its purest form, public performances are given.

still 283,000 horses; by 1973 only 30,000. Since then the stock has been increasing again, by around 1000 a year. The proportion of cold-bloods has fallen to 50 per cent while that of Haflingers has risen to 30 per cent. Warm-bloods – mostly imported saddle-horses – now constitute about 12 per cent of the total stock.

The bloodstock industry in Austria is small, and racing at Freudenau, Vienna, encounters difficulties from time to time, but the classic races are nevertheless held. Trotter breeding, on the other hand, has been quite successful and is producing a steady supply of good quality stallions.

The Spanish Riding-School

This riding-school is the last remaining institution where the classical art of equitation is still fostered in its purest form and is brought to the pitch of perfection described in the writings of Xenophon (c. 400 BC) and depicted in impressive bas-reliefs and old engravings. This establishment derives its name from the fact that the horses schooled here are exclusively of Spanish origin – Lipizzaners; they are also all stallions. The concept of Haute Ecole in the classical sense implies the development of the whole of the horse's musculature by gymnastic training so as to attain the ability to perform with perfect control the most difficult exercises consonant with the natural action of the horse.

The first recorded mention of the Spanish Riding-School is in a document dated 1572, where it is designated as the *Spainischer Reithsall*. Its original responsibility was to educate young nobles in the art of riding. Nowdays it serves an important purpose by preserving the heritage of classical equitation theories and by its general influence on dressage riding; in addition, it is responsible for testing Lipizzaner products. The magnificent hall was erected between 1729 and 1735, and in 1743 Maria Theresa herself led the quadrille in the instantly famous 'ladies' carousel'. Until the end of the First World War only the Emperor's guests were allowed in to see the performances.

Piber

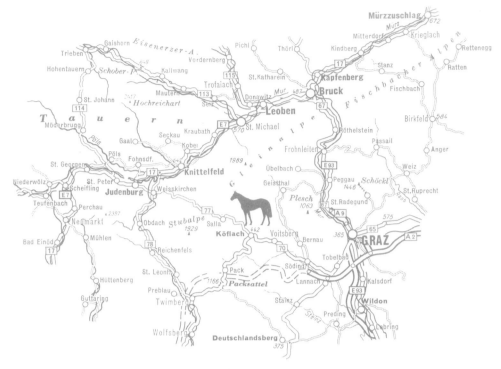

In 1869 these Lipizzaners, which had very useful qualities, were transferred from Piber to Radautz. The authentic Spanish Riding-School Lipizzaners did not arrive at Piber until 1920 when, in the course of post-war developments, the Lipizza foundation stud-farm, situated to the north of Trieste, came into the possession of Italy. Piber is today the only state-owned stud-farm in Austria to carry on the tradition of the imperial court stud-farm at Lipizza by breeding Lipizzaners for the Spanish Riding-School in Vienna.

The Piber Stud was founded in 1798. Used at first as a cavalry remount centre and then as a military stud-farm, it remained entirely under military control until 1867. After a short period of civilian management the stud-farm was actually closed down, but soon afterwards re-opened as a remount centre and finally, again as a stud-farm, administered by the so-called Military Stud Branch up to the end of the First World War in 1918. In those days Piber was attached to Radautz, the most distinguished stud-farm of the Austro-Hungarian empire (see above, p. 184).

Piber has successfully devoted its main efforts to high-class bloodstock: the Arabs and Anglo-Arabs bred there are reckoned to have been very good. English Thoroughbreds and half-breeds also do well at Piber. Lipizzaners were first bred at Piber in 1857. However, these were not court Lipizzaners, but horses of the type used by farmer-breeders, as is still the practice in Hungary, Czechoslovakia and Yugoslavia.

(Top) The Piber stud-farm, with the landmark of the Romanesque church, which was mentioned in a document dating from as long ago as 1066.

(Above) The spacious riding-school.

(Left) Parade of Lipizzaner brood-mares with foals at a reception for Queen Elizabeth II in 1969.

(Right) The present Piber Castle was built in 1696, in the Renaissance style, by the Italian architect Domenico Sciasso. It now houses the stud directorate.

(Far right) Brood-mares and foals run free in the wide, lush pastures and at night are brought in to their roomy stables. The stock of Lipizzaners numbers some 130 to 150 stud horses.

(Below) The inner courtyard of the castle with its three-storey gallery.

(Overleaf) Three-year-old Lipizzaners.

Here Lipizzaners are bred according to principles of production relevant to the suitability of the horses for Haute Ecole. The paramount objective is to produce a traditional horse for parade and display.

The Second World War brought problems to Piber once more. In 1942 the entire establishment was transferred to Hostinec in the Bohemian Forest and was combined with Italian and Yugoslav Lipizzaners to form one large stud-farm. At the end of the war, in 1945, the most valuable horses were taken to the American zone by a US Army unit under the command of General Patton, in a notable coup. After the return of the Yugoslav and Italian horses the remaining stock of the stud-farm came back to Piber in 1947. It took a great deal of effort to restore the stud-farm to its previous level.

Alongside the Lipizzaners, a relatively small stud-farm of warm-bloods is maintained at Piber, consisting of descendants of the old Austrian cavalry horses of Radautz type. The stud-farm numbers fifty or sixty horses.

Hungary

In former times the Magyars were a race of true horsemen. Travelling over great distances on horseback, they ultimately conquered the Carpathian plain.

But times have changed. Although many horses are still to be seen working on the roads and in the fields of Hungary, this animal no longer plays a leading part in agriculture. More and more it is being used only for leisure and sporting activities.

The Magyars of ancient times were nomads who lived by hunting and cattle breeding and who were probably already riding horses more than 4000 years ago in their original homeland in the Urals. They were certainly on horseback when, splitting off from the Finno-Ugrian stock, they made their way to the west; and when they reached the Carpathian region the swiftness of their horses and the fury of their attacks struck terror into the hearts of the peoples settled there.

What sort of horses did the Hungarians ride? They must have been fast, undemanding animals with tremendous endurance; for otherwise they could not have covered such great distances and appeared so suddenly. The first indication of the quality of the Magyars' horses is to be found in the works of the Roman historian Tacitus; writing in the first century AD he recorded that the Roman horse-dealers bought 'hungurian' horses for preference.

From their original homeland to the west of the Urals they migrated first eastward and then southward to the Central Volga regions, where they remained for several centuries. Then they moved on slowly to the northern spurs of the Caucasus and from there continued through southern Russia and the Ukraine and across the Carpathians, finally reaching Pannonia, where they settled. The story of their wanderings is interesting for a very particular reason: it contains the answer to our question.

Two hypotheses are advanced in the literature on the subject. The first of these maintains that the Magyars' horses were descended from the wild horse of the Asiatic steppes, also known – after its discoverer – as Przewalski's horse. The second hypothesis asserts that the nomads rode the wild horse of the southern Russian steppes – the Tarpan. It must be assumed that the Hungarians rode Przewalski's horse first and got hold of the Tarpan later, in southern Russia.

In a record from the period when the Hungarians seized the country, their horses are described as follows: 'The size is small; the head noble, with keen eyes; the body is wiry; the joints are neat and the sinews very hard. Mostly their colour is dark mouse-grey, with light-coloured hair on the belly. There is a black stripe on the back, and shoulders and forearms are often darker. White horses are not uncommon, there are different shades of grey, and some have many markings.'

The Tarpans, the wild horses which finally became extinct in the nineteenth century, were mouse-grey and had short, noble heads, with a slightly concave profile.

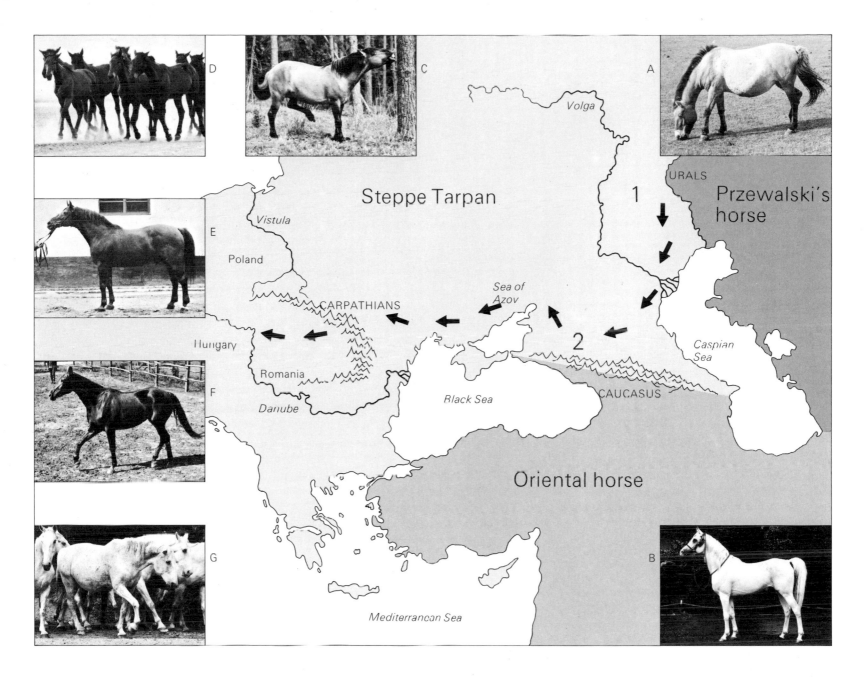

The Hungarians are descendants of the race which inhabited the steppes between the Volga and the Urals (1) some 4000 years ago, and it is believed that at that period they were already riding horses, most probably descendants of the wild Przewalski horses (native to that region (A)). These nomads subsequently migrated in a south-westerly direction and reached the northern spurs of the Caucasus (2). There is some evidence that they came into contact there with tribes who were riding Arab-type horses (B). As they migrated further westward they came to the region inhabited by the wild horses of the western steppes, the Tarpans (C). All these varieties influenced the Hungarian breed. Finally, over 1000 years ago, they reached the Carpathian basin, where they settled. The Magyars have maintained a close relationship with the horse up to the present day. They have produced such breeds as the Nonius (D), the Gidran (E) and the Furioso-North-Star (F) and developed the Hungarian Tulipan foundation line of the Lipizzaner breed (G).

(p. 190) On festive occasions in Hungary the wild horsemanship of the steppes comes to life again.

The somewhat larger and heavier Przewalski of the eastern steppes, by contrast, is yellow-dun to brownish-yellow and has quite a large, rather spherical-shaped head. The occurrence of greys and those with markings indicates, moreover, that the Magyars were already improving their stock with Arabs.

The first stud-farm in Hungary was founded by the tribal leader Arpád (889–907) on an island in the Danube which still bears the name of the first stud director, Csepel. Moreover, several place names on this island are connected with horse breeding.

The battle of Lechfeld (955) marked a significant turning point in the history of Hungary. Raids by armies and robber bands in search of adventure throughout Europe grew less frequent. Arpád's grandson Géza (972–97) and his son Wojk, who became known as Stephen I (St Stephen, King of Hungary 997–1038), were

baptized, and the latter finally succeeded in persuading the nomads to settle and establishing Christianity in the country.

That horses were of great importance to Stephen I is evidenced by a law which forbade working with horses on Sundays and festival days. Those who broke this law had to relinquish their teams to the State. Stephen's successors also showed great interest in horse breeding and gave it encouragement by various laws. Widely renowned for their swiftness, their endurance, and their undemanding nature, the horses found an enthusiastic market in other countries. When ultimately the situation arose that, on account of home requirements, the heavy export demand could not be met, King László (1077–95) passed a law forbidding the export of any breeding stock.

King Lájos (1516–26) introduced some new ideas into Hungarian horse breeding. During his reign horseraces were run in the country for the first time, and horses from the neighbouring kingdom of Poland took part in them. Up to this point practically no foreign types had been successfully bred.

The year 1526 marked the start of a new phase in the history of horse breeding in Hungary. After the battle of Mohács Hungary came under Turkish rule for 150 years. Though marked by troubles in other spheres, this Turkish period brought great gains to horse breeding. At first through the taking of war booty and later, during the occupation, by purchases and gifts, much new blood was infused into the native stock, for the Turkish cavalry had many Arab horses. The breeders soon recognized the fine qualities and the good influence of the Arabs, and this breed became very much sought after. Crossing with Arabs greatly ennobled the type of the Hungarian horses and improved their action.

In the first half of the nineteenth century horse breeding in Hungary was given a great impetus by Count Stephan Szechenyi. He founded the first racing club and organized the first Thoroughbred races, at Pressburg (Bratislava) and later, in 1826, in Pest. He convinced his compatriots that the Thoroughbred could have a good influence on the country's breeding industry. He had realized early on that by being crossed in this way the Hungarian horses not only became faster but were also greatly refined and improved as regards appearance.

The government authorities also recognized the fine qualities of English horses and in 1853 founded the third state stud-farm at Kisber. This establishment was responsible for breeding Thoroughbreds which could be used for general breeding purposes under expert supervision. Up to 1867 the three state stud-farms were controlled by the Austrian Habsburg regime; at that point they came into the possession of the Hungarian State. From then on Mezöhegyes, Babolna and Kisber supplied the country with high-quality animals for breeding. But there were also numerous private breeders with excellent horses. At the beginning of the twentieth century the breeding industry suffered another reverse. Agriculture became more intensive, great expanses of pastureland came under the plough, and the first negative effects of mechanization made themselves felt.

The damage caused by the First World War was very great. A large part of the good breeding material still available was requisitioned by the army and was left on the battlefield.

Early in the 1920s the Hungarians began to rebuild their horse breeding industry. By the end of the 1920s they were already in a position to supply at least part of the requirements of those countries which traditionally acquired their horses from Hungary. However, the quality still left something to be desired.

The following figures speak for themselves.

1911 (within the old boundaries of Hungary):	2,000,611 horses
1935 (within the post-Trianon boundaries):	885,859 horses
1940:	989,450 horses
1944:	859,976 horses
1945 (in September, after the end of the war):	328,234 horses

These figures are a clear indication of the devastating effect of the Second World War on horse breeding. And it must be borne in mind that not only did the number of horses decrease by 58 per cent in the last year of the war, the quality also suffered. After the war practically all that was left were old, sick, half-starved or wounded animals of little, if any, use for breeding purposes.

It was not until the early 1960s that horse breeding in Hungary began gradually to recover from this heavy blow.

(Above) *Kincsem* was far and away the most famous and most successful Thoroughbred ever produced in Hungary. Between 1876 and 1880 this mare ran in fifty-four races in six countries, without ever being beaten. Between April and November for four years she spent more nights jogging along in cattle-carts than in her stable. No wonder the Hungarian Jockey Club buildings erected at that time were named *'Kincsem Houses'*, and that there was a *'Kincsem'* tavern' close to the Budapest racecourse. In addition, a commemorative medal was struck for *Kincsem*; there was a *'Kincsem'* racing paper and a *'Kincsem'* lottery.

(Right) For decades Hungarian two-, four- and five-in-hand teams have been highly successful in international competition. The Hungarian driving style has been taken up all over the world; but there is no country where the sport is practised with such enormous enthusiasm as it is in Hungary.

Mezöhegyes

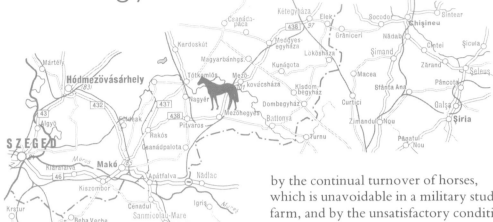

Situated in the extreme south-east of the Hungarian plain is the oldest and most important of the country's state stud-farms: Mezöhegyes. It was founded in 1785. The man on whose recommendation Joseph II (1741–90) ordered the stud-farm to be built was Josef Csekonics, who was also responsible for establishing the Babolna Stud soon afterwards.

In the early stages of its existence the stud-farm had many troubles to overcome, especially sickness. This was caused mainly by the continual turnover of horses, which is unavoidable in a military stud-farm, and by the unsatisfactory conditions of hygiene. There were always several thousand horses standing at the stud-farm. In 1793 alone, 830 foals were produced by about 1000 mares. On the other hand, the records for 1809 show that some 1000 horses died within a short period due to diseases introduced from outside. In 1814 the remount centre was closed down, and from then on breeding was the stud-farm's only activity. At the same time the establishment's farming activities were developed, so that it was not necessary to buy in the whole of the forage requirements from outside. There is still a big farming industry at Mezöhegyes today.

In 1810 an Anglo-Norman was born in France who received the name *Nonius*. His ancestry and place of birth are not known with certainty – various statements have been made in this connection. What is known is that his breeding included a high proportion of English Thoroughbred blood, that his early life was unsettled and that he was brought to Mezöhegyes in 1816 as war booty.

This *Nonius Senior* inaugurated a new epoch in Hungarian horse breeding and became the foundation sire of the best-known Hungarian breed. He stood at the stud-farm until his death in 1832. At first mares of all types were sent to him; however, as a result of systematic breeding and the genetic potency of this stallion a homogeneous type was soon established.

(p. 194) The old buildings at Mezöhegyes are still standing, almost in their original state. Above is shown a section of the façade; below, the side view of the riding hall.

(Below) One of the stable units at Mezöhegyes.

(Right) *Ramzes junior*, born in 1960 and acquired from Germany, is having a big influence on the production of jumpers in Hungary.

(Far right) *Ramzes junior*'s son *Zeus*, born in 1969.

The aim was to breed an unpretentious, hardy, somewhat heavier, but nevertheless agile type especially suitable for agricultural work. From 1860 onwards English Thoroughbred blood was introduced, making the Nonius lighter and eliminating most of the defects of conformation, in particular the heavy 'ram's head' with the small deep-set eyes, and the badly coupled loins.

In 1861 the breed began to be subdivided into two types: the lighter, small Nonius, standing less than 160 cm (16 hands), and the large draught animal.

From 1885 onward Nonius types were also bred at Debrecen in the puszta of Hortobagy; in 1961 all Nonius breeding was moved to Hortobagy.

The Hungarian line of Anglo-Arabs – the Gidran – was also started at Mezöhegyes. The foundation sire was the original chestnut Arab stallion *Gidran Senior*, by whom the Spanish mare *Arrogante* foaled the colt *Gidran II*. This breed was subsequently improved by the infusion of much English Thoroughbred blood, and the Gidran became known as an excellent saddle- and carriage-horse. At the present time the Gidran is bred at Sütveny and also outside Hungary, in Romania and Bulgaria.

Finally, a third breed was developed at Mezöhegyes, the Furioso-North-Star, also known as the Mezöhegyes half-bred or simply as the Furioso. The two foundations sires were both English Thoroughbred stallions. *Furioso* arrived in 1841, from the stud-farm of Count Karolyi, while *The North Star* was imported from England. The mares sent to these two stallions were the stud-farm's own products and mainly of Hungarian origin. The two lines were at first bred separately, but from 1885 onwards they were intercrossed, giving rise to the hyphenated name. However, the Furioso strain has remained dominant.

The Furioso-North-Star is a strong horse with a big frame, standing up well to carriage work and highly versatile as a saddle horse, being particularly suitable for heavy riders. At the present time it is bred mainly at the Apajpuszta stud-farm, between the Danube and the Theiss.

As a consequence of the changing uses for horses in recent times, Mezöhegyes has had to face new breeding tasks. Thus, as well as Thoroughbreds and trotters, the so-called Hungarian sporting horse is now mainly bred here. The existing Hungarian stock is improved by much crossing with Thoroughbreds, and more and more horses of proven sports ability are brought in from West Germany. It is hoped by this means to bring about a lasting improvement. Moreover, the aim of breeding is no longer to produce an impeccable appearance, but rather to select according to the results of performance trials.

(Above) The herd of mares at Mezöhegyes, photographed in 1932.

(Right) There is a long and greatly cherished tradition of team driving in Hungary. The harnesses are masterpieces of the harness-maker's art. Finely braided straps and bands with pretty ornamentation decorate the horses. The typical thin parade-straps of the head harness serve not only as decoration but also as protection against insects.

Babolna

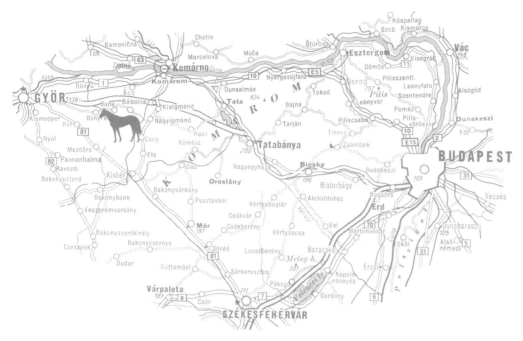

Hungary's second oldest state stud-farm – Babolna – lies about 15 kilometres (9½ miles) to the south of the district town, Komarom. At the time of the Romans there was already a settlement here, but this is believed to have been destroyed by the Tartars. The first records date from the thirteenth century. It was a noble seat, known as Babunapuszta. The property was acquired in 1662 by the family of Count Szapary, from whom it was bought by the Government in 1789 in order to establish a branch of the Mezöhegyes stud-farm. Accordingly Babolna, as the property was now called, came under the control of Captain Csekonics, and its main task at first was to accommodate overflow horses from Mezöhegyes (see pp. 194–95). But there were also some horses of foreign origin here, particularly from Spain.

Breeding proper started in 1807, after Babolna had been elevated by royal decree to independent status. No records are available regarding the work of the early years. After the battle of Györ in 1809

Napoleon's troops also attacked Babolna. The horses were evacuated to Mezöhegyes in good time, but some of the buildings were burnt down, and the first stud books with them.

Systematic breeding was resumed in 1816. The top military administration directed that Arab types were to be produced. Accordingly, the stallions *Thibon*, *Ulysso*, *Mustaphe* and *Tharax*, as well as some others, were obtained from France; all of them carried a high proportion of Arab blood. From Arabia there came the stallions *Siglavy-Gidran* and *Ebchen*, together with the mare *Tiffle*. Further stud-horses were bought from the Near East on different occasions, and the pure breeding with the existing animals would certainly have had a good effect in time. Unfortunately, however, it was decided to try to strengthen the light bone structure of the Arabs by introducing three Thoroughbred stallions and some Spanish ones, and this ruined the whole breeding programme. In 1833 there was an outbreak

of dourine, causing the death of fifty-two mares. In order to infuse fresh blood into the breeding stock, some Syrian stallions were bought; among them was *Shagya*, who founded a line still flourishing today.

Until 1850 the policy was to attempt to breed horses of Arab type using Arab stallions and a variety of mares; then it was decided to breed pure Arabs at Babolna and, using these home-bred Arabs, to produce a constant Arab type by crossing. For this purpose another mission was sent

(Left) This memorial to the horses killed in war stands in the yard at Babolna.

(Right) The black stallion *Obajan XIV*, born in 1963; his family came originally from Syria.

(Below) The avenue leading to the main entrance at Babolna. The estate is about 700 years old and was formerly, under the name Babunapuszta, a country seat, changing hands frequently until it came into the possession of Count Szapary in 1662. In 1789 the Government bought the property from the family for 450,000 gold forints.

(Left) A Babolna five-in-hand. An imposing parade of Oriental horses can sometimes be seen in the riding-hall at Babolna. The present management is however often very cool towards visitors, unlike other stud-farms in Hungary.

the introduction of performance tests. Fresh blood was infused by various purchases organized under the expert management of the stud director, Fadlala El Hedad, who had come to Babolna as a boy of fourteen with a convoy of horses from Arabia.

Babolna experienced its greatest prosperity during the period between the two World Wars. According to reports, there was at that time no other stud-farm in the world with so many Arab horses of such outstanding quality – not even in the land of their origin. The most famous sires of that period were *Kuhaylan-Zaid* and *Sven Hedin*, the latter being an Arab stallion bred at Weil, in Württemberg, and renamed *Kemir* when he stood at Babolna.

By the end of the Second World War the stock was almost completely destroyed. It was only because they had been brand-marked as foals that a small number of them were traced, with a great deal of difficulty.

It was not until the 1960s that the breeding of Arabs flourished once more at Babolna. Standing at the stud-farm then were the notable *Gaza VII*, the superb black *Obajan XIII*, *Shagya XXXVI*, *Kemir II* and *Jussuf VII*. An import from the Egyptian State stud at El Zahraa was the silver-grey *Farag*, whose sire *Morafie* now rates as an important sire in the United States.

In 1973 there were nine stallions standing at stud, of whom five were Babolna-bred and four were imported from Egypt. The number of mares is now about eighty.

to Syria, returning to Europe with no fewer than 16 stallions, 50 mares and 14 foals. Some of these horses were taken to the court stud-farm at Lipizza (now in Yugoslavia), but the majority came to Babolna.

On 1 January 1869 the establishment, which had hitherto been administered by the military authorities, was placed under the control of the Hungarian ministry of agriculture. The most important innovation resulting from this change was

In 1973 there were nine stud-horses standing at Babolna, of whom five were bred there and four were imported from Egypt. The magnificent chestnut stallion *Ibn Galal*, born in 1966, left, and the white *Ghalion*, born in 1965, right, are original desert Arabs. *Shagya XLIII*, born in 1961, above, was born at Babolna; his ancestral sire *Shagya* came to Hungary from Syria in 1834.

Sümeg

The ruins of the medieval castle can be seen from afar, dominating the hill at Sümeg. In the princely old stables with the double row of columns supporting the vaulted roof some fifty stud-horses of various breeds are now standing. The bishop's grain store formerly occupied the first floor. The saddle room is arranged as a museum, with harnesses and saddling gear, including the splendid saddle shown here, part of the booty taken in the Turkish wars.

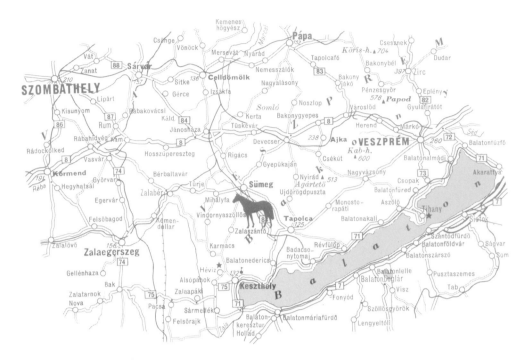

The picturesque little town of Sümeg lies to the north of Lake Balaton, at the western end of the Bakony mountains. It was founded at the time of King Bela IV who, after the Mongols invaded Hungary in 1241, built several castles, including the mighty defensive installation at Sümeg. The old town was completely destroyed by fire in 1701. In the middle of the eighteenth century it was rebuilt by Bishops Acsadi and Biro, and many splendid baroque buildings were erected at that time. The princely stables which now accommodate the stallion centre date from the same period.

Formerly, the Sümeg district was not actually a horse breeding region, though it was well-known for its donkeys, which were prized by the small farmers of the neighbourhood. It was only with the foundation of the State agricultural associations that the horses arrived. In 1969 one of Hungary's three stallion centres was installed in the ancient stables.

Szilvasvarad

The origin of the Hungarian Lipizzaner breed goes back to the early part of the nineteenth century. At that time the court stud of Lipizza fled before the advancing troops of Napoleon to Mezöhegyes where it remained until 1815, when it returned to its original home. However, some of the horses stayed at Mezöhegyes, where they formed the foundation stock for the Hungarian Lipizzaner breed.

As it turned out, the South Hungarian plain did not suit the grey horses from the rocky Karst. To overcome the detrimental effects, in 1874 a state stud-farm for the Hungarian Lipizzaners was established at Fogaras in Transylvania. In 1920 the stock had to be moved again, this time to Babolna, as after the conclusion of the Peace of Trianon Hungary had ceded Fogaras to Romania. Since the Lipizzaners were not suited to the climate and soil conditions at Babolna either, the search was continued, and finally an area was found, in the Bükk mountains to the north of the great plain, where the conditions were

roughly the same as in the Lipizzaners' original home.

About 25 kilometres (15 miles) to the north of Egra (Erlau) – a town famous for its wine – lies the government-owned estate of Szilvasvarad; it was there that the Hungarian Lipizzaners finally settled in 1951. The stallions were splendidly housed in the old stables of Szilvasvarad castle; stabling for the mares was erected on the hill opposite. Weaned foals and young horses live in the Csipkeskut farm high up in the mountains.

Compared with the Central European stock, the Hungarian Lipizzaners are somewhat heavier and clumsier. Seven lines are bred in accordance with the old classical principles: *Conversano, Favory, Incitato, Maestoso, Neapolitano, Pluto* and *Siglavy-Capriola*. In addition, the *Tulipan* line developed in Hungary is naturally also bred. There are at present about seventy brood-mares at the establishment.

Lipizzaners are also bred at other state-owned centres.

(Above) *Csikos*, mounted herdsmen, drive the mares from the hilly pastures to their stables in the evening.

(Left) *Neapolitano*, one of the most impressive Lipizzaner stallions at Szilvasvarad. The Hungarian Lipizzaners are somewhat heavier than their congeners in Yugoslavia and Austria. There are altogether some 4500 Lipizzaners in Hungary, constituting about 3 per cent of the total stock of horses. During the covering season there are about sixty-five Lipizzaner stallions at the various covering stations.

(p. 200) The chalky soil and harsh climate in the Bükk mountains of northern Hungary provide ideal conditions for breeding Lipizzaners. Nestling between the hills is the Szilvasvarad main stud-farm; high above it is the Csipkeskut farm where the foals are kept.

Since 1951 the Lipizzaner stud horses have been housed in the former stables of Szilvasvarad castle. The seven old lines, together with the Tulipan line developed in Hungary, are bred here on classical principles.

(Right) The black stallion *Conversano* provides striking evidence that Lipizzaners are by no means always greys. There are a few chestnuts among the mares also.

201

Czechoslovakia

In Bohemia, as also in Slovakia, there is a rich tradition of horse breeding. While the type of horse bred in Bohemia is marked by the influence of heavy sires, horse breeding in Slovakia adheres more closely to the types favoured in Hungary.

A notable advance in horse breeding was made in the eighteenth century with the introduction of numerous measures aimed at producing horses to meet the requirements of the army. Registration procedures were instituted and dimensions

individual provinces of Bohemia, Moravia, Silesia and Slovakia in accordance with their autonomous status and in co-operation with the breeders' associations. Both warm-bloods and cold-bloods were bred, in fairly precisely delimited regions. The volume of cold-blood production was determined by the requirements for traction power. Warm-blood breeders, on the other hand, opposed this trend towards increasing the bulk of their horses. Following the introduction of large

were stipulated for registration. But it was not until the second half of the nineteenth century that a substantial improvement was achieved in the general level of breeding. Faced with the rapid development of industry, agricultural productivity also had to be raised.

Between 1918 and 1945 horse breeding in Czechoslovakia was adapted to meet the needs of agriculture, transport and the army. Breeding was controlled by the ministry of agriculture and by the

numbers of Oldenburger and East Friesian stallions, a new type was developed, the Czech warm-blood. This was a smaller horse than the Oldenburger, but it was well adapted to the needs of agriculture. It matured earlier and was of a more compact build; on the other hand its constitution was not so tough and its hoofs were not so good. The Czech warm-blood was bred in Bohemia and especially in the district around the provincial stud-farm at Nemosice.

In Moravia warm-blood breeding was modified under the influence of English half-breed stallions of a lighter type and, in the southern part of the province, also under the influence of Arab half-breeds, especially of the Shagya, Gidran and Dahomen strains. The Moravian half-bred was more refined and lighter than the Bohemian.

At the beginning of the twentieth century there was a big increase in the production of cold-bloods in Bohemia.

(Top) The Horse Breeding Research Station at Slatiňany includes a museum with one of the most comprehensive collections in the world. As well as a great variety of objects of interest for the history of art and culture there is a wonderful collection of saddles and harnesses from all over the world.

(Above, left) The stallion *154 Furioso XIII*, a typical representative of the noble $A\frac{1}{2}$, who proved himself as a sire in the province of Moravia.

(Centre) *Furioso XVIII* was one of the best known half-bred principal sires at Kladrub.

(Right) The stallion *288 Marquis Lechoticky*, son of the imported Belgian *9 Marquis de Vraiomont*, founded a famous blood-line in Moravia.

Stallions, especially Brabants, were imported and used to cover large numbers of warm-blood mares also. By crossing in this way the herd was gradually formed into the type known as the Bohemian cold-blood. In Moravia breeding was influenced more by imported Ardennais.

In addition to the use of these Belgian horses in Bohemia and Moravia, Norikers also were bred in both provinces, mainly in the foot-hills of the mountains of southern Bohemia and northern Moravia.

In Slovakia, heavy Nonius horses and English half-breds were commonly bred in the southern and western regions. In the middle of the country there were medium-sized Nonius horses, lighter half-breds and Lipizzancrs, and in the foot-hills there were Lipizzancrs and Arab half-breds. Finally, in the mountain regions the little Huzul ponies were bred.

Whereas in 1900 the ratio of warm-bloods to cold-bloods in Bohemia was 92:8, in 1920 it was 48:52 and in 1940 it was 42:58.

During the last thirty years the number of horses in Czechoslovakia has dropped. Whereas between 1920 and 1938 the average number was about 666,000, it has decreased by nearly 90 per cent since 1947, as the following figures show: 658,000 in 1947; 590,000 in 1950; 543,000 in 1955; 389,000 in 1960; 204,000 in 1965; 144,000 in 1970; 72,000 in 1975.

After the Second World War, and particularly in the 1960s, there was a very distinct change in breeding objectives, the aim being now to produce a modern, versatile, utility type of warm-blood.

This change was associated with a merging of various types within the warm-blood and cold-blood breeds.

In Czechoslovakia, as elsewhere, equestrian sports are widely enjoyed, and the number of riding-clubs is increasing all the time. Coupled with this growing interest, the breeding of English Thoroughbreds is being intensified, and new racing stables and racecourses are being created. The central racecourse is situated at Chuchle near Prague.

At Slatiňany there is an equine research station, primarily concerned with horse breeding. This institute includes a museum which is recognized all over the world as one of the greatest in its field. It was created in 1947 at the instigation of the well-known equine expert, Professor Dr František Bílek. This comprehensive collection is housed in a castle and includes a great many objects of significance in the history of art and culture. One section is concerned with the historical evolution of the horse and another deals with the significance of the horse in veterinary and human medicine. The collection of saddles and harnesses from all parts of the world is exceptionally rich, and there is also a library with a large number of books on equine subjects.

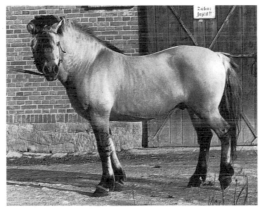

(Above, left) In the mountain regions the Huzul is bred, a small but exceptionally tough draught- and pack-horse.

(Centre) In recent years Norwegian Fjord horses have been imported in large numbers.

(Right) By crossing these two breeds, Czechoslovakia has produced the highly successful Fjord-Huzul.

(Left) At Kladrub there is also a small herd of Isabels. The illustration shows the stallion *Notar*.

(Overleaf) A Huzul.

Topolcianky

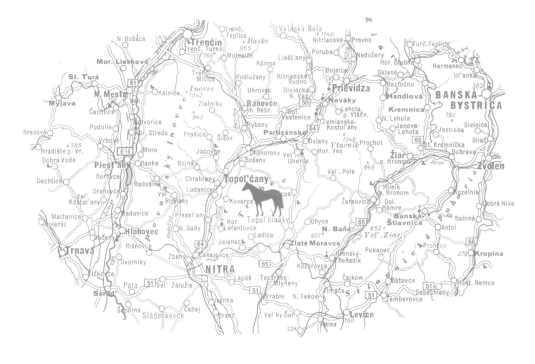

After the foundation of the Czechoslovak Republic in 1918 the country's horse breeding industry was reorganized. It became apparent that there was a need to create a state stud-farm where stallions could be stood to provide for the country's breeding requirements. On the basis of its geographical position and breeding tradition the new republic was best suited to breed high-class horses; warm-bloods had already been bred here for a long time.

On 15 October 1921 the Topolcianky state stud-farm was established, and it was here that the new breeding programme was to be implemented. In view of the soil and climatic conditions and the structure of industry in Slovakia, practically all the Central European warm-blood types – from the little Huzul through Arabs and Lipizzaners to Nonius – were bred here, with the exception of the English half-bred.

The first Nonius herd was developed from horses imported from Yugoslavia. The foundation stock of Arabs came from the Radautz and Babolna stud-farms. The Lipizzaners came from Lipizza and here continued to be bred pure. The Huzuls came from Radautz.

In 1954 the herd of Nonius was transferred to the recently created state stud-farm at Novy Tekov. At about the same time, as part of a programme of specialization, the breeding of English half-breds was started, the foundation stock being obtained from other stud-farms in the country.

(Top) The riding-hall at Topolcianky. The stable-blocks for the riding-horses are to the left and right of the little steeple.

(Above) The Lipizzaner stallion *Siglavy VIII Canissa*, born in 1959, by *Siglavy IV Sallo* out of *733 Canissa*.

(Left) The original Arab stallion *Kasr El Nil*, born in 1971, by *Bint El Nil* out of *Tuhotmos*, shown here as a three-year-old. This magnificent stallion, imported from Egypt, has been standing at stud since 1975.

Topolcianky is situated in the Nitra district. Pastures and farms are spread over the hills at altitudes between 220 and 480 m (about 700–1500 feet) above sea-level. The soil is chalky in some parts, but mostly clayey, and the climate is mild. The site is sheltered from cold north and west winds by the Carpathians and the Tribec and Vtacnik mountains. The basin is open towards the plain of the Danube to the south. The annual average temperature is between 6.5°C and 10°C (43–50°F), and the amount of precipitation is between 460 and 830 mm (18–32 inches). There are deciduous woods on all the farms.

Topolcianky has three stud-farms and two other farms where cattle are bred; mushrooms and vines are also cultivated on the estate.

The administration buildings are quite close to the castle, as are the grounds where the young horses are schooled, the centre for training sporting horses and the auction ring.

Topolcianky Castle is one of Czechoslovakia's favourite tourist spots. The first-floor gallery overlooking the inner courtyard is particularly impressive. Under the cross-vaulted roof, many red deer trophies testify to the excellent hunting in this neighbourhood. One great attraction at the castle is the collection of elegant furniture from various periods.

The stallion shown on this page is the English half-bred *North Star V*, born in 1964, by *North Star III* out of *386 Furioso XIV*. He sires good sporting horses.

207

Kladrub

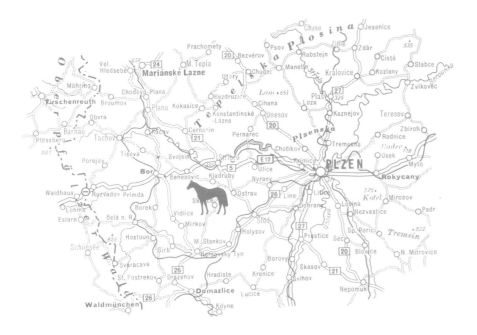

(Below) Kladruby and English mares running out of the ancient stables at Kladrub.

The photographs in this section, except for those of the stallions, are from the archives of the German Horse Museum; they were taken soon after the turn of the century.

The main stud-farm at Kladrub is one of the oldest in the world still in business; it was founded by Emperor Rudolph II in 1597.

After its establishment horses were imported from Spain and later also from Italy. The stud-farm enjoyed its greatest prosperity during the reign of Charles VI, in the first half of the eighteenth century, when there were up to 1000 horses here.

In 1757, during the Seven Years War, some of the buildings were destroyed by fire; the establishment was transferred to Kopčany and did not return to Kladrub until the reign of Emperor Joseph II.

The old Kladruby type, known in earlier centuries as *Equus bohemicus*, is a powerful coach-horse. His majestic appearance and the imposing gait and the trot with a high knee action marked him out for court ceremonial parades. The sole aim of breeding was to produce coach-horses for display occasions, especially as required by the Imperial Court in Vienna. White horses were used for court ceremonies and black ones for ecclesiastical ceremonies. There always had to be twelve white and twelve black stallions ready in the imperial stables.

The old Kladruby white strain was founded by the Italian-Spanish black stallion *Peppoli*. His mating with *Aurora 1775* produced the stallion *Imperatore*; he in turn covered *Mosca* to produce the stallion *Generale*, who became the foundation sire of the Kladruby lines *Generale* and *Generalissimus*.

(Above) The great courtyard at Kladrub. The first building on the left is the boarding stable with foaling boxes and accommodation for brood-mares. The taller building next to it is the stable for the saddle horses and working horses and the young brood-mares. Next to it is another low stable block for carriage horses and more working horses and brood-mares. To the right of the little church a part of the castle roof can be seen.

(Left) An open stable for foals at the Franzenshof farm.

(Right) *Generale Alba XIII*, principal sire around the turn of the century. The foundation sire of the old Kladruby white line was the black stallion *Peppoli* (born in 1764) from the Ferrari private stud-farm in northern Italy. Mated with *Aurora*, in 1774 he got the stallion *Imperatore*, whose mating with *Mosca* in turn produced *Generale* in 1787. This *Generale* was the foundation sire of the *Generale* and *Generalissimus* white strains bred at Kladrub.

(Below) The stallion *Sacramoso XXIX*, born in 1920, by *Sacramoso XXVII Aja* out of *85 Napoleone Ragusa*. He sired all three of the stallions used in the first phase of the regeneration process, and is a typical example of the carriage horse.

The stallion *Sacramoso* from the stud-farm of the Marquis Sacramoso at Verona founded the black line bearing that name. The second black line, that of *Napoleone*, died out in 1927.

In the same year the breeding organizations decided to give up breeding blacks. Eleven years later Professor F. Bílek developed a programme for regenerating this unique breed. This programme has now reached the final phase; a definite transformation has been established by introducing Lipizzaner blood.

The small herd of Kladruby blacks is now kept at the Horse Breeding Research Station at Slatiňany. The white herd, also re-invigorated by Lipizzaner blood, is still, as before, at the Kladruby establishment. As at Slatiňany, English half-breds are produced there as well.

(Above) Mares coming in from pasture, around 1900.

(Left) The principal sire *Siglavy Pakra I*, by the imported Lipizzaner *Siglavy Pakra* out of *191 Favorina*. In the final phase of the process of regenerating Kladruby blacks, carried out at the Slatiňany Research Station, this stallion produced progeny of great promise although he himself is somewhat lacking in substance.

(Right) The black stallion *Sacramoso* was one of the most important sires at the beginning of this century.

209

Poland

Poland has more horses than any other country in Europe; her total stock numbers some three million. But not only is the number of horses large; their quality is also very high. It may be precisely because Poland had such an agitated history that its people became such excellent breeders of horses.

Private Arab stud-farms in Poland were world-famous for many decades right up to the Second World War. The first Arab horses arrived as war booty; later on, breeders of high rank sent their agents to the Middle East to find horses and purchase them. Prince Sanguszko was the first; as far back as 1803 he had original desert Arabs at his stud-farm. His descendant, Count Potocki, founded the excellent Antoniny stud-farm which, like the famous Sawran, Jarezowce, Pelkinie, Bialocerkiev and Guminska private stud-farms, is no longer in existence. However, the state stud-farm at Janow Podlaski still maintains the old tradition and is at present breeding Arab horses which are among the best and most coveted in the world.

As well as the famous Polish Arab, the Anglo-Arab – the Malopolska – also has a very good reputation. This cross between the English Thoroughbred and the Arab was developed separately in France, Hungary and Poland. However, the foundation stock used in Poland comprised mares of the native Tarpan type; these were mated with Arab stallions. Using horses with a high proportion of Arab and English Thoroughbred blood, two Anglo-Arab types were subsequently developed. In the first of these two types, produced mainly at Janow Podlaski, the influence of the Shagya strain is obvious, especially in the finely-shaped head; this type is the closest to the Arab of all the Anglo-Arabs. At Walewice and some other stud-farms the type of Anglo-Arab produced, while not so impressive in appearance, is on the other hand extremely versatile; this type was founded mainly on the Hungarian Furioso and the Gidran, the Hungarian-bred Anglo-Arab. After the Second World War Poland also imported French Anglo-Arabs and even improved their quality at the Pruchna main stud-farm. Standing 160 cm (16 hands) or more, this is the biggest type.

The Wielkopolska now ranks as the most important of Poland's warm-bloods. This is bred in northern Poland and to some extent also in what used to be East Prussia, and is actually a direct descendant of the East Prussian horse of former times. The two types of Wielkopolska, now scarcely distinguishable from one another, are the Posener, which has been bred in Poland for about a hundred years, and in which East Prussian blood still predominates, and the Mazur, the Polish Trakehnen. Using as foundation the remarkable old-established Trakehnen horses, breeding has been conducted with the utmost care and with skilfully judged infusions of Thoroughbred, Arab and Anglo-Arab blood. At present the Trakehnen type is being produced at five main stud-farms – of which Liski is the most important – with

Even at the present time, it is impossible to imagine the Polish landscape without horses. Most of the numerous small farmers continue to work the land with horses, as they always have, and take their produce to market or to the dealer by cart.

(Right) The parade ring at the Warsaw racecourse. It is here that the renowned Polish Arabs and Anglo-Arabs are trained and tested. At the age of two-and-a-half they are prepared for a Derby course of 3000 m (15 furlongs or 3281 yards).

(Right) The Popielno Research Stud is situated on an island in the lake district of northern Poland. Here, as well as in the National Park in the Bialowieza Forest, there are herds of retrogressively-bred Tarpans very similar as regards appearance and behaviour to the genuine Tarpans which became extinct in the nineteenth century. Popielno maintains a wild herd which is left unmolested, as well as a number of Tarpans which are kept under supervision, for research purposes.

(Overleaf) Young warm-bloods rushing out of their stables.

more than 400 brood-mares; 600 brood-mares of the Posener type are spread over six main stud-farms.

Polish breeds most worthy of mention are the Konik, the Huzul and the Tarpan.

'Konik' just means 'pony', and this is the most widespread breed of ponies in Poland; it will be indispensable for small farmers for a long time to come. The Konik is a direct descendant of the Tarpan, from whom it has inherited the small, very pretty head with the often dished profile and the intelligent, lively eyes. Many Koniks have retained the colouring of the wild Tarpan, the mouse-grey coat with the strongly marked black stripe. The others are mostly dark-brown or black, or occasionally chestnut. The Konik is good-tempered and has great endurance, a tough constitution and longevity. It is still used mainly as a draught animal, but it can also serve very well as a leisure riding-horse.

The Huzul, also known as the mountain Tarpan, is associated with the Carpathian mountains, and is bred mainly in Romania, though also in the Carpathians of Czechoslovakia and Poland as well as in Bulgaria and Austria. It is more compact than the Konik and about the same size, standing some 135 cm (13 hands), and very similar in type. However, the colour, which is not infrequently yellowish dun, and the often somewhat coarser head suggest a stronger genetic influence: the wild sub-species (Przewalski's horse).

The Tarpan, as bred today at the Popielno Research Stud and in the forest reserve of Bielowieza, is no longer the true wild horse of old, though it is a direct descendant and has a similar appearance. The true Tarpan died out in the nineteenth century. The Berlin zoologist Heck, working mainly with Koniks resembling Tarpans as closely as possible, carried out a so-called retrogressive breeding operation which, while it cannot be recognized scientifically – for however closely the product may resemble the Tarpan it is still not a genuine Tarpan – is nevertheless interesting, since it demonstrates in living form just what a Tarpan looked like and how greatly it differed from Przewalski's horse.

Finally it must be mentioned that several western-type cold-blood breeds are also produced in Poland.

Liski

The Polish stud-farm at Liski is situated in the Bartoszyce (Bartenstein) district of East Prussia. It was opened in the spring of 1947 as a state horse breeding establishment. The buildings are for the most part old German ones. Liski itself, along with the Domarady (Dompandehl) and Zawiersze farms, was a remount centre. Before the war, Judijty (Juditten) together with the Park, Gulkajmy and Przewarszyty farms constituted the largest private stud-farm in East Prussia, and belonged to Herr von Kuenheim. The total area of these properties amounted to 2235 hectares (5527 acres).

Liski's original function as an enterprise belonging to the Polish Government was to produce Mazur horses.

Horses began to arrive at Liski in May 1947; the first to come were East Prussian and Hanoverian mares bought in West Germany. The next purchases were made from UNRRA, and included Döle and Fjord mares and the following Trakehnen stallions: *Pyrrhus*, born in 1939, *Polarstern*,

(Right) The English Thoroughbred stallion *6636 Parysow*, born in 1969 in England, by *Quorum* out of *Palinode*, by *Pall Mall*.

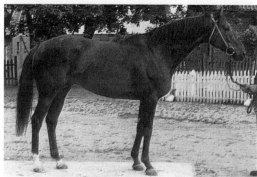

(Above) The castle of Judijty, formerly Juditten. During the period between the two World Wars it belonged to Herr von Kuenheim, whose private stud-farm here was the largest in East Prussia.

(Left) Stables and paddocks with yearlings at Liski.

(Below) Team of chestnut mares at the Domarady farm. On the left, *Dendrologia*, born in 1958, by *Flower* out of *Chronologia*, by *Midas*. On the right, *Cyklawa*, born in 1958, by *Chryzalit* out of *Cina*, by *Termit*. Fourteen mares at the stud-farm are available for farm-work.

born in 1930; *Tamerlan*, born in 1937; and lastly, in 1950, *Celsius*, born in 1943.

In 1951, twenty-eight mares were bought from Germany, many of whom made an honourable name for themselves at Liski: *Huryska, Elida, Depesza, Cartagina* and others founded outstanding lines and produced some champion stallions.

The aim of the Liski stud-farm was to produce powerful half-breds of high quality. They were bred from the female Trakehnen lines, and, using this foundation,

a start was made to re-establish the old Trakehnen lines. Of the Trakehnen stud lines, originally numbering thirty-two in 1921, four are now to be found at Liski: *60 Demant*, born in 1776; *137 Luftsprung*, born in 1775; *165 Tiberiussche*, born in 1782; and *177 Fatme*, born in 1787; in addition there is the new Trakehnen family of the mare *Lore*, born in 1905.

The stallions used for breeding were mainly from the following Trakehnen lines: *Tempelhüter, Ararat, Dampfross,*

Parsifal, Astor, Luftgott and *Eiserner Fleiss*.

Since the beginning of its operations, Liski has sold 377 stud-horses; since 1956, 675 horses have been exported to 14 countries. In December 1976 the establishment had a stock of 428 horses, including 6 stallions and 165 brood-mares. The horses are kept at 5 stud-farms, grouped in herds according to colour.

(Above left) The avenue of birches at Liski.

(Above) *Dyskobol*, born in 1954, by *Dziegel XX* out of *Chronologia*, by *Midas*.

(Far left) *6744 Bulat*, born in 1967, by *Haakon* out of *Balanda XX*, by *Dar Es Salam XX*.

(Left) *5440 Poprad*, born in 1961, by *Traum* out of *Poprawka*, by *Pilgrim*.

Janow Podlaski

The stud-farm at Janow Podlaski was founded in 1817 as a state breeding establishment.

For almost a hundred years warm-bloods were bred here. Frequent use was made of Thoroughbred stallions from England and Arab stallions from the then-famous private Polish establishments such as Branicki, Dzieduszycki, Potocki and Sanguszko.

In 1914 all the horses from Janow were taken to Russia; they never came back.

In 1919 a start was made on reconstructing the Polish horse breeding industry, and Janow was selected to be the foundation stud-farm. Until other stud-farms were created, a very great variety of breeds were to be found here. At that stage, however, it was decided to produce three breeds: (1) Pure Arabs, a reconstruction based partly on the lines of mares imported from Arabia in 1845; (2) Half-bred Arabs, based on mares from the Austro-Hungarian stud-farm at Radautz; and (3) Anglo-Arabs, produced by mating English Thoroughbred stallions with half-bred Arab mares.

The Arabs produced there soon became famous far beyond the country's borders; since 1929 pure Arabs have been exported to many European and overseas countries.

In September 1939 more than 90 per cent of the horses from Janow were lost, and the German forces took over the administration of the stud-farm. With the help of Polish personnel, efforts were made to reconstruct the breeding industry, horses being sought out and brought back to Janow from other parts of Poland and then from various other occupied countries, including Yugoslavia and France.

In July 1944 the Germans removed the horses from Janow to a remount station in Saxony, taking many of the Polish personnel with them. In February 1945 the horses were again transferred, this time to the Schönbecken-Graven remount station.

After the war, in May 1945, an office was created in Germany for dealing with the Polish stud-horses; this was directed first by

(Above) Most of the buildings at Janow Podlaski were erected in the nineteenth century. The famous 'clock stable' dates from 1846.

(Right) The pure Arab stallion *Banzaj*, born in 1965, by *Czort* out of *Bandola*. *Czort* was one of the best sires of the post-war period, a son of *Wielki Szlem* and grandson of the famous *Ofir*.

(Top) The Anglo-Arab *Felix*, born in 1967, by *Celix* out of *Figa*, by *Shagya XXXIII-2*; his unusual colouring is very striking.

(Above) The pure Arab stallion *Partner*, born in 1970, by *Elenzis* out of *Parma*.

(Right) A gateway at the 'élite' stable, the oldest building at Janow Podlaski, erected in 1941.

(Far left) The exquisite head of the pure Arab mare *Bandola*, born in 1948, by *Witraz* out of *Balalajka*, photographed at the age of twenty-five. She is a sister of the famous stallion *Bask*, now in the USA, and dam of *Babdos*, leading sire at Janow.

(Left and below) Brood-mares at the water-trough and coming in from the pastures.

Colonel W. Rozwadowski and afterwards by Colonel S. Zamoyski. This office, located in the British Zone, had under its control some 1500 horses and 550 Polish personnel.

In 1946 the horses from Janow were returned to Poland and installed at the Posadowo stud-farm at Poznan (Posen). A year later the pure Arabs were taken to a more suitable district. In 1950 the first of the half-bred Arabs came back to Janow

Podlaski and in 1960, at last, the pure Arabs as well.

At the present time both pure Arabs and Anglo-Arabs are bred at Janow; many experts say that the world's best Arabs now come from Janow.

Since the end of the war more than 200 Anglo-Arab stud horses have been produced and reared at Janow and supplied to stallion centres, and 250 pure Arabs have been sold abroad since 1960.

Walewice

There are certain events associated with the history of the Walewice stud-farm which should not be left without mention, even though they have no direct bearing on horse breeding. These events occurred during the period of the Napoleonic wars, when there was a love affair between Napoleon I and Maria Colonna-Walewska.

The name Walewice appears in old records dating as far back as 1316. It is linked with the name of the Walewski family, to whom the property belonged until 1831. Walewice's hey-day was towards the end of the eighteenth century, when Anastazy Colonna-Walewski, the proprietor, became Chamberlain to King Stanislas Augustus, from whom he obtained substantial assistance, enabling him in 1783 to erect the castle to replace the timber-built house.

In 1807 Anastazy brought his third wife, Maria Laczynska, to his castle, from Kiernozie. Shortly before this, on 1 January of the same year, the beautiful Maria had made the acquaintance of Napoleon at Jablonna. During the succeeding years the Emperor met Maria on frequent occasions, and the affair resulted in the birth of their son Alexander Florian on 4 May 1810. After the death of the Chamberlain in 1814, Alexander Florian inherited Walewice. However, on account of his involvement in the 1831 insurrection, Napoleon's son was forced to leave the country. In 1845 the property was acquired by the Grabinski family, in whose possession it remained for exactly one hundred years.

Until the First World War Arab horses were bred at Walewice; then production was switched to Anglo-Arabs.

On 16 July 1945 the Walewice estate was taken over by the government horse breeding organization. The whole stud establishment had to be entirely re-organized. There were only sixteen mares left, and most of the good horses from the other Polish stud-farms had been carried off by the German troops as they retreated. Immediately after the war the remaining breeding stock was rounded up. The aim was to breed Anglo-Arabs, using as a foundation some descendants of Shagya mares and the stallion *Fils du Vent XX* from France, a descendant of the famous *Flying Fox*. Good results were obtained from the newly re-organized stud-farm right from the start. At the present time there are 400 horses at the establishment. The whole of the breeding stock is very well established in the Anglo-Arab type.

The classic castle of Walewice is mirrored in the little river Mroga. As Chamberlain to King Stanislas Augustus, who was very generous to him, Anastazy Colonna-Walewski was able to replace his timber-built house with this edifice in 1783. Twenty-five years later his third wife, Maria Laczynska, came to live here. She became well-known through her love affair with Napoleon I.

In former times Arabs were bred at Walewice. After the First World War the establishment switched to Anglo-Arabs. During the Second World War almost all the horses were lost. The breeding industry, by then under state control, had to be completely rebuilt. At the present time there are about 400 Anglo-Arabs at Walewice. Breeding with the greatest care, from a small but excellent stock, the establishment has earned a very high reputation, reaching far beyond the country's borders.

Soviet Union

(Left) Horseback sports are probably as old as horse-riding itself, in which case they would be oldest of all in Mongolia. For it is believed to be here, in the vast open steppes, that men first tamed and rode horses. The wild daring needed for this activity is still to be seen in the reckless horseback sports of the present day. Whenever these age-old contests are held, the 'masters of the saddle' arrive from all directions to take part in them (see overleaf).

Russia has always been a great country for horses. For the nomads of the wide-open steppes, their tough ponies were the basis of existence as long ago as three or four thousand years, or even earlier. Right up to the present century the horse had a unique role in Russia: around the turn of the century the country possessed about a third of the world's total stock of horses – some 34 million out of about 100 million. Today Russia still has some 8 million horses.

Russia's first royal stud-farm was created in the reign of Tsar Alexis, the father of Peter the Great. He imported bloodstock stallions from Asia and from the Baltic provinces. His son took an even greater interest in breeding; he founded further stud-farms at Kiev and imported mares from Silesia and Prussia. In 1722 he also instituted races for testing the performance of his horses.

After Peter's death the breeding and racing industry declined, but was revived under the reign of Catherine the Great, when it reached an unexampled prosperity. At that time a large number of Thoroughbreds were brought in from England, including at least four classic champions: *Noble*, *Tartar*, *Daedalus* and *Symmetry*. Though a great many breeding experiments were made, the results were not very successful.

Count Alexis Grigorievich Orlov, who is believed to have strangled Peter III in the palace revolution of 1762 and in 1770, as Admiral of the Russian fleet, gained the victory over the Turks in the naval battle of Cheshme in the Aegean, began to breed horses when peace returned – and was even more successful in this field than in war. He imported from Greece a pure Arab stallion called *Smetanka*, to whom he sent a Friesian Harddraver mare (according to some reports, a Frederiksborg mare). These Harddravers, when mated in England with Thoroughbreds also produced the splendid Norfolk Trotter, a breed which later exercised a strong influence on many others, particularly the American Standard Trotter and the French Trotter. The mating of *Smetanka* with the Friesian mare produced a highly promising stallion, named *Polkan*; he in turn was mated with a Harddraver mare and got the stallion *Barss*. Orlov certainly took great pleasure in experimenting, but he obviously went about it quite scientifically – and also had great good luck. *Barss* had three outstanding sons: *Lubesnoy* was foaled by an Arab-Mecklenburger mare, *Dobroy*'s dam was an English Thoroughbred, and *Lebed*'s dam was a cross between English Thoroughbred, Arab and Mecklenburger. However, these three stallions all resembled one another as regards fundamental characteristics; they were long, strong horses with a notably high, but nevertheless well extended, trotting action. They provided the foundation for the whole Orlov Trotter breed.

Orlov Trotters were for a long time the fastest trotter breed in the world. They exercised their influence on many other breeds not only in Russia but also in western Europe.

After the death of Count Orlov his widow sold the establishment to the Government. During the nineteenth century some English Thoroughbred blood was introduced, without, however, producing any substantial improvement. Gradually the Orlov Trotter was outclassed by the American Standard Trotter.

For conditions in Russia the Orlovs were undoubtedly excellent horses. They were not only good racers; they were also quite able to wait in the street during the course of a state dinner in the Russian winter without coming to any harm.

Around the turn of the century the Russians crossed a great many American Standard Trotters with Orlov Trotters and thus produced a new breed, the Russian Trotter; but even so they could not equal the Americans.

Alongside trotters, the Russians were also breeding Thoroughbreds. In 1815 Tsar Alexander, who was very fond of Thoroughbreds but does not appear to have understood much about them, bought a number of these horses. After the conclusion of peace, two English horse-dealers arrived in Russia who fully lived up to the traditionally unsavoury reputation of this profession. They supplied the Tsar's court with an assortment of miserable specimens of English bloodstock which were not exactly suitable for increasing the popularity of Thoroughbreds in Russia, and which confirmed the Cossacks in the opinion that their horses were better. They planned to prove this by means of a race. It was arranged that two Cossack horses should run against two Thoroughbreds on 4 August 1825. The race was held near St Petersburg, on public roads, over a distance of 75 kilometres (47 miles). The Cossack horses were alleged to have been champions, whereas *Mina* and *Charper*, the Thoroughbreds, were only second-class horses – so, at least, goes the version told by the English. Moreover the Thoroughbreds are said to have been carrying twenty kilograms (forty-four pounds) more weight. The race took a highly dramatic turn. At half the distance *Mina* went lame and her rider had to give up. As for *Charper*, one of the stirrup leathers broke, which frightened him so much that he bolted and did not calm down again until he was completely exhausted. In the meantime however one of the Cossack horses, also completely exhausted, had to be taken out of the race. The other appeared to be so strained by the exertion that the rider dismounted and put a child in

(Below) Steering the troika, the traditional Russian three-in-hand, demands finger-tip control. The middle horse under the arch (the *duga*) is usually an Orlov Trotter and has to trot all the time. The side horses, by contrast, are 'loose' on the outer side and go at a gallop.

the saddle. According to the story, the child had to be held up by helpers on both sides for the rest of the course. *Charper*, now carrying much more than forty kilograms (eighty-eight pounds) of extra weight, won the race – with a lead of eight minutes.

As a result of this incident more Thoroughbreds were imported and more races were organized. In 1836 the first Thoroughbred stud book to be published in Russia appeared. Some time before then the construction of the Moscow racecourse was completed, and in 1841 the St Petersburg racecourse was also opened.

For a long time, however, pure Thoroughbreds were produced only to a limited extent. They were used mainly for improving the native breeds and thus for the production of horses for hunting and for the cavalry.

Since about 1890 the breeding industry has produced large numbers of horses and is also well organized. But it has never been really successful. The best horses come to the west every year to take part in races, but up to the present only a few have made much of a show.

One of these was *Garnir*, who won the 1958 Russian Derby and the President's Prize in East Germany and remained unbeaten in a number of other races. He has been standing at stud since 1962, and has proved himself well. Many of his descendants have been victorious on Russian racetracks. *Garnir* was foaled in 1955 at the Voskhod Thoroughbred stud-farm, but it is not easy to see from his pedigree where his good qualities come from. His sire was *Raufbold*, a son of *Oleander*; shortly before the end of the Second World War, in Germany, *Raufbold* fell into Russian hands and in this way arrived at Voskhod.

Zabeg was foaled at the same establishment in 1957; he exhibited a quite extraordinary competitive spirit and was incredibly tough. As well as in his home country, he raced in East Germany, Poland, Norway, Sweden and the USA. In thirty-five races he came first fifteen times and was placed on nine occasions. It was entirely in view of these qualities, and not at all on account of his pedigree, which did not include a single well-known name, that he was taken to Ireland in 1965 to stand at stud for two years there, and later in the USA.

The greatest racehorse ever to come out of Russia was *Anilin*; he also was foaled at Voskhod, in 1961. Out of twenty-eight races he won twenty-two and was placed three times. On two occasions he collected the Grand Prix of the Socialist countries,

and came second in the Washington DC International. In the Prix de l'Arc de Triomphe, running against a field of really top-class horses from all over the world, including *Seabird*, *Reliance*, *Meadow Court*, *Marco Visconti* and *Diatome*, he obtained an honourable fifth place. He gave his most magnificent performances in the Europa Prize, where he always came up against top-class opposition, such as *Luciano*, which did not prevent him from winning three times. What distinguished him above all was his enormous staying power. In the last couple of hundred metres he overtook his competitors one after another, with lengthened strides. He has been standing at stud since 1967 and is the great hope of Russian bloodstock breeding.

As well as trotters and Thoroughbreds, quite a variety of other breeds are raised in Russia, and many of them have excellent characteristics. Apart from the Russian Arab, which ranks with the best in the world and which is bred mainly at Tula, half-way between Moscow and Voronezh, the Akhal Teke is probably the highest-class breed in Russia. This breed originated in the arid steppes of Turkmenistan where, for thousands of years, and under extremely harsh prevailing conditions, it perpetuated the heritage of speed, toughness and endurance which it shares with its close kin, the Arab. With its elegant appearance it stands half-way between the Arab and the English Thoroughbred. At the present time it is bred all the way from the Caspian Sea to China, the most

- ANILIN -

J. Koblischek

important stud-farms being Makhmut Kuli near Ashkhabad, Lugovsk in Kazakhstan, Tersk in the northern Caucasus and Alma-Ata.

Closely related to the Akhal Teke is the Turkmen, which originated in the same steppes and which is said to be the ancestor of the Arab. Whether or not this is so, the Turkmen played, and in many Asiatic Soviet republics is still playing, as great a part in the improvement of other breeds as the Arab in the western world.

Other breeds with noble blood and closely related to the Arab are the Karabai, the Karabakh and the Kabardin. The Karabai is the horse of the Uzbeks; it is bred nowadays at the Dzhizak stud-farm, as well as privately. While it was originally used only as a saddle horse, a somewhat heavier, longer draught-horse type has also been developed by selection.

Karabakhs mostly stand scarcely over 140 cm (14 hands), so in size they are really

ponies. Their appearance, however, is so refined and harmonious that they count among the most beautiful horses. They are bred at the Akdam stud in Azerbaidzhan as well as privately, and are much favoured for the wild equestrian sports of the district.

The Kabardin is bred at the Malokarachayev stud-farm in the Northern Caucasus; this is a mountain horse, marvellously sure-footed and tough, and of great endurance. These horses demonstrated their exceptional capacity for performing under extremely adverse weather and ground conditions in a riding trip round the Caucasus in the winter of 1936, when they covered 3000 km (over 1800 miles) in 37 days.

Like all nomads, the Kirgiz, near the Chinese border, have horses of exceptional toughness. In recent times they have been crossed with Thoroughbreds and Don horses to obtain an animal of larger size.

In the Kirgiz Republic and in

Kazakhstan, Don horses are bred at the Zimovnikov and Budyonny stud-farms. These have been developed from the little Kalmuk horses which were taken over by the Don Cossacks. Quite early on these tough steppe horses were improved by crossing with Karabakhs, Turkmens and Arab-like Persians. They are now versatile warm-bloods of medium size, also useful for draught work, although they are certainly not as tough as their ancestors who in 1812 carried the Don Cossacks when they overcame Napoleon in one of his worst defeats.

The Budyonny horse – named after the hero of the Revolution Marshal Budyonny – was developed soon after the Second World War at the Rostov military stud-farm, and ranks as one of Russia's greatest breeding successes. It was produced by crossing Don horses with English bloodstock. The indifference to all kinds of weather and the robust constitution

characteristic of the Don horse combined very happily with the outstandingly good action and endurance of the Thoroughbred. Originally intended as a cavalry horse, the Budyonny is splendidly adapted for military and hunting purposes, but also for show-jumping and even for agriculture.

In addition to these and several other warm-bloods, Russia also produces various fine cold-bloods which of course have all been bred from western cold-bloods or at least strongly influenced by them. Among these the Byeloruss, a descendant of the Tarpan, is notable for its especially undemanding nature. Its size and weight have been increased by crossing with Belgians, Swedish Ardennais and Bretons, and its good action has come from Norfolk Trotters, Arabs and several other breeds. It stands only a little over 150 cm (about 15 hands) and weighs about 500 kg (78 stone or 1100 pounds). The breed became recognized in about 1920.

The Vladimir breed, recognized since 1946, was developed after the Revolution in the region to the east of Moscow, and is at present bred in the state stud-farms at Vladimir, Yaroslavl, Ivanovo and Tambov. Ancestresses of the breed were the local mares, who were mated impartially with a whole series of cold-bloods – Percheron, Ardennais, Suffolk Punch, Clydesdale and Shire. Cleveland Bays and trotters also played a part. This horse stands about 160 cm (16 hands) and is considerably heavier than the Byeloruss.

The history of the Voronezh horse – formerly known as the Bityug, from the River Bityuga, a tributary of the Don – began soon after 1700, when Peter the Great had the native mares covered by Netherlands stallions. During the past 250 years, however, this type has been modified several times; warm-bloods were brought in to make it lighter, and cold-bloods to make it heavier again. The present medium-weight type, which is useful for many agricultural purposes, was evolved after 1920.

The Russian cold-blood, which, like the Byeloruss, stands only about 150 cm (15 hands) but is extremely powerful, was developed in the Ukraine. This horse was also crossed with various breeds; as well as Belgian horses, Ardennais and Orlov Trotters contributed to the improvement of the local type. The Novo-Alexander and Kuedin stud-farms are particularly concerned with this valuable working breed.

After the Revolution the Soviet cold-blood was developed in northern Russia, mainly by introducing Belgian stallions. This animal stands about 160 cm (16 hands) and weighs about 800 kg (126 stone or 1760 pounds); it is bred at the Pochinkov and Modovian stud-farms and on collective farms, particularly in the Vladimir district.

That the Akhal Teke, in spite of its nervous and sometimes difficult temperament, can attain world class in dressage, was demonstrated by *Absent*, carrying S. Filatov, shown here at Aachen in 1960. In the same year he won the Olympic Gold Medal in Rome. According to some sources, however, *Absent* is not a pure Akhal Teke, but carries some Trakehnen blood – which seems very possible from his appearance.

Near East

Im feld byn ich ftets bey im ftecken
Zu meynen auffgenetten hoffecken

Noch in Ofterreych zu Wien
Stach es mir an dem goller hyn

It was in the Nedjd, the wild highlands in the heart of the Arabian Peninsula, that a type of horse was developed which exercised an unequalled influence on horse breeding all over the world. Scarcely a single breed exists which has not at some time or other been improved by an infusion of Arab blood. The English Thoroughbred, the acme of modern horses, without which any warm-blood breeding would be unthinkable, is founded on three Arab stallions and some thirty mares who also already carried much Arab blood. Even cold-bloods have derived spirit and good action from the Arab, while most ponies have inherited better riding characteristics from the same source.

The origin of these wonderful horses has always been shrouded in mystery. However, recent work in the field of evolutionary research seems to suggest that far back in prehistoric times a geographic sub-species of the primitive wild horse living in this region already possessed the characteristic features of the Arab. It is known that the Egyptian pharaohs bred horses of great nobility and that such horses were later ridden by the Bedouin in the Arabian highlands.

This horse, already endowed with a superlative heritage, was developed by the Bedouin to become the noblest of all horses. The inexorable natural selection in the cruel desert, the relentless struggle for existence and the fanatical lengths to which the Bedouin would go in the interests of pure breeding – when necessary taking immensely long journeys to find the best stallions for their mares – have created a horse of superlative merit, unequalled in beauty and brilliance.

The Bedouin proudly claim these qualities for their horses: 'their faithfulness to type and genetic potency; their indestructible good health, longevity and fertility; their refinement, beauty, harmonious proportions and bodily perfection; the friendliness of their nature, blending good temper with fiery spirit and great vitality; their adaptability and

(Above) Turkish lancer (Uhlan), from a wood-cut by Niklas Stoer, around 1530. It was purely thanks to their far superior horses that in the fifteenth and sixteenth centuries the Turks were able to attain the position of leading power in eastern Europe.

(Left) The Turkish Grand Vizier Ahmed Pasha. Engraving by Paulus Fürst, c.1665.

(Right) Theodor Horschelt, pupil of Albrecht Adam, the well-known painter of horses, painted this *Bedouin on the Lookout* in 1854; it has since become famous.

(Below) This lithograph of a Bedouin on his Djodar-Arab was made by Victor Adam around 1860.

readiness to learn; their toughness and steely sinews; their undemandingness and power of recovery after exhausting efforts; their good manners and intelligence.'

Those who know the pure-bred Arab will acknowledge the truth of the Bedouin's claims. The triumphal advance of Islam in former times was founded on the superiority of this horse.

Karacabey, Turkey

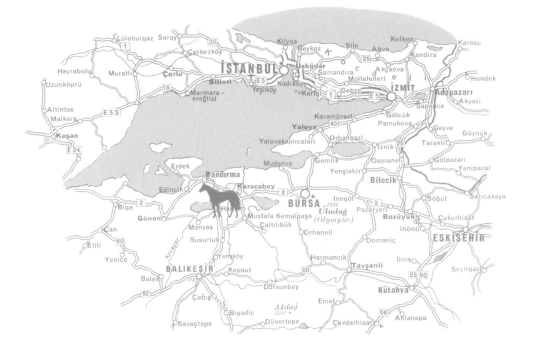

(Below) The inscription on the memorial to *Baba* (Father) *Kurus*, and below that a photograph of the splendid Arab. This stallion ranks as the most important foundation sire for the whole of modern Arab breeding in Turkey. He was bred by Anese Bedouin in Lebanon and sold to Syria. While at stud at Karacabey he got 141 foals.

BABA KURUŞ
1921–1945
ORİJİNİ:Suriye. Şam,Helbe Köyü
Haramızda Çalıştığı 11 Yıl İçinde
141 Tay Alınmış,Arap Atçılığımızın
Kuruluşunda Önemli Rol Oynamıştır

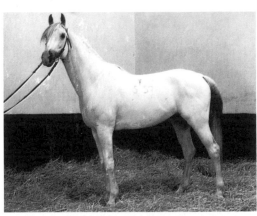

To the visitor to Istanbul the significance and presence of the horse in the Turkish Empire is revealed at one of the most famous places of interest: at the gateway to the Blue Mosque, 300 years after the construction was finished, there still hang massive iron chains which used to prevent horsemen from going the last part of the way to the meeting-place of the Faithful in arrogant style on horseback. In front of this mosque stretches the ancient Hippodrome across which, 500 years ago, Sultan Mehmet II, mounted on a magnificently decorated white horse, made his entry into Constantinople as conqueror.

Not far from the former capital, Bursa – with its old-style Turkish architecture a frequent subject for artists, and already famous as a thermal spa in the Hellenic era – lies Karacabey, Turkey's largest and most important state-owned stud-farm.

The foundation for this establishment was laid by Köse Mihal, 'Beardless Michael'. Over 600 years ago he gave the estate to his daughter as a dowry when she

(Above, left) Haflingers are enjoying increasing popularity in Turkey. At Karacabey they are bred both pure and crossed with the Karacabey warm-blood, the latter system resulting in an excellent work-horse with a very good action.

(Right) The Karacabey horse plays an important part throughout Turkey. This extremely refined warm-blood was produced by crossing high-bred Turkish mares with pure Arab stallions.

(Right) Arab mare with foal. As well as the locally developed warm-blood Karacabey-Nonius and Karacabey-Haflinger, pure Arabs and English Thoroughbreds are also bred at Karacabey.

married Orhan, the second Sultan of the Osman Empire. After the son-in-law, a succession of princely rulers inherited the Michael Farm; this name was changed in 1924 by decision of a Ministerial Council.

More than 500 people are employed at Karacabey, in agriculture and in breeding horses, cattle, sheep and poultry. Apart from Arab and English Thoroughbreds, the principal type produced here is the Karacabey horse, a refined and compact warm-blood. But Turkish horse-owners also use two cross-breeds: the Karacabey-Haflinger and the Karacabey-Nonius. (The Nonius itself, which came from Hungary, was originally bred pure for the army, and was later crossed with the Karacabey and improved; nowadays only a few remain.)

(Left) Colts trying their strength in play.

(Above) The brand-mark of Karacabey.

229

Royal Stables, Jordan

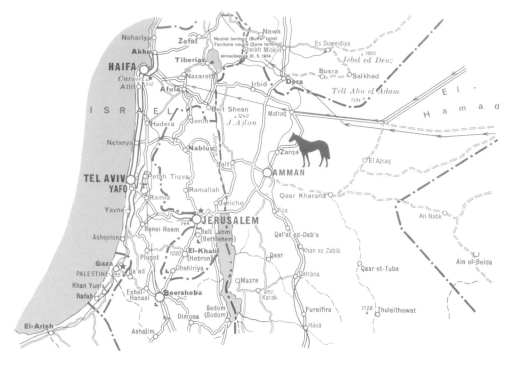

horses. Thanks to his political skill he succeeded in fusing the disunited groups formed by the Bedouin tribes. Abdullah was murdered in 1951, while attending Friday prayers at the El-Aqsa Mosque in Jerusalem. His stock of horses was dispersed.

It took long years of searching to reconstitute the Royal Stables: the horses had disappeared in all directions; many had fallen into the hands of Bedouin and farmers.

King Hussein is descended from the family of the Prophet Mohammed. All pure-bred Arab horses trace their ancestry back to the five mares of Mohammed – so runs the legend. But it is known for a fact that the Prophet, by the strict commandments laid down in the Koran, contributed greatly to maintaining the purity and unrivalled quality of this breed. And it is not really surprising that his followers have maintained this love of horses and this understanding of the secrets of noble blood strains, even though there may have been occasional generations which were not gifted in this way. These faculties appear to be inherent in all the sons of Allah; no wonder, therefore, that the horses in the royal stables are the peak of perfection for beauty and quality.

The stables and paddocks of the ruler of the Hashemite Kingdom are situated outside the capital city, Amman. The stud-farm was founded by Emir Abdullah, the grandfather of the present king; he was a lover of Arabic poetry as well as pure-bred

(Right) The mare *Reemer*. Her enchanting foal, sired by the leading stud horse *Baharein*, was born the day before this photograph was taken.

(Above) A desert Arab in the snow. This splendid horse, from the royal stables, is *Samiha*, by *Al Mozabor* out of *Farha*. The stallion *Al Mozabor* was bought in the late 1940s from the Arab stud-farm of the Duke of Veragua in Spain, and was brought to Jordan.

(Right) Princess Bint al Hussein at dressage practice on her Iraqi racehorse.

(Below) At the centre of the white-washed stud-yard is the drinking-trough, an octagonal fountain decorated with tiles and spanned by a wrought iron arch surmounted by the crown.

(Below) *Baheb* is a typical example of the Near East racehorse.

One mare named *Gazella* was not found until five years after the start of the search; she was doing farm-work, and was in a pitiable condition. She had become snow-white, but on being brought back to the stud-farm she recovered her health. Through her dam, *Emira 1st*, she is a Kuhailan Kurush, and her sire was the stallion *Al Mozabor*, who was imported from Spain.

231

El Zahraa, Egypt

(Below) From the fertile plains in the valley of the Nile a camel has brought carrots for the horses in the stud-farm. *Maysha* immediately tries one.

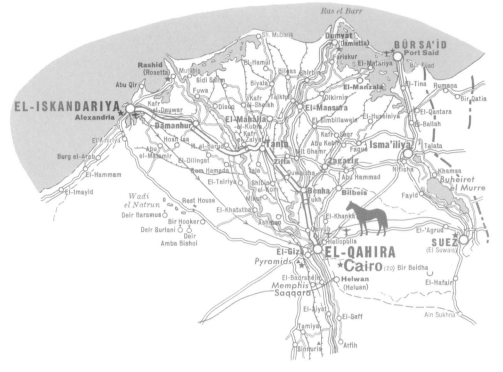

In the ancient Egyptian civilization, the breeding of noble Arab horses was from very early times reserved for the rich and powerful. Only they were permitted to import specially selected horses from Arabia.

The now world-famous state stud-farm at El Zahraa was founded in 1908. At that time it was under the control of the Royal Agricultural Society. After the Second World War, when the royal horse breeding establishment was lying in ruins, the re-organization of the stud-farm was entrusted to a Hungarian stud director, Tibor von Pettkö-Szandtner. His job was beset with very great difficulties. At that time the Egyptians had practically no idea of the value of the Arab horse and no understanding of breeding according to European principles. It took years of searching to get hold of suitable breeding stock. Good stallions were scattered throughout the country and were mostly in private hands. Some mares were obtained from the police stud-farms at Inshass and Batim. But the stud director even had to concern himself with providing the daily forage for the horses. Good individual animals, such as *Nazeer*, had to be almost literally unearthed. *Nazeer*'s sons *Ghazal*, out of *Burka*, *Hadban Enzahi*, out of *Kamla*, and *Kaisoon*, out of *Bint Kateefa*, are among the most important progenitors in Arab breeding in Germany. The world's experts particularly praise the riding qualities of *Ghazal*'s progeny, true to type. These

El Zahraa was founded in 1908 as a royal stud-farm. After the Second World War it needed to be completely re-organized. The stables of the principal stallions are now occupied once more by carefully selected and extremely valuable horses. Most of them come from the Nedjd, the Arabian Highlands where for thousands of years, under extremely difficult conditions and exercising great skill, the Bedouin have been breeding the best horses in the world.

(Left) Throughout the ages it has been the custom in Egypt to enhance the handsome appearance of horses by means of gaily coloured and richly decorated saddles and bridles. Thus for the Mameluke Sultans of the thirteenth and fourteenth centuries the elaboration of gorgeous display was a matter of course, and for the succeeding kings, princes and pashas the possession of a pure Arab horse was a status symbol.

(Below) Two elite stallions from El Zahraa. The blood of the stallions from these stables flows in Arabs and many warm-bloods all over the world.

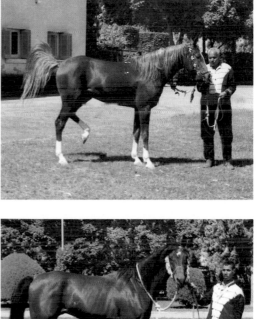

animals are distinguished by their splendid bearing and great aptitude for dressage. The two other stallions sent to Germany from El Zahraa also show evidence of first-class type transmission. The descendants of *Hadban Enzahi* have qualities of toughness and vigour, while those of *Kaisoon* have a particularly nice nature, with a pleasant spirit and ready obedience.

The present stud director, Dr Mohammed Marsafi, is making every effort to maintain the original pure blood-lines.

That he is succeeding in this purpose is proved especially by the many so-called 'gazelle' heads with markedly high foreheads and distinctly concave profiles. The only criteria applied in the selection of stud-horses are pedigree and beauty; evidence as regards performance is not demanded. Only a few animals are sent to the racetrack; this explains why a stallion highly esteemed at El Zahraa might not always fulfil the expectations of a European owner.

There are about 250 horses at El Zahraa; some 65 of the stallions are made available to owners of mares at various agricultural stations without a covering fee.

The mares at El Zahraa are also distinguished by extraordinary beauty, the principal features being the wonderful 'gazelle' head with prominent forehead, wide 'wind-drinker' nostrils and large eyes.

Japan

Horseback sports, especially combined with religious ceremonies, have been common in Japan for far longer than a thousand years. Horses – or, more accurately, ponies – were bred here in the pre-Christian era. Some of the primitive pony breeds are still to be found in Japan – for example, the Dosanko, to name only the best known; this is bred mainly on the large northern island of Hokkaido. The origin of these ponies is not really known, but it may be assumed that Mongolian ponies, especially of the types which have been kept for thousands of years in Korea and Manchuria, were the foundation ancestors of the Japanese ponies.

Some of the old religious horseback sports are still practised today and regularly attract a large and enthusiastic public. The riders wear traditional costume and generally use the old-style saddle and bridle; and for many events only the original-type Japanese ponies may be used. The production of these ponies is entirely in the hands of farmers and small breeders.

The old sports included races in which the riders sat upright in the expertly made Yamato saddles and drew through the air behind them green-and-white or red-and-white striped tubular flags. But European-style racing, as organized throughout the world nowadays, arrived in the Japanese islands relatively late.

After a period of 280 years during which a policy of isolation was followed, the harbours of Nagasaki, Yokohama, Kobe, Hakodate and several others were at last opened for international shipping in 1858. Yokohama was the most important of these harbours, and the greatest trading place for raw silk and tea. A great many Englishmen settled here, and before long they installed at Yokohama the first, improvised, oval racetrack. The first 'English' race was held in May 1862. This new and completely secular equestrian style did not find immediate acceptance, as demonstrated by the fact that in August of that same year several English riders were attacked by Samurai warriors of the Satsuma clan, and killed. Following this incident, the government offered the Englishmen a piece of ground suitable for riding, by the sea at Negishi near Yokohama, for their exclusive use. Here, in 1867, the Negishi racetrack was constructed, and on this first proper western course two race-meetings were held in the following year. In 1880 the Nippon Race Club was founded here, and Japanese were also allowed to join the club.

On 10 May 1881 the Emperor Meiji paid his first visit to the racecourse. His enthusiasm was so great that up to 1899 he made the trip to Negishi thirteen times to see the races.

In those days pure-bred horses were rarely seen on this racetrack. Most of the runners were Chinese horses imported from Shanghai, which were considerably faster than the Japanese ponies.

In 1895 horses were brought in from Australia for the first time. From 1902 onward the Nippon Race Club only imported foals, which were allocated to club members by lot, for rearing. If the performance of these animals during their

234

(p. 234, below) Emperor Meiji, a great racing enthusiast, watching a race at Ueno, in Tokyo, around the turn of the century.

(Right) Soma Nomaoi is an equestrian sport which originated in the Teicho period (923). Originally it consisted of a complicated drive by the mounted

soldiers of Prince Taira No Masakado. Nowadays it is performed every July at Haramachi, under the old rules and with the traditional trappings, and is to some extent a religious occasion.

(Below) Running out in the winter at Japan's main breeding district on the Island of Hokkaido.

racing career was satisfactory, they were subsequently sent to stud. *Hikaruimai*, who won the 1971 Tokyo Yuushun (the Japanese Derby), was in fact a descendant of *Mira*, who was imported from Australia in 1899.

In 1906 the authorities developed a thirty-year plan for improving the production of Japanese ponies, especially regarding their suitability for the army. At the same time they tacitly approved the proposal of the Nippon Race Club to sell

betting tickets. In November 1906 a race was held at Ikegami in Tokyo, for which tickets were sold in the club. This was followed by a rapid growth of enthusiasm for racing throughout the country. Three years later there were already fifteen racecourses in Japan.

At the present time Japan has forty-one racecourses altogether, ten national and thirty-one regional. There are about 2800 races every year, and 300 of them are held at the national racetracks. Flat-racing is the

(Below) A historic race with full traditional
equipment. Of the many events held at the Equestrian
Park in Tokyo, traditional horseback sports, performed
in the original-style costumes, are the favourites. The
different sports include dare-devil acrobatics and
various old forms of polo and horseback archery. In
some of these sports only Japanese ponies may be
ridden.

(p. 237) *Shinzan*, winner of the Triple Crown in 1964.

most common, but there are also steeplechases. On the island of Hokkaido, moreover, there are also traditional races with cold-blood horses. Most of the cold-bloods are Percherons of French origin.

Racehorse breeding

Hokkaido is the principal district for breeding racehorses; some 68 per cent are produced here. As well as Thoroughbreds, Anglo-Arabs are also great favourites for racing. Out of about 10,000 racehorses produced every year, some 4000 are Anglo-Arabs. In order to ensure that there are no very great differences in performance between horses of this breed, they are obliged to carry not less than 25 per cent of Arab blood.

Even racehorses are bred almost exclusively by general farmers; there are very few stud-farms as such. Only about 1 per cent of breeders have twenty or more mares, 82 per cent have no more than five animals. Nearly all the larger breeders produce Thoroughbreds; the smaller ones breed mainly Anglo-Arabs.

It is a characteristic of the situation in Japan that very few racehorse owners are also breeders. They buy young horses, have them trained and enter them for races; at the end of the animals' racing career they are resold. The breeders themselves usually have little or nothing to do with racing.

The entire racehorse breeding industry is supervised by the Japan Light Breed Horse Association. This Association organizes sales and owns some 70 stud horses which stand at covering stations all round the country. Among these stallions there are always about fifteen imported champion Thoroughbreds.

Altogether there are some 400 Thoroughbred stallions in Japan and 230 Anglo-Arab stallions. The stock of brood-mares numbers about 18,000. More than 200 of the Thoroughbred stallions are imports; these cover some 80 per cent of the Thoroughbred mares.

Since the Second World War about 350 stallions have been imported, from England, Ireland, France, Italy, America, Australia, New Zealand and Argentina. Recently a champion stallion was leased from Ireland for the first time. Over the same period some 2000 brood-mares have been imported.

The high population density in Japan constitutes a serious problem for horse breeding. It is usual elsewhere to reckon about five acres (2 hectares) of pastureland for one brood-mare; here few breeders can allow so much land per mare, and most have to manage with far less. In particular the farmers producing Anglo-Arabs often have to keep their horses in extremely small paddocks. The foals thus tend to suffer from too little natural activity, so it is the regular practice to have them exercised by mounted attendants, galloping round an oval track; this encourages the healthy development of the bone structure, the muscle and respiratory systems and the heart.

Equestrian Park

The Equestrian Park at Setagaya in Tokyo was established in 1940. On account of the war, however, only a small part of the

planned arrangements was completed at first. At the beginning the park was used for the instruction of jockeys, trainers, racing technicians and riding-masters. Towards the end of the war even this was almost completely abandoned. In 1947, however, the school started up again and began to train jockeys and Anglo-Arabs.

When, in 1959, it was settled that the XVIIIth Olympic Games would be held in Japan, it was decided to adopt the Equestrian Park for the Olympic riding competitions; the great riding-hall built in 1963–64 was one of the numerous additions. During the Olympics, in October 1964, the splendidly laid out and luxuriantly planted park inspired great admiration.

At the present time the park is a training centre for a wide range of equestrian and breeding activities. It offers facilities for all kinds of sporting events and exhibitions involving horses.

The large stud-farms

The most important of the Japanese horse breeding establishments are the Meiwa Stud, the Onward Stud and Yoshida Farm. As already mentioned, only Thoroughbreds – and not all of these – are produced at those establishments which are genuine stud-farms. The three stud-farms mentioned above are all situated on the island of Hokkaido, Japan's principal horse breeding region.

The Meiwa Stud was founded as recently as 1971, by Ryusuke Morioka, as a branch of his industrial enterprise. The establishment covers 150 hectares (370 acres) and has a training track 1500 m (1640 yards) long as well as a covered 500 m (547-

(Top, left) Aerial photograph of Tokyo racecourse, 25 kilometres (15½ miles) from the city centre. The main track measures 2100 m (2296 yards), the second track 1900 m (2078 yards), the steeplechase courses 1696 and 638 m (1855 and 698 yards), the training tracks 1438 and 410 m (1573 and 448 yards); there are 1109 boxes for racehorses. Since 1932 the Japanese Derby has been run here every year on the last Sunday in May.

(Right) The Kokura Racecourse at Kita-Kyushu. The main track measures 1623 m (1775 yards); there are 540 boxes. The most important race held here is the Kokura-Kinen.

(Top, right) Japan Lightbreed Horse Association yearling sales on Hokkaido.

(Above) The Ritto Training Centre, completed in 1969. It has an area of 153 hectares (378 acres), with boxes for more than 2000 horses and housing for more than 4700 personnel and their families. Five training tracks are provided, of lengths ranging from 1400 to 2200 m (1530–2406 yards).

Another training centre is under construction at Miko. It will have an area of 182 hectares (450 acres) with accommodation for 2300 horses and 5000 personnel.

yard) track. The three stallions now standing at stud there (February 1977) are: *Father's Image*, a son of the famous *Swaps*; *Silver Shark*, by *Buisson Ardent*; and *Haseiko*, by *China Rock*. The forty-strong herd of mares includes *San San*, *North Broadway*, *Marching Matilda* and *Princess of Iran*.

The Onward Stud, founded in 1960, covers 100 hectares (246 acres) and has one training track of 1400 m (1530 yards) and two of 500 m (547 yards). Here also there are stallions whose pedigrees include famous names, such as *Hard to Beat*, by *Hardicanute*; *Fuji Onward*, by *Ribot*; *Great Onward*, by *Sir Ivor*; *Onward Bary*, by *No Robbery*. Among the forty mares are *Miss Onward*, *Renown*, *Himawari* and *Irena*.

The Yoshida Farm comprises 330 hectares (815 acres). The three stallions are: *Contrite*, by *Never Say Die*; *Cover Up Nisei* by *Cover Up*; *Gold Rising*, by *Rising Flame*. The thirty-five mares include *Gineora*, *Typecast*, *Northern Princess* and *Wakakumo*. The history of this important stud-farm started in 1908 with the importation of a few mares and one stallion from Australia by the farmer Gontaro Yoshida.

Australia and New Zealand

(Below) Founded on the old Lindsay Park estate as recently as 1965, this stud-farm is at present the most important bloodstock breeding establishment in Australia.

(p. 241, top left) Lindsay Park owner-trainer Colin Hayes with his magnificent stallion *Without Fear*, whose first batch of foals have already broken a world record. Sire of *Without Fear* is the Two Thousand Guineas winner *Baldric II*, and his dam is the Oaks winner *Never Too Lok*, by *Never Say Die*.

Conditions in Australia and New Zealand are ideal for horse breeding. In Australia alone there are nearly 500 racetracks, and the race-meetings number over 3000 a year. Four thousand trainers have 42,000 horses in preparation for racing, while 7464 breeders owned 16,308 Thoroughbred brood-mares at the beginning of 1977. The most important race is the Melbourne Cup; the day on which this is held is a holiday in the State of Victoria, and during the broadcast of the race the whole country holds its breath.

The first horses to be brought to Australia came from the Cape of Good Hope in 1788, and were followed a little later by imports from Chile. The farmers immediately arranged races with these horses, known as Capers or Caper-Chileans, and the first organized meeting of this kind was held at Parramatta, near Sydney, in 1810. At this same period the first Thoroughbred stallions arrived from England. They were promptly set to serve the Caper-Chilean mares, and a new type of horse was produced – the Waler. After several years of repeated crossings with Thoroughbreds, the Walers came to resemble them closely in appearance and performance.

Just as in the North American West, in Australia too a great many horses escaped into the desert, especially during the gold rush around 1850. With the passage of time they became quite wild, and developed into a tough bush breed. It is almost impossible to tame these 'Brumbies'. They provide ideal bucking horses for rodeos, and only the best riders can stay on them for twenty seconds.

Rodeo sports, which here, as in America, have developed from the working activities of mounted cattle herdsmen, are extremely popular. But all the other types of equestrian sport – including jumping, military, dressage and leisure riding – are also practised intensively, as a result of which horse breeding is flourishing. Trotting is developing also. The high quality of Australian horses and riders has

been demonstrated by a number of Thoroughbreds at big international trials, as well as by army teams which have reached medal class in Melbourne and Montreal and won an Olympic Gold Medal at Rome in 1960.

Around 1840 the first sizeable batches of horses arrived in New Zealand from Australia. The first race, to the best of our knowledge, was run in 1855, and the first race of Thoroughbreds in 1860. Steeplechasing became more popular here than in Australia, and the best horses for long 'chases were produced from Thoroughbred stallions and crossed warm-blood mares. One such horse, named *Moiffaa*, travelled to England in 1904 and was victorious there in the world's most difficult steeplechase, the Grand National. Quite recently the New Zealand racehorse *Grand Canyon* won renown in Europe and in the USA.

(Left) Lindsay Park is not only a stud-farm but also a training centre, and is well up to the standard of any similar establishment in the world. As well as grass and sand training tracks there are heated boxes and a swimming-pool for the horses, and small clinic with a permanent veterinary surgeon, and other absolutely modern arrangements. The breeder-trainer, Colin Hayes, has produced more than 2500 winners up to the present and ranks as Australia's best bloodstock expert.

(Left) It is nearly fifty years since Seton Otway, eighty-three years old in 1976, founded the Trelawney stud-farm. His *Alcimedes*, now twenty-three years old and thus also getting on in years is one of the great stallions in New Zealand's racing history. In carrying off the Melbourne Cup, *Alcimedes'* son *Galilee* won the most important race in Australia, and his descendants *Divide and Rule*, *Prince Grant* and *Pegs Pride* also distinguished themselves by their tremendous staying power.

Lindsay Park

The history of this stud-farm began as recently as 1965, although the estate itself, with its beautiful old colonial-style house, has a rich tradition. The green Barrassa valley in the south of Australia was settled mainly by German Lutherans, and the landowner Angus Fife, who built Lindsay House, had a fatherly relationship to these early settlers.

Colin Hayes, the founder of the stud-farm, built up his Thoroughbred stock with great care. In ten years Lindsay Park had become a phenomenon in the racing world. During the 1975–76 racing season thirty horses of *Without Fear*'s first year's batch of foals won forty-nine races. With this result the Lindsay stallion easily beat a sixty-year world record.

The splendid qualities of the Lindsay horses are due not only to the excellent breeding and training conditions but also to their pedigrees, where names such as *Ribot*, *Bold Ruler*, *Buckpasser* and *Star Dust* appear.

Trelawney

Trelawney ranks as the most important Thoroughbred stud-farm in New Zealand; it was founded by Seton Otway nearly fifty years ago. A mare named *Persis*, which he bought for the modest sum of £18, was destined to become one of New Zealand's greatest foundation dams. The first stallion to arrive at the stud-farm became even more famous: *Foxbridge* was New Zealand's leading stud-horse for twelve years, three times champion sire of the Empire, and finally top sire of brood-mares for twelve years – all in all, New Zealand's best ever stallion.

(Left) The Lindsay Park stud-farm lies in the green countryside of the Barassa Valley in South Australia, and enjoys a very mild climate.

(Above) Yearlings at the Trelawney stud-farm, probably the most successful bloodstock establishment in New Zealand. Trelawney is located at Waikato, some 140 km (87 miles) from Auckland, in a district well-known throughout the country for its excellent pastures. The management of the stud-farm was recently taken over by Jim Otway, son of the founder. At the beginning of 1977 he bought the colt *Val du Fair*, who comes from the same French stable as *Allez France* and *Pawneese*. *Val du Fair* won

$50,000 in France and came fourth in the French Derby. Mated with the excellent mares at Trelawney, this stallion is expected to prove a worthy successor to his forebears, although the phenomenal success in New Zealand of *Foxbridge*, the stud-farm's first sire, may perhaps never be repeated.

Argentina

Pedro de Mendoza founded Buenos Aires, the present capital of Argentina, in 1535. The success of the Spanish Conquistador's bloody campaign through Chile and Argentina was due in great measure to his Andalusian horses.

During the power struggle many of these horses ran wild, and fifty years later they had formed sizeable herds roaming the wide grass-covered pampas. These Argentine mustangs later provided the foundation for the Criollos, the horses of

(Above) The gauchos of the Argentine pampas make use of an extremely effective device which can be used both as a lasso and as a weapon. This *bola* consists of long plaited leather strips with two or three balls made of metal, stone or occasionally even bones attached to the ends. When hunting, especially in pursuit of the nandu ostrich, the *bola* is hurled like a lasso, and its loaded ends loop round the neck or legs of the creature and bring it down.

the gauchos. On the foundation of these unsurpassed horses the Argentines have over the centuries become one of the greatest horse breeding nations in the world. From the indigent gaucho to the richest estanciero, everybody needed a horse. In this way a close relationship developed with this animal, and also a profound basic understanding of everything connected with the horse as a way of life.

From the international and equestrian sports point of view Criollos have no particular significance, but they have made excellent horse breeders of the Argentines, who have fully demonstrated their ability to breed not only hard-as-nails horses for cowboys, but also splendid animals up to international standards for polo and racing.

The fact that Argentine representatives of the 'Sangre pura de Carrera' breed have for several years been winning important races in Brazil and North America has caused trainers, breeders and owners in other countries to sit up and take notice. Between 1961 and 1975, 9702 Argentinian Thoroughbreds were exported to a long list of countries, especially the USA, Venezuela, Brazil and Panama, but also including countries in Europe. Since 1974 exports have indeed dropped sharply; this is, however, not the fault of the breeding industry, which continues to operate as energetically and conscientiously as ever – the causes are political. The country's most important Thoroughbred stud-farms are Comalal, Argentino, El Pelado, El Turf, Don Yayo and Malal Hue.

The Comalal establishment, which has a rich tradition, was Argentina's leading stud-farm in the 1960s. Although it came fifth in the 1975 statistics for stud-farms with the highest number of winners, nevertheless it still rates as excellent on account of the high-quality breeding material produced since its foundation in 1957. The founder, incidentally, was one of the most remarkable racing personalities in Argentina, Don Miguel Martínez de Hoz.

The list of Comalal winners of classic races is itself worthy of mention. *Pontia*, by

Sideral (1959), *Melodie*, by *Seductor* (1960), *Pasión*, by *Sideral* (1961), *Tacha*, by *Tantán* (1962), and *Rafale*, by *Court Harwell* (1967), won the Polla de Potrancas (One Thousand Guineas). *Napoles*, by *Prince Canaria*, won the Polla di Potrillos in 1961; the Gran Premio Selección was carried off by *Pasión* in 1961, by *Sweet Sue* (by *Sideral*) in 1965, and again in 1967 by *Rafale*; the Gran Premio Internacional Carlos Pellegrini was won in 1963 by *El Centauro* (by *Sideral*) and in 1967 by *Rafale*; *El Centauro* triumphed in the Gran Premio Honor in 1963, and *Elegio* – another son of *Sideral* – in 1967.

From the above list it will be seen that *Sideral*, born in 1948, by *Seductor* out of *Starling II*, by *Noble Star*, represents one of the main pillars of bloodstock breeding in Argentina. In 1976, moreover, he accomplished a feat rare even among top-class horses, in becoming both champion sire and champion sire of brood-mares.

The Argentino stud-farm, while it does not cover a particularly large area, is important from the point of view of breeding, above all in view of its successes in the recent past. This stud-farm, situated near Lugán, came second in 1975 in the annual statistics for highest number of winners. It was formerly associated with the very best names in bloodstock, such as *Gulf Stream*, by *Hyperion*, champion sire in Argentina in 1955, 1958 and 1959. It was no doubt as a result of mating the good Gulf Stream mares with cheap imported stallions that the stud-farm declined in the early 1960s. It owes its restoration to the ranks of

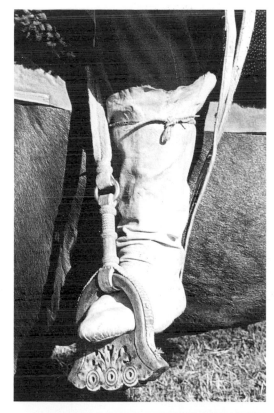

In the course of its history which goes back a hundred years, the Argentine gauchos have developed their own tradition, which is evident in their saddles, bridles and dress. It is not uncommon to find the harness richly decorated, and the large disc-shaped stirrups reveal great artistry. Like the heavy wooden stirrups of the North American cowboys, they are also highly functional.

the big-winner stud-farms somewhat surprisingly to *In the Gloaming*, by *Crepello* out of Oaks winner *Sun Cap*. This stallion has links with a great era, when *Macón*, by *Sandal*, won the Derby and the Gran Premio Internacional Carlos Pellegrini, and *Tiny* won the Derby.

El Pelado, where things are rather quiet at present, became well-known mainly on account of the world-famous sire *Congreve*, by *Copy Right* out of *Per Noir*, by *Perrier*. The enterprise as a whole is one of the largest in Argentina, but only about an eighth of the 5000 hectares (over 12,000 acres) is available for horse breeding. In the mid-1960s the leading stallion at the stud-farm was *Vitelio* whose sire, *Claro*, had won the Irish Two Thousand Guineas and was champion sire in Argentina in 1954. Eleven years later *Vitelio* himself became champion sire; he owed this honour mainly to his daughter *Vit Reina*, winner of the Gran Premio Carlos Pellegrini in 1965. Later on it was her full brother *Vin Vin* who was most successful.

(Left) When breaking in a horse the gaucho certainly does apply these terrible looking wheel-spurs a few times, but after that he does not need to use such force – the gaucho horse knows what he has to do. He reacts to the slightest touch, and accomplishes his many and various tasks with admirable skill. The gaucho's boots are usually made of soft, tanned horse-hide with pliable soles. A particular piece of hide from the animal's leg is used, and the knee or heel corresponds to the rider's heel in the finished boot.

245

It is said that during Pedro de Mendoza's bloody conquest of Argentina, seventy-six of his horses ran off. Whatever the actual number, these animals multiplied freely in the wide open pampas, so that fifty years later Governor Váldez commented that 'There are so many horses here that from a distance they look like a forest.'

These horses and the large numbers of cattle which had also run wild provided the basis of life for the Argentinians, and made them first-class horsemen.

The Haras El Turf – not a very large establishment – has long been well-known as the enterprise of the two polo players Julio and Carlos Menditeguy. This stud-farm became famous on account of *Pronto*, by *Timor*, who won a number of classic victories and was an outstanding sire. His son *Practicante*, out of *Extrañeza*, was horse of the year in 1969, winning the Gran Premio du Jockey Club, the Gran Premio Nacional and the Gran Premio Carlos Pellegrini.

In the latter half of the 1960s the Haras Don Yayo possessed a champion stallion in the grey *Good Time*, a grandson of *Court Martial*; he won twelve races. His first crop at stud included horses such as *El Califa*.

In 1976 *Con Brio*, by *Ribot* out of *Patronella*, by *Petition*, made a big name for himself. This chestnut, born in 1961, won the Ripon Champion Two-Year-Old Trophy and the Brighton Derby Trial Stakes. *Con Brio* came to the fore in 1977 as

the new star in the firmament of Argentine sires, for both the 800-metre and the 900-metre track records were sensationally beaten by one of his descendants.

Malal Hue

The Malal Hue stud-farm, where the creeper-clad mansion reflects the old tradition, still ranks as one of the most important bloodstock breeding establishments in Argentina. Like its sister stud-farm, Comalal, it has a place among the top seven in the list of establishments with the highest numbers of wins in 1975. The basis of this success is the superb stallion *D. Board*.

This stud-farm, with an area of about 2000 hectares (5000 acres), is situated some 20 km (13 miles) from Mar del Plata, about 500 km (300 miles) south of Buenos Aires. It has a rich tradition, and around the turn of the century was rated as one of the best establishments for the Hackney breed, then held in great honour. Since 1913 it has specialized in breeding Thoroughbreds.

The name of the founder, José de Martínez de Hoz, is inseparably linked with horse breeding in Argentina. After his death in 1935 the two brothers José Alfredo and Miguel continued to run the stud-farm at Chapadmalal. They imported mares of exceptional quality and bought the stallion *Rustam Pasha*, by *Son-in-Law*. The supreme class of this stallion, acquired by the Aga Khan in 1937, was evident in his progeny. Thanks to him and to *Embrujo* (by *Congreve*), winner of the Argentine Triple Crown, Chapadmalal had at its disposal a stallion potential almost without equal. In 1945 the stud-farm acquired *Bahram*, the unbeaten winner of the English Triple

Crown. In 1958 the stud-farm was split up into the Haras Malal Hue and the Haras Comalal, mentioned above.

247

USA

There is no doubt that without the horse the cultural history of mankind would have followed a totally different course. America's history without the horse is simply unthinkable.

The widely held view, that the Spaniards brought horses to America for the first time, is based on a mistaken idea. Horses originated in America. In the course of some fifty million years they evolved here from the little rabbit-sized *Hyracotherium* to the genus *Equus* which, like its predecessors, migrated across the land-bridge to Asia and on to Europe and Africa. While in the Old World *Equus* has managed to maintain itself up to the present time in the form of horses, zebras and asses, in America it died out about 8000 years ago, through unknown causes.

After an epoch without horses it appears, from the most recent research findings, that the Vikings brought little horses to America on their dragon-ships about 1000 years ago, but these do not seem to have taken a hold here.

The arrival of the Spanish horses, on the other hand, had a lasting effect. Columbus actually introduced saddle horses into the New World. When he landed on the Caribbean island of Hispaniola he brought with him thirty horses. Following him, scarcely a Spanish ship landed in America without horses on board.

During the course of the bloody Spanish conquest and the subsequent period of colonial domination in the south-west of America, thousands of horses escaped and ran wild in the wide expanses of the prairies; the same thing happened with the imported cattle. In the middle of last century the number of mustangs ran into millions. In Texas alone there were estimated to be three million cattle. Hundreds of thousands of mustangs were rounded up, and most of them ended their lives on the battle-fields of the Boer War and the First World War. Hundreds of thousands more were slaughtered to manufacture fertilizer and poultry food,

and still more were killed off by the cattle breeders as competitors for the available forage. The present stock is estimated to be about 10,000; though protected by law they are still being hunted.

(Left) At the time of the colonization of America, scarcely a Spanish ship landed without horses on board. They were used both as an indispensable means of transport in the new and unknown continent, and on the other hand as ballast on the ships, at that stage still empty. Throughout the voyage, which then took about three months, they had to remain hoisted aloft in slings.

(Below) Most of the 'cowboy' horses still carry Spanish blood today, while their saddles, bridles and spurs echo the equipment of the Latin-American *vaqueros*.

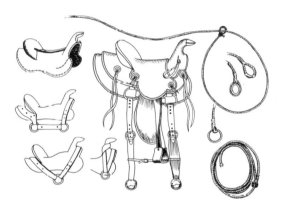

It is easy to imagine the shock the Indians received on first encountering these great animals on which the white men rode. But they soon realized that it was not necessary to be white in order to ride such an animal, and acquired 'big dogs' for themselves, either by catching horses that had run wild, or by bartering, or again simply by stealing them from the Spanish haciendas. It was not long before they were riding their horses like the devil, and in North America the tables were turned: the conquerors were put to flight and forced back to the other side of the Rio Grande. Thanks to their horses, the Indians of the American West were able to hold their ground for another two hundred years.

The Indians were highly skilled horsemen. Some of them later also proved to be talented breeders. They favoured above all striking piebald and spotted horses, and many tribes undertook more or less systematic breeding. However, these nomads of the plains were not concerned about putting up fences. Innumerable horses escaped and ran wild, and only a few were ever caught again. It was much simpler to ride south to Mexico, attack the haciendas, and carry off the Spaniards' horses.

The picture (left) by Bodmer, the Swiss, famous for his paintings of Indians, is taken from the book, *Indianer waren meine Freunde* (Indians were my Friends).

In the middle of the last century cattle breeding in Texas began to flourish; in 1848 there were six head of cattle for every inhabitant of Texas. However, this abundance did litttle for the Texans, since they received only three dollars here for a fat beast, whereas in the East and in California people were paying eighty. The cattle breeder Edward Piper had an idea which, though novel, proved not impossible to carry out – this was to drive the cattle in great herds to the places where they were needed; thus a new era opened in the history of America. Before long, herds were on their way northward, eastward and westward, over distances of anything up to 3000 km (over 1800 miles), with often as many as 2000 animals, driven by men as skilful as they were tough and fearless, who lived under the open skies for months at a stretch, stayed in the saddle up to twenty hours a day and defended themselves against Indians, cattle rustlers and the forces of nature – all for forty dollars a month.

The era of this great trek is past. But although there are now trucks and railways to transport cattle over these long distances to the giant ranches where they are rounded up, sorted and brought in, cowboys are still with us, and will long remain, just as horses will.

The motto of the American Mustang Association is: 'The horses that made America'. And this is not a great exaggeration, for it was not only the legendary cattle drovers that the horses served. They were used as cavalry horses, pulled the stage coaches and 'trail' wagons in teams of four or six, and were harnessed to the plough.

From the original Spanish (i.e. Oriental) horses, various breeds and types have been developed, largely as a result of systematic breeding by certain tribes; these include the piebald Pinto, the unusual Appaloosa and the golden-coloured Palomino.

Spanish horses made history in America. But naturally immigrants from other European countries also brought their horses with them, and these also were by no means unimportant. As well as whole shiploads of Irish horses which came to Virginia, the Swedes, Finns, Dutch, Germans, French and above all of course the English, brought their horses over.

In the middle of the eighteenth century regular importation of English Thoroughbreds started; and these also had a tremendous influence in America. *Count Fleet*, *Citation*, *Tom Fool*, *Native Dancer*, *Swaps*, *Nashua*, *Kelso*, *Buckpasser*, the legendary *Man O' War* and finally *Secretariat* are just a few of the resounding names. At the present time the bloodstock industry, with its main centre in Kentucky, is the largest in the world.

Important breeds in America include Hackneys, Cleveland Bays and Arabs, and among the cold-bloods Belgians, Percherons, Suffolk Punches, the Shire Horse and the Clydesdale, together with a whole range of pony breeds. But America has also developed her own breeds: the versatile Morgan, for which a register was started in 1850; the American Saddle Horse, formerly above all an excellent cavalry horse, but now demoted to a mere show horse; the Tennessee Walking Horse, another show horse, whose widely famed high knee action is developed by highly improper training practices; the Quarter Horse, whose qualities are so varied and phenomenal that the numbers of this breed have risen to far more than a million since the register was started in 1940; and finally the American breed with the widest international fame, the Standard Trotter, the fastest horse in the sulky, which can be compared with the Thoroughbred in popularity and in the magnitude of its breeding industry.

Calumet

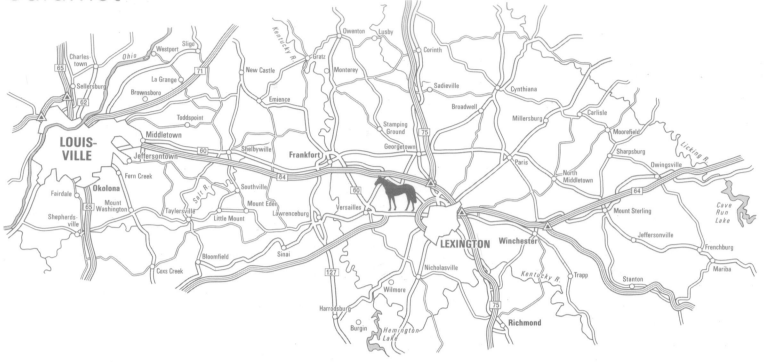

The trotter *Calumet Butler* won the Hambletonian in 1931. That was the glorious conclusion of the relatively short period when Trotters were bred at the Calumet stud-farm. In that same year William Monroe Wright made the establishment over to Warren Wright, who immediately began to switch to breeding Thoroughbreds.

A *calumet* is the Indian 'pipe of peace'. It is also the name of a well-known American baking-powder, and when the Wrights withdrew from this industry and built their stud-farm at Lexington, in the state of Kentucky, in 1928, they gave it the same name, Calumet.

At the Saratoga auction sales in 1931 Warren Wright bought three yearlings, which he named *Flirting*, *Lucille Wright* and *Warren Jr*; they formed the basis of one of America's greatest Thoroughbred stud-farms.

In the following year the new stable colours registered one victory, one second and two third places and winnings

amounting to $1150. In 1933 the winnings amounted to $22,055, and in 1934 to $88,060; the peak of success was reached in 1947, when no less than $1,402,436 was won with 100 triumphs, 44 second places and 26 thirds. This was, moreover, the first time in America's racing history that any one stable had won over a million dollars. The total prize money amassed by the Calumet stable between 1932 and 1975 was $21,863,076.

It was in the Kentucky Derby that the establishment won its finest laurels. Calumet sent altogether eighteen horses to this great test of performance. Eight of them gained victories and six more were placed; eight victories – four more than any other breeder has managed to register up to now.

Calumet horses collected the magnificent total of thirty-two titles: five times 'horse of the year', five times 'handicap horse', five times 'handicap mare', 'once sprinter', four times 'three-year-old', three times 'three-year-old colt', three times 'three-

year-old filly', twice 'two-year-old', twice 'two-year-old colt' and twice 'two-year-old filly'.

At the Saratoga sales in 1936 Warren Wright purchased *Bull Lea* for $14,000; this was to prove the most worthwhile investment ever made in the bloodstock business. This horse won a tidy $100,000 in prizes – not an overwhelming sum, although a considerable one. At stud, however, he broke no less than ten records. Up to 1969, the last year in which his sons

and daughters raced, his direct progeny had won $13,589,181 in prize money.

He sired twenty-eight horses, each of whom won $100,000 or more, seventeen of them collecting over $200,000 each. He got fifty-eight stakes victors, including resounding names such as *Citation*, *Armed* and *Bewitch*.

Bull Lea was champion sire five times – in 1947, 1948, 1949, 1952 and 1953. He sired his twenty-fourth and last crop of foals in 1964; the last of them, *Mon Zigue*,

was born on 5 April 1964, and became a champion. *Bull Lea* died on 16 June of the same year, aged twenty-nine.

Another stallion who had a profound influence on the Calumet stock was *Blenheim II*. He was imported in 1936 by a syndicate of American breeders in which Calumet had a quarter share. Until his death in 1958, *Blenheim II* stood at the Claiborne Farm at Paris, Kentucky. The best of his offspring got on Calumet mares were *Mar-Kell*, *Nelly L.*, *Proud One*, *A*

Gleam, *Fervent*, *Blenweed* and *Whirlaway* who in 1941 was the first of the Calumet horses to win the Kentucky Derby.

The finest son of the great *Bull Lea* was *Citation*. With winnings of $1,085,760 he was the first 'Thoroughbred millionaire'. In 1948 he won the 8th Triple Crown with ease. It was a full quarter-century before another horse managed to achieve this feat – which *Secretariat* did, in 1973.

Pensive, winner of the Kentucky Derby in 1944, proved himself an outstanding sire.

Anybody driving on the road from the west to Lexington is not likely to miss the Calumet stud-farm, shortly before reaching the town; its pretty red-and-white wooden buildings are set among lush, wide pastures.

The Calumet stud-farm was built in 1928 by the baking-powder manufacturer William Monroe Wright; during the first three years it bred Trotters, including a Hambletonian winner. In 1931 the stud-farm was taken over by Warren Wright, who switched to breeding Thoroughbreds.

(Right) The first of the eight Kentucky Derby winners to run in the Calumet colours: *Whirlaway*, born in 1938, by *Blenheim II* out of *Dustwhirl*. The jockey was Eddie Arcaro, the trainer B.A. Jones.

(Below) The marble memorial to Calumet's eight Kentucky Derby winners. The last of them, *Forward Pass*, who won this race in 1968, is not listed here.

(Below) Two Kentucky Derby winners: *Pensive*, winner in 1944; born in 1941, by *Hyperion* out of *Penicuik II*. The jockey was Conn McCreary, the trainer B.A. Jones.
Citation, winner in 1948, born in 1945, by *Bull Lea* out of *Hydroplane II*. As in 1941, the successful jockey was Eddie Arcaro and the trainer B.A. Jones.

One of his first crop, *Ponder*, won the Kentucky Derby in 1949. *Ponder*'s own first crop included *Needles*, who won the same race in 1956.

'Racing class in mares produces racing class.' Calumet has always been guided by this theory, but has also had the courage to experiment. The blood-lines of *Bull Lea* and *Blenheim II*, crossed in various ways, produced several horses who contributed substantially to the successes of the 1940s. Some of the champions from this establishment were produced by dams who had never run a race.

In 1976, there were six stallions standing at Calumet: *Best Turn*, *Forward Pass*, *Gleaming*, *Raise a Cup*, *Reverse* and *Tim Tam*.

The herd of brood-mares has gradually been reduced in number from the original sixty to thirty-three. The fifteen to twenty-two foals produced annually are all retained, so that they can be raced in the stable's own colours.

Of the many large and splendid stud-

WHIRLAWAY
1941
PENSIVE
1944
CITATION
1948
PONDER
1949
HILL GAIL
1952
IRON LIEGE
1957
TIM TAM
1958

farms in Kentucky's Bluegrass region, Calumet is undoubtedly one of the most beautiful. Its red-and-white wooden houses form a picturesque arrangement amid the wide green pastures surrounded by white-painted oak fences, with a blue haze veiling the scene in the twilight. The fences have a total length of 37 km (23 miles) and there are more than 10 km (6 miles) of roads connecting the different parts of the establishment.

After *Whirlaway* won the Kentucky

(Above) *Ponder*, winner of the Kentucky Derby in 1949; born in 1946, by *Pensive* out of *Miss Rushin*. On this occasion the trainer B.A. Jones had Steve Brooks on this champion horse. In the same year *Ponder* also won the Peter Pan Handicap, the Arlington Classic, the Lawrence Realisation and the Jockey Club Gold Cup.

(Above, right) *Hill Gail*, winner of the Kentucky Derby in 1952, born in 1949, by *Bull Lea* out of *Jane Gail*. Eddie Arcaro was the winning jockey for the third time, and B.A. Jones was the winning trainer for the fifth time.

(Left) *Iron Liege*, winner of the Kentucky Derby in 1957, born in 1954, by *Bull Lea* out of *Iron Maiden*. The jockey was Bill Hartack and the trainer was yet again B.A. Jones, who was able to celebrate the same victory for the seventh and last time a year later. In the same year *Iron Liege* collected another three wins, five second places and three third places.

(Right) *Tim Tam*, born in 1955, by *Tom Fool* out of *Two Lea*. This stallion, winner of the Kentucky Derby in 1958, was still standing at stud at Calumet in 1976.

(Below) *Forward Pass*, born in 1965, by *On and On* out of *Princess Turia*. In 1968 he was eighth and last of the Calumet horses to win the Kentucky Derby; he has been standing at the stud-farm since 1970.

(Below) *Bull Lea*'s grave. He was bought in 1936 as a yearling, for $14,000, and this purchase turned out to be the best ever investment in the bloodstock business. He himself collected just on $100,000 in prize money, while his offspring won altogether far more than thirteen million dollars. He was 'Sire of the Year' five times.

Derby in 1941 Calumet became known in remote circles not directly connected with the bloodstock industry. The number of visitors to the farm continuously increased, and at first the owners were pleased at the interest shown by the public. Unfortunately, however, as time went on, this flood of visitors became intolerable. On some days there were several hundred of them, even a thousand, which naturally caused great disturbance and considerable damage. During the 1960s, however,

visitors caused a number of fires on stud-farms, and under pressure from the insurance companies most of the establishments in the neighbourhood of Lexington, including Calumet, were closed to the public.

(Left) The 1975 Kentucky Derby. The field at the first bend. In the background is the grandstand with its distinctive twin towers. It was here, on the Churchill Downs in Louisville, that the first Kentucky Derby was run a hundred years earlier, on 17 May 1875.

Darby Dan

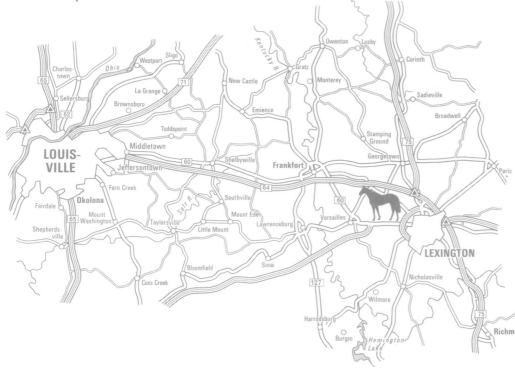

Darby Dan Farm of today is the nucleus of what was one of the most famous and successful breeding establishments in Central Kentucky: Colonel E. R. Bradley's Idle Hour Stock Farm.

Colonel Bradley, who died in 1946, first purchased land in the Bluegrass in 1910, and founded his bloodstock farm there. He bred and raised four Kentucky Derby winners: *Behave Yourself* (1921), *Bubbling Over* (1926), *Burgoo King* (1932), and *Broker's Tip* (1933).

On Colonel Bradley's death, his farm was sold to Robert Kleberg, owner of the Texas-based King Ranch, and Edward S. Moore. Mr Kleberg left the 700 acres he purchased to his granddaughter. Mr Moore sold 186 acres before he died, and since that time, his widow has sold the balance.

Present owner of Darby Dan Farm is John W. Galbreath of Columbus, Ohio. He purchased 173 hectares (428 acres) of the original Idle Hour Stock Farm in 1957, and in 1962 acquired additional acreage to bring

(Right) *Graustark*, born in 1963, by *Ribot* out of *Flower Bowl*, whose grandsire was *Hyperion*. During his short racing career *Graustark* was reckoned by experts to be the fastest horse in America. He was unbeaten up to his eighth race, when he broke a bone in his foot, which caused him to lose the race by a few inches. He was bought by a syndicate for $2,400,000, which made him the most expensive stallion of his day. He is now worth $8,000,000.

(Below) *Chateaugay*, born in 1960, by *Swaps* out of *Banquet Bell*, shown here after his victory in the 1963 Kentucky Derby, with jockey Braulio Baeza in the saddle. Also leading the field was the top favourite *Never Bend*. In the same year *Chateaugay* won the Bluegrass Stakes, the Belmont Stakes, and the Jerome Handicap.

Darby Dan Farm to its present 250 hectares (618 acres). In addition to Darby Dan Farm in Kentucky, Mr Galbreath owns and operates Darby Dan Farm near Galloway, Ohio. This farm consists of 1820 hectares (4500 acres).

In the last four decades, the Galbreaths have bred more than seventy-five stakes winners, including the 1963 Kentucky Derby and Belmont Stakes winner *Chateaugay*, the 1967 Kentucky Derby winner *Proud Clarion*, the 1972 English Derby winner *Roberto*, and the 1974 Preakness and Belmont Stakes winner *Little Current*. Mr Galbreath is the only man who has won Derbies on both sides of the Atlantic.

Standing at Darby Dan Farm in Kentucky in 1976 were *Graustark*, *Roberto*, *His Majesty*, *Good Counsel*, *Little Current*, and *True Knight*.

Graustark, bred and owned by Mr and Mrs John W. Galbreath, was one of the most publicized horses ever in training and

was a hot favourite to win the 1967 Kentucky Derby. Running in the Blue Grass Stakes ten days before the Derby, he broke a bone in his foot, losing the race by a nose – his only defeat in eight starts.

Roberto raced in England, Ireland, and France. He was the champion two-year-old in Ireland in 1971 and won the Derby Stakes at Epsom in 1972.

His Majesty, a full brother to *Graustark*, is a stakes winner of $99,430, but his racing career was cut short by an injury. *Good Counsel*, bred and owned by Mrs Galbreath, is a stakes winner of $246,554. *Little Current*, bred and owned by Mr Galbreath, is a stakes winner of $354,704. *True Knight*, bred and owned by Mr Galbreath, won or was placed in twenty-two stakes races and earned $739,673. His sire was the great *Chateaugay*.

(Above) The mansion at Darby Dan, built in the colonial style.

(Left) The extensive white-fenced stallion paddocks at Darby Dan. Exercising in the paddock in the foreground is the outstanding *Graustark*.

(Left) The statue of *Black Tony*, one of the many great horses to come into the world here, to carry the Darby Dan colours to victory, and to pass on their splendid qualities at stud.

Spendthrift

(p. 259, top left) *Sham*, the most promising of the young stallions. The first of his foals appeared on the racetrack in 1977.

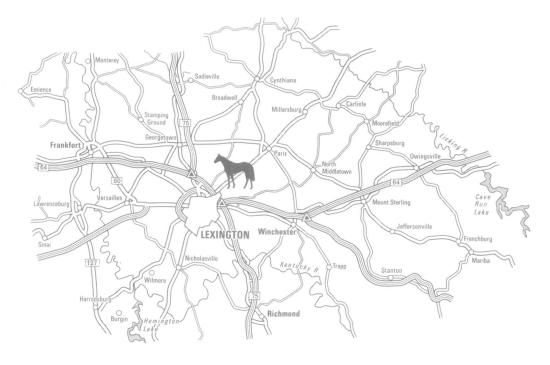

worse. *Beau Père* died shortly after his arrival in Lexington, before he could even cover a single mare – he was uninsured as well.

Undaunted, Combs returned to California six months later, to look at Mayer's *Alibhai*. This stallion had never run a race, but he was a son of *Hyperion*, and some of his offspring had also showed great promise on the track. Mayer asked $500,000 for the horse. Back in Kentucky, Combs tried to collect the money by

In 1937 Leslie Combs II came down from the hills of West Virginia to the Bluegrass region of Lexington in Kentucky. He had inherited money from his grandmother and decided to use this to make a start in horse breeding. He found the land he needed, and also acquired some good mares, but success at first eluded him. It was extremely difficult to get hold of really first-class stallions.

It was ten years before Combs met film magnate and horse breeder Louis B. Mayer in California and was thus able to acquire the outstanding stallion *Beau Père*. Mayer wanted $100,000 for him. This was not really too high a price, taking into account what fine horses this stallion had already sired; but *Beau Père* at that time was already twenty years old. Combs, however, did not possess anything like $100,000 in ready money. So he rounded up twenty friends in the area and thereby fixed up his first syndicate deal. By selling $5000 shares to each of them he collected the sum required.

The affair could not have turned out

(Above) The entrance to Spendthrift Farm, one of the most successful Thoroughbred stud-farms in the world. It is situated near Lexington, Kentucky, in the heart of the Bluegrass region.

(Left) The residence, well-known for its hospitality.

dividing it into thirty shares, but he managed to sell only twenty. Mayer accordingly kept ten shares. This time the deal paid off.

Alibhai got first-class offspring such as *Bardstown, Determine, Traffic Judge, Flower Bowl, Hasseyampa, Chevation* and many more.

When Combs came to Lexington in 1937 he bought the Spendthrift farm. He knew the neighbourhood well, for it was close to the farm of his great-grandfather, Daniel Swigert, who had in fact bred the 1881, 1882 and 1886 Kentucky Derby winners.

Combs developed the syndication system extremely successfully. He bought nine stallions on this system, paying over a million dollars for each of them – $1,800,000 for *Majestic Prince* and $2,625,000 for *Raise a Native*.

There are now some 200 brood-mares at Spendthrift. In 1972 the establishment's horses won the biggest amount for any single breeder. In the past ten years horses bred here have won more than $15 million. Combs has been the leading consigner to the Keeneland Summer Sales, in 1967 was the first commercial breeder whose grass sales amounted to more than a million dollars, and in 1972 more than two million.

Thirty-five Spendthrift yearlings have fetched a selling price of $100,000 or more each, another record in the industry. *Majestic Prince*, again syndicated after his racing career, fetched $250,000, *Exemplary*

(Above) One of the stable blocks. Around 200 brood-mares are lodged at Spendthrift.

$280,000, *Crown Prince* $510,000, *Kentucky Gold* $625,000 and *Elegant Prince* a remarkable $715,000.

Between 1966 and 1975 more than 100 stakes winners came from Spendthrift. In 1976, some thirty stallions were stood there.

(Above) *Never Bend* ranks as the establishment's most important sire. Up to 1976 he had got thirty-nine stakes winners and also the champion of England and France, *Mill Reef*, now standing at the British National Stud.

(Left) *Raise a Native* is as good a horse as *Never Bend*. His descendants include one Kentucky Derby winner and one European champion.

(Overleaf) In America, flat races are normally run over shorter courses than in Europe, but at correspondingly higher speeds.

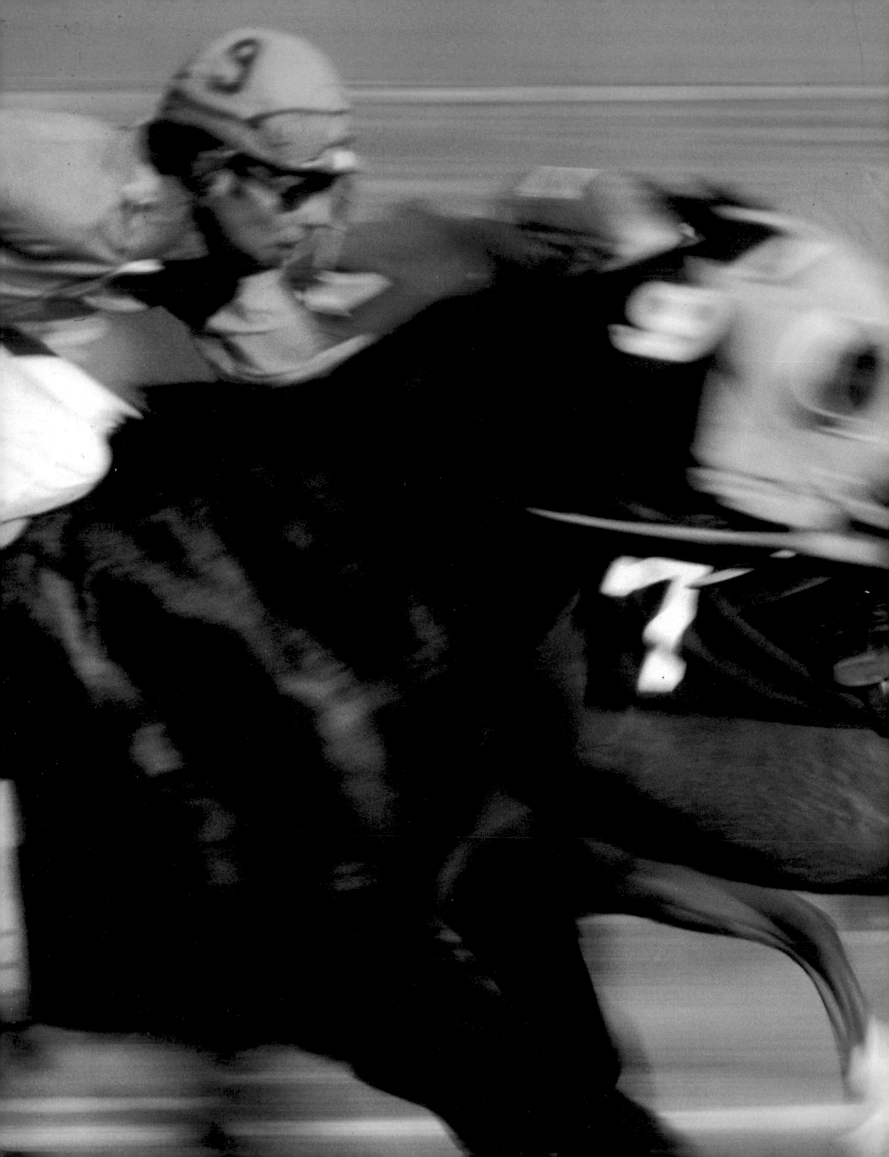

Hanover Shoe

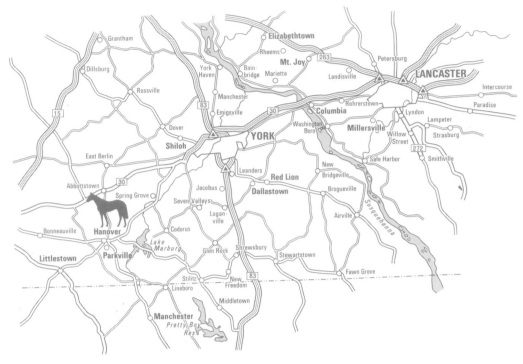

In May 1926 Lawrence B. Sheppard, at that time still in his twenties, purchased for $150,000 the whole stock of horses – sixty-nine Standard Trotters – left by the late breeder A. B. Coxe. With these he founded the Hanover Shoe Farms in southern Pennsylvania, later to become the largest and most famous of trotter stud-farms.

Among these horses were two first-class animals: the stallion *Dillon Axworthy*, who had already sired some very fast offspring, and his daughter, *Miss Bertha Dillon*, soon

to become well-known as the dam of three foals who ran the mile in two minutes. She is recognized today as the foundation dam of the 'Royal Family' of Hanover, the leading line of two-minute Trotters and Pacers.

Together with his father, Harper D. Sheppard, and the latter's partner, Clinton D. Myers, who in 1899 had founded the Hanover Shoe Company, the enterprising Lawrence B. Sheppard set to work building and equipping the stud-farm.

In the airy yellow stables and in the paddocks of the 1620-hectare (4000-acre) farm there were in 1976 14 stallions and some 300 brood-mares. In the spring there are usually about 1700 horses on the farm. Every November nearly all the yearlings are sold at the trotter auction in Harrisburg.

The two most important classic trotter races are considered to be the Hambletonian, instituted in 1926, and the Little Brown Jug, founded in 1946. Of the first forty-eight winners of the

(Right) *Best of All*, born in 1964, by *Good Time* out of *Besta Hanover*, produced many winners, including *Boyden Hanover*.

(Below) Two great stallions: *Columbia George*, born in 1967, by *Good Time* out of *Mitzi Eden*, put up five world records and won twenty-eight races; and *Star's Pride*, born in 1947, by *Worthy Boy* out of *Stardrift*, reckoned to be the all-time greatest Trotter stallion. He got eight Hambletonian winners and twenty-six world champions.

(Below) *Tar Heel*, born in 1948, by *Billy Direct* out of *Leta Long*, sired no fewer than eighty foals who ran the mile in two minutes or less. His offspring won more than twenty-two million dollars.

(Centre) *Albatross*, born in 1968, by *Meadow Skipper* out of *Voodoo Hanover*. *Tar Heel* is one of his great-grandsires. The fastest pacer and all-time fastest horse pulling the sulky. World champion in three classes as two-, three- and four-year-old.

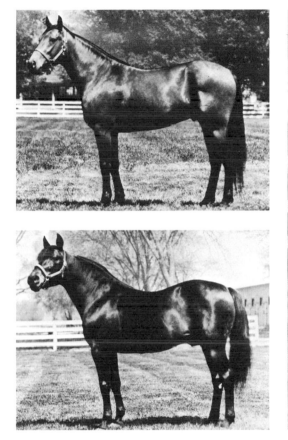

The title of 'Pacer of the Year' is repeatedly gained by Hanover horses. In 1972 this title was awarded almost unanimously to the stallion *Albatross*, who had set a great many world and track records, some of which will possibly never be broken. He ended his career as the most successful pacer of his time and is now standing at stud at Hanover. His first foals were born in 1974.

Albatross's stable-mate *Supper Bowl* kept him company by winning the title 'Trotter of the Year'. With the Hambletonian, the Kentucky Futurity and the Yonkers Futurity he won the Triple Trotter Crown and more money than any other trotter in one season.

In 1973 *Starlark Hanover* and *Boyden Hanover* easily won all the trotter and pacer prizes for two-year-olds, and *Delmonica* was hailed as the best trotter mare in the world.

Hambletonian, twenty-seven were bred or raised at Hanover, or were later brought here as stud-horses. And of the first twenty-five Jug winners twenty were similarly connected with Hanover.

Since 1964 the United States Trotting Association has been compiling comprehensive statistics on breeders. Hanover Shoe Farm has been at the top every year. In 1972 Hanover-bred horses won a total just short of four million dollars. A year later the amount was almost four and a half million.

The ten top sires of 1972 included four Hanover stallions, and in the same year five of the best brood-mare sires were from Hanover. In the two-year-old and three-year-old class five Hanover horses were among the first ten. The first places were taken by *Tar Heel* ($1,684,119 winnings) and *Adios* ($1,278,552); both are now standing at the stud.

(Right) Left to right: John Simpson, President of Hanover Shoe Farms Inc., Jonel Chiriacos and Lawrence B. Sheppard, the founder, who died in 1968, shown holding a trophy of the European champion mare *Elma*, by *Hickory Smoke* out of *Cassin Hanover*. *Elma* had won the $64,000 Grand Lottery Prize on 4 April 1965. She was the first American-bred and American-owned Trotter mare to collect this

internationally open title. Bred by Mrs Charlotte Sheppard, she was at first trained and driven in the USA by John Simpson. In Europe she went to the stable of trainer Jonel Chiriacos. She was driven by Johannes Frömming, the most successful driver of his time. He took *Elma* to victories in Italy, France, Germany and Sweden, in 1965 and 1966. *Elma* is now a brood-mare at Hanover Shoe Farm.

Walnut Hall

(p. 265, top) The architectural style of the barns at Walnut Hall is typical of Kentucky. The horses and cattle are housed on the ground floor, hay and straw are stored on the first floor, and in the top storey the tobacco is hung up to ferment.

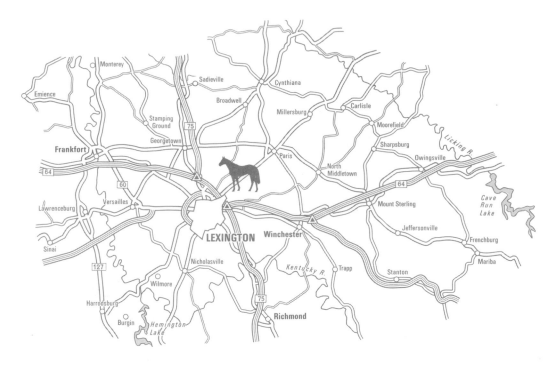

In 1777 Colonel William Christie, of Virginia, was rewarded for his services in the Franco-Indian war of 1765 with a piece of land in Kentucky; this was the foundation for Walnut Hall.

However, it was not until a good hundred years later that horses were bred here. After changing hands several times the farm was bought in 1879 by John S. Clark. He took full advantage of the Kentucky Bluegrass region's highly suitable conditions for breeding Thoroughbreds,

which he also raced. Up to that time only very few trotters had crossed the mountains from the Eastern States to come south. Later, however, Clark began to take an interest in Standard Trotters also. His best Trotter was named after himself, and ran the mile (1.6 km) in the very respectable time of 2 minutes 19 seconds.

In 1891 Lamon Vanderberg Harkness came to Kentucky to buy carriage horses. But his brief glimpse of Trotter breeding here made him so enthusiastic that he

purchased Walnut Hall. He extended the property to over 2000 hectares (5000 acres), put up new stable blocks, sheds and staff accommodation, and modernized the residence.

In 1882 he bought the best mare he could find: the four-year-old *Mother Carey*.

After two decades Walnut Hall possessed one of the finest herds of Standard Trotter mares and several top-class stallions, and enjoyed an excellent reputation throughout the trotter world.

After several comparatively quiet years, Walnut Hall made news again in 1930, when Lamon Vanderberg's young granddaughter Katherine took up Trotter racing and won records in two continents with the mare *Margaret Castleton*. At that time also, famous horses such as *Protector*, *Guy Axworthy* and *Scotland* were standing at Walnut Hall.

In 1960 *Impish* was foaled. She broke nine world records on the Red Mile at Lexington as a two-year-old, and retired unbeaten from the racetrack to take her

(Above) Close to the stallion stables are the last resting-places of Walnut Hall's great horses, including *Peter Volo, Volomite, Guy Abby, Guy Day, Danley, Demon Hanover, Scotland* and *Guy Axworthy*.

(Right) In 1842 the original Walnut Hall residence was burnt down. The then owner, Victor Flournoy, built this new residence soon afterwards. He took advantage of the availability of a large supply of walnut trees to use this wood in the creation of a splendid interior.

place in the brood-mare herd. Her records still stand. Early in 1977 there were more than ninety brood-mares at Walnut Hall.

The stud-farm also maintains a large herd of cattle, which is beneficial for the pastures. Another activity of the farm is the large-scale cultivation of tobacco which, after harvesting, is allowed to ferment on the top floor of the enormous barns.

(Far left) The weathervane over the foaling unit, also visible in the top picture.
In the friendly and rural atmosphere of the stallion stables at Walnut Hall we encounter such distinguished names such as *Duane Hanover*, *Sampson Direct*, *Silent Majority* and *Uncle Sam*. Among the most outstanding sires are *Dayan* (above), born in 1966, and *Florlis* (left), born in 1960.

265

Castleton

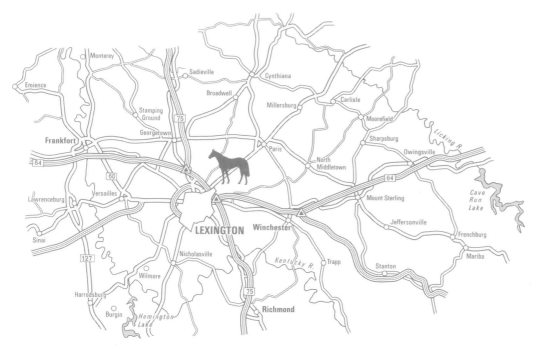

(Right) Part of the extensive complex of stables and paddocks at Castleton, viewed from the water tower.

(Below) The wall, 3 km (1¾ miles) long, separates the establishment from the road and was built in the 1930s by the then owner, Sam Look. The entrance gateway, then over 150 years old and about to disintegrate, was rebuilt exactly as before, stone by stone.
During the rebuilding work a wooden water-conduit of the same age was discovered, leading to a spring a kilometre (over half a mile) away; it was still in good condition.

The history of Castleton goes back to the last decades of the eighteenth century. That was when John Breckinridge left Virginia for Kentucky and bought the piece of land near Lexington.

When, in 1806, his daughter Mary Ann married David Castleman, he made over a part of the land to her and built her a splendid mansion. The young couple called their estate Castleton.

David Castleman's son, a general in the Civil War, was a great horse expert. This John B. Castleman had a big share in the development of the American Saddle Horse, one of the favourite American breeds, which subsequently gave first-class service as a cavalry mount and as a show horse nowadays has many admirers. This was the beginning of Castleton's fame as a breeding establishment.

In the 1880s, Castleton Farm was bought by Steward M. Ford, owner of Ford's Theatre in Washington, where President Lincoln was assassinated. Ford bred carriage horses and show horses at Castleton.

(Above) In 1911 David M. Look, from New York, spent more than three million dollars on a complete conversion of the residence, which was then at least a hundred years old. On his wife's arrival in Kentucky, she encountered a shoot-out in the hotel lobby; she immediately returned to New York, and would never live in the mansion.

(Far left) *Bret Hanover*. In 1966 this pacer ran the mile in 1 minute 53.3 seconds, making him world champion, still unbeaten. A statue was erected in his honour while he was still alive.

(Left) A memento of colonial times: a slave cabin.

In 1903 the stud-farm was bought by James R. Keene, a well-known personality in American racing at that time. Many years previously he had acquired from the grandfather of Leslie Combs II, founder of the Spendthrift stud-farm, two top-class yearling colts, *Miser* and *Spendthrift*, who were as successful in America as in France and England. At Castleton he bred a number of high-class horses.

When, in 1911, Keene fell ill he sold Castleton to the New Yorker David M. Look, who started one of the most important Trotter stud-farms here. He had extensive alterations made to the vast mansion at a cost of over three million dollars, but still could not persuade his wife to live here; she regarded Kentucky as a jungle. The house stood empty until 1930, when Look's son Sam married and brought his wife to live here.

In 1945 the estate was bought by Mr and Mrs Van Lennep. At that time, Mrs Van Lennep had already been breeding Saddle Horses for eighteen years, and at Castleton

she now started to breed Standard Trotters also. This soon pushed the breeding of show horses into the background, and in 1975 the Saddle Horses were given up altogether.

In 1976 Castleton had some 250 Trotter mares of its own and also boards 450 visiting Trotter mares during the covering season.

(Centre) Colts.

(Above) An old picture from the early days of Trotter racing.

(Far left) *Strike Out* ran the mile in 1 minute 56.3 seconds and won twenty-nine out of forty-four races, came second nine times and third once. He was the all-time fastest three-year-old over the half-mile.

(Left) *Speedy Scott* ran the mile in 1 minute 56.4 seconds, won the Triple Crown and collected $650,909 in his Trotter racing career. His descendants include numerous winners of difficult races.

Breeds and types

At the present time more than 300 breeds, types and varieties of horses are distinguished. They are all descended from a species of wild horse, *Equus przewalskii*, which spread over wide stretches of Europe, Asia and North Africa about a million years ago. The scientific designation often leads to the erroneous assumption that the animal known as 'Przewalski's horse' is the progenitor of all domesticated horses. In fact, the Przewalski is only one of the various geographic breeds or sub-species of *Equus przewalskii*, namely *Equus przewalskii przewalskii*. The Tarpan of the Steppes was another sub-species of the

same species and is named *Equus przewalskii gmelini*, and the Forest Tarpan is named *Equus przewalskii silvaticus*.

Undoubtedly, all these three kinds of wild horse became domesticated. It is now thought that other races of wild horses, in particular the South Asian and North African, also became domesticated. From them are descended, for example, the Arabs and the Barbs, two domesticated breeds whose basic distinctive characteristics were certainly not developed simply as a result of selective breeding but were acquired earlier, in the course of their evolutionary history (albeit these characteristics are now not so easy to distinguish, since the Barbs have for over a thousand years received infusions of Arab blood).

Prehistoric horses will not be discussed in detail here. It is simply pointed out, with all due regard to the splendid results achieved by breeding, that the essential differences in conformation and behaviour of the various basic breeds already existed before the domestication of horses. The art of horse breeding – and it may very well be described as an art, in the sense of being a creative activity – consisted and consists in the production of horses for all types of use, for any climate, for widely varied types of ground, and for all tastes, by careful selection and systematic crossing of existing breeds. Nowadays, however, there is a strong tendency for breeds to become merged. Apart from specialities such as Thoroughbreds and trotters for racing and ponies for leisure riding, efforts are generally directed to the production of a versatile sports/saddle horse. Hence it is possible to recognize the impending arrival of a European warm-blood breed of horse.

In the following pages, forty-eight of the most important breeds and types of horses are described. As is appropriate to the subject of this book, the examples chosen are essentially types which are bred on stud-farms. Although ponies are almost entirely excluded, this should not be interpreted as a value judgment: we, the authors, ourselves breed ponies.

(Left) In former times Przewalski's horse, the wild horse of the eastern steppes, was to be found throughout the region stretching from the Urals across central Asia as far as Mongolia. Typical of this type of horse is the reddish-yellow to brownish-yellow colour, the short bristling mane without forelock and the large coarse head. Wild animals of this breed were last sighted during the 1950s in the remotest and most desolate parts of the Gobi Desert. There are now probably no more genuine wild specimens in existence. The last of them may have mated with Mongolian ponies. But though these last true wild horses have been rooted out of their own habitat, nevertheless the type is not extinct. About seventy years ago a few dozen specimens of Przewalski's horse were imported into Europe for zoological gardens. When the danger of extinction was recognized, breeding groups were made up in various zoos from the descendants of these imported animals. At the Prague zoo an international breeding register has been kept since 1960. By systematic breeding, mainly at the Prague zoo, at Catskill near New York, at Whipsnade in England, and at the Munich-Hellabrunn zoo, the total number of these animals has been increased from about 50 to over 200. Our photograph was taken at the Warsaw Zoo.

(Right) In the steppes of southern Russia lived the Steppe Tarpan, a wild horse of mouse-grey colour with black mane and tail, a strongly marked dorsal stripe and a very pretty, short head with a slightly concave profile. Its appearance was altogether more refined than that of Przewalski's horse. The last Steppe Tarpans perished during the second half of the nineteenth century. Using domestic horses containing a high proportion of Tarpan blood, and exercising very careful selection, these animals have now been 're-bred'. The results, which can be seen in various zoos and in two wild-animal reserves in Poland, are horses which look like, but are not, true Tarpans. Somewhat smaller was the Forest Tarpan, which lived in central and eastern Europe. It was more lightly built than the Steppe Tarpan, and in the winter its colour was lighter. It perished earlier, in the eighteenth century. The stallion in the illustration is a re-bred Steppe Tarpan living wild in the Popielno Reserve in northern Poland.

Akhal Teke

Illustration: Akhal Teke stallion from the stables of the Swiss circus, Knie.
Description: Swift, noble saddle-horse of high endurance, similar to the English Thoroughbred. Refined head, long sloping shoulders, high withers, long legs, very dry limbs.

The writings of the famous world traveller Marco Polo show that he was already acquainted with these horses by the end of the thirteenth century. According to his account, Alexander the Great's fiery stallion Bucephalus was the foundation sire of this breed.

The homeland of the Akhal Teke lies in the steppes of Turkmenistan. For endurance and toughness this breed can only be compared with the Arab, to which, moreover, it is closely related. In 1935 Akhal Tekes were tested on a long-distance run from Ashkhabad to Moscow, a distance of 4300 km (over 2600 miles); they reached their destination in eighty-four days.

At the present time they are being bred at several studs in Russia and are ridden in high-power sports.

American Saddle

Illustration: American Saddle Horse stallion in California. It is in Kentucky and Virginia that most of these horses are bred.
Description: Very handsomely modelled head, arched 'swan neck', compact muscular trunk, high withers, back and croup short and level, sound limbs, tail carried high as a result of cutting two tendons and tying high.

The Saddle Horse started out as a type having great stamina for riding round the great plantations of Kentucky and Virginia. It evolved as the product of crossing English Thoroughbreds, Hackneys, Morgan Horses, and Canadian and American Pacers, from which it inherited its tendency towards unusual gaits.

It is now purely a show horse, the sense and purpose of which can be argued about, but which nevertheless has an enthusiastic following of thousands of Americans at the shows. There are two types: the three-gait, which has tail and mane cut short; and the five-gait, whose tail and mane are left long, and whose gaits include, as well as the walk, the trot and the canter, the so-called 'slow gait' and the 'rack'.

Anglo-Arab

Illustration: Anglo-Arab brood-mares at the Pompadour stud-farm in France.
Description: Developed by crossing English Thoroughbreds with Orientals on a limited basis. Found mainly in France. This method of breeding is interesting and often produces worthwhile results when the intrinsic properties and the external features of the two breeds combine harmoniously or complement one another effectively. Recognized as improving breed.

During the last century Arabs and English Thoroughbreds were already being crossed in various countries of Europe, so as to combine the good features of the two breeds. In the course of time the composite Anglo-Arab evolved, and various types have been developed in different regions. The most important are the Polish Malopolska, which often closely resembles the Arab, the Hungarian Gidran, and lastly the French Anglo-Arab, which is regarded as the ideal type. This last type is bred mainly at the famous Pompadour stud-farm in the South of France, and tends to be a very good jumper. Similar horses were to be found there as early as the eighteenth century. Around the middle of the nineteenth century the present type was evolved from two Oriental stallions and three Thoroughbred mares.

Anglo-Norman

Illustration: The stallion Fend l'Air, born 1971, belonging to the French Government stallion centre at Saint-Lô in Normandy.
Description: This was originally exclusively a cross between a heavy farm horse, based on a mixture of warm-blood and cold-blood, and the English Thoroughbred. Since about 1955 a 'Selle' stud book has been collecting the types predominantly free of cold blood and selecting them to develop a consolidated riding type.

According to old records, the horses which were already being bred in Normandy at the beginning of our millennium were descended from the old Armoricans which spread through France at the time of the Moors. These 'Normandy horses' had almost died out by the middle of the nineteenth century, when systematic breeding was started from the remaining stock. A large number of English Thoroughbreds and half-breds were crossed in.

The foundation sire of the modern Anglo-Norman breed was a Norfolk Trotter called Young Rattler. Towards the end of the nineteenth century the powerful and good-tempered Anglo-Norman was in demand as a coach-horse. Around the 1930s there was a sharp decline in the breed, but the successful development of a saddle-horse type restored the breed to great favour.

American Standard Trotter

Illustration: Standard Trotter at the moment of suspension. Description: Thoroughbred type, but legs not so long. Long, very sloping shoulders, high croup. Hurried and irregular in the walk, not very impressive in the gallop, this breed puts all its energy into its long-striding trot. The two types, Trotter and Pacer, race separately.

Towards the end of the eighteenth century impromptu races were already being organized in eastern North America with trotters both ridden and harnessed. With the passage of the decades many different types of horses were selected for breeding and were crossed with one another: Morgan Horses, Cleveland Bays, Canadian and Narragansett Pacers, etc. *Hambletonian*, born 1849, son of the Thoroughbred *Messenger*, had a decisive influence on the breed.

It was the ambition of the breeders to produce a horse capable of trotting the mile in less than two minutes. The Pacer *Star Pointer* accomplished this in 1897, and the mare *Lon Dillon* in 1903 became the first Standard Trotter to manage it. The fastest Standardbred, the Pacer *Bret Hanover*, covered the mile in 1 minute 53.6 seconds in 1966.

Andalusian

Illustration: Andalusian stallion at the Cortijo de Quarto stud-farm near Seville. Description: Noble and elegant appearance, with nicely rounded lines. In the old type the head is rather large, with convex profile; after infusion of Arab blood this is now smaller and more refined. Docile and good-natured, but with a fiery temperament. Mostly grey, but also some black and bay.

On their Barb and Arab horses, unbeatable at that period for swiftness and endurance, the Moors in AD 711 took the Iberian Peninsula by storm. When their long period of dominion came to an end they left behind not only palaces and mosques but also wonderful horses, thanks to which – by the irony of fate – the Spaniards themselves were able to conquer a world-wide empire.

While in the royal stud-farms northern horses were crossed with the desert types to make them larger and heavier, pure strains were raised in three Carthusian monasteries. From the sixteenth century onwards these 'Spanish horses', or Andalusians, came to be the most desired breed in Europe and constituted the foundation of all the horses bred for Baroque pomp and parade.

Appaloosa

Illustration: Prize-winning Appaloosa at the Agricultural Fair, Tulsa, Oklahoma, 1975. Description: Striking spotted coat with four different hair patterns. The head is straight and light, though the profile is often convex; the neck is beautifully arched, the shoulders well set, main and tail short and thin; muzzle usually with pigment-free patches ('toad' muzzle); character extremely friendly and gentle.

This is a breed which, though not bred at the major stud-farms, should, on account of its unusual beauty and great popularity in America, not be left without mention.

Spanish horses, among which there were formerly many spotted specimens, were the foundation sires of the Appaloosas, as of all the horses of the American West. The Nez Percé Indians of the region which is now Idaho bred these horses in a systematic manner.

In 1877 American troops overcame the Nez Percé and seized about 200 of these striking horses. Some of them were bred pure by ranchers, and in 1938 the Appaloosa Stud Book was started. At the present time there are about 150,000 registered Appaloosas.

Arab

Illustration: The Arab *Aramus*, born 1962 in Poland, is at present top stallion at the stud of the singer Wayne Newton, near Las Vegas, Nevada. Description: The noblest and most beautiful breed of horse, unrivalled in strength, stamina and intelligence. Neck set high, refined marvellously beautiful head with large expressive eyes and wide nostrils. Light trunk, muscular limbs, tail carried high, spirited appearance. Mostly grey, sometimes chestnut or other colours.

The origin of the Arab remains shrouded in uncertainty; nevertheless it is probable that this breed is descended from a type of wild horse which was indigenous in the Arabian peninsula in the last Ice Age and already possessed the most important characteristics of the desert horse. The Prophet Mohammed understood the laws of selective breeding and handed down to his followers instructions for maintaining pure blood-lines. By far the best horses were bred by the Bedouin in the highlands. In this region the combination of climate, the pitiless elimination of poor specimens and the fanatical pursuit of purity resulted in the production of horses of incomparable quality. Pure Arab stocks fall into one of three biotypes: the male *Kuhaykan*, the female *Saqlawi* and the exceptionally swift *Muniqi*.

Ardennais

Illustration: Ardennais stallion at the Pompadour stud in the south of France.
Description: Medium heavy, powerful working horse. Well-proportioned head, strong neck, short back and croup, muscular limbs, large hoofs, feather. Energetic, astonishingly long stride. Extremely adaptable and very robust. Grey, chestnut, bay or cream. Blacks are not liked.

An extremely important cold-blood type which has had a decisive influence on the creation and improvement of many other breeds. It is probably descended from the prehistoric Solutrean horse. Bred by farmers in the Ardennes, its use has however by no means been confined to agriculture; it was highly esteemed by the Romans and the Crusaders, provided the foundation for the tournament horses of the Middle Ages, dragged Napoleon's cannon as far as Russia and indefatigably pulled the army's heavy vehicles right up to World War II.

The Ardennais is still bred in various countries, and particularly in Sweden is very common and popular. The Swedish Ardennais has little or no feather.

Barb

Illustration: *Fantasia* in the Moroccan *Moussem de Moulay*.
Description: Elegant, light, high-spirited but reliable saddle horse. Profile not so convex as in earlier times, sometimes actually quite straight. Somewhat coarser bones than Arabs. Short stride, relaxed trot, gallop covering more or less ground.

The Greeks and Romans were already aware of the properties of the Barb – its robustness, versatility and stamina. Under the rule of the Vandals in North Africa cold-bloods were crossed in, but their influence was not sustained. Much more important were the effects of the Moslem conquest of the North African countries in the seventh century, which brought in 75,000 Arab horses. The improvement produced by these Arabs turned the Barb into a horse whose properties filled the whole of Baroque Europe with enthusiasm. His descendants, the Andalusians, founded famous breeds such as the Neapolitan, Lipizzaner, Kladruby and Frederiksborg. One of the three foundation sires of the English Thoroughbred breed was a Moroccan Barb stallion, *Godolphin Barb*.

Clydesdale

Illustration: The Busch Breweries of St Louis, Missouri, have their own Clydesdale stud-farm. The products are often paraded on public holidays as eight-in-hand teams and they are a very popular advertisement for beer all over America.
Description: One of the most magnificent draught-horses. Well-proportioned head, beautifully arched neck, very powerful but not clumsy general appearance. Bay, rarely black, with a lot of white on the head and legs and sometimes also on the belly. Luxuriant feather.

This breed originated in the valley of the River Clyde in Scotland in the eighteenth century, when native mares were crossed with Belgian stallions to produce a powerful pack- and draught-horse. Clydesdales stand about 165–170 cm (16–17 hands) and weigh up to 1000 kg (one ton). They are distinguished by a lively but sober temperament and an energetic, long-striding walk and trot. After a marked decline in their numbers these horses have recently regained great popularity, and many are exported, especially to America, New Zealand, Australia and South Africa. In the USA, moreover, they have established their own breeders' society.

Connemara Pony

Illustration: Young Connemara mare, belonging to the outstanding breeder John Daly, at Lough Mask in Connemara, Ireland.
Description: Refined riding-pony, with scarcely any typical pony characteristics. Light, expressive head, neck carried well, strong back with good saddle-seating, sound joints, excellent in all three gaits, tremendous jumping capacity. Stands 135 cm to 145 cm (13 to 14 hands). This type is now found all over the world.

The Celts, who, borne by their tough ponies, conquered large parts of Europe between 4000 and 2300 years ago, came to the British Isles in the fourth century BC, and settled in Wales, in south-west England and in Ireland. Their descendants are still excellent horsemen.

Gradually their ponies vanished from Ireland, making way for larger horses. Only in the far north-west, in the barren, rocky, wind-swept countryside of Connemara, did they manage to maintain a foot-hold. Oriental blood was infused as long ago as 2000 years, and later on English Thoroughbred blood was introduced. Connemara Ponies mated with Thoroughbred stallions produced some fabulous sporting horses, some of which reached world championship level.

Breton

Illustration: Breton stallion at the Pompadour stud-farm in the south of France.
Description: Heavy cold-blood, with straight head, well-proportioned neck, thick-set trunk, short, strong legs with large hoofs and little or no feather. Energetic and undemanding. Mostly chestnut, but not uncommonly light bay or chestnut-grey.

The expertise of the French in breeding cold-bloods is well demonstrated in the Breton; this horse is also used for improving various foreign breeds. A native of Brittany, its foundations are the same as those of the other French cold-bloods. Three types are bred, the best known being the Big Breton, standing over 160 cm (about 16 hands) on average, and weighing at least 550 kg (1200 pounds or 85 stone). Less well known in other countries is the Highland Breton, lighter and more active, standing only about 150 cm (15 hands or less). Lastly, the Postier, which was developed by crossing-in Norfolk Trotters and which has inherited from them its spirited gait.

Cleveland Bay

Illustration: *Knaresborough Justice*, 1967, stud-horse at Wymondham in Norfolk.
Description: Medium-heavy warm-blood. Longish head and swan neck. Long back and croup, well-set shoulders, sound limbs. Bay, with black legs and black mane and tail. White markings are undesirable.

In the Cleveland Hills of north-east England these horses were formerly used as draught animals by the woodcutters, with whose disappearance in the eighteenth century they also almost vanished from the scene. Their outstanding, versatile qualities were however rediscovered, and the breed was improved and redeveloped as a coach-horse which soon took over the principal role as carriage-horse at the royal court. A number of Cleveland stallions played a part in building up the Hanoverian breed. At the present time Queen Elizabeth II still maintains a Cleveland Bay stud-farm in Norfolk. By crossing with Thoroughbreds, really excellent hunters, jumpers and military horses have been produced.

Criollo

Illustration: Criollo of typical dun colour, with dorsal stripe and zebra-striped legs.
Description: Rather heterogenous. Head medium-sized with straight profile, but sometimes quite large and with convex profile; withers usually good; powerful short back and sloping croup; sound joints and hoofs. Characteristics common to all are indestructible good health and tremendous stamina. Height about 135 cm to 150 cm (13–15 hands).

Criollos (or Creoles) is the name given to all Central American and South American horses descended from Spanish stock. As in the North American West, many of the Spanish and Portuguese conquerors' saddle horses escaped into the wild. Nowadays they are bred nearly everywhere under unrestricted conditions and are ridden mainly by cowherds. It is estimated that there is one horse for every seven inhabitants in Latin America.

Dun, mouse-dun and chestnut-dun colourings are common and desirable, with dorsal stripe and zebra-striped legs; but there is a wide range of other colours, and spotted patterns are frequent. The Criollo is most numerous in Argentina, where it is put through a trial comprising a race lasting for several days. There are also Criollos of various types in Brazil, Chile, Peru, Colombia and Venezuela.

English Thoroughbred

Illustration: English Thoroughbred, reared in America, under training on a track in Virginia.
Description: Bred to produce the inherent qualities necessary for tough competition. Strong nerves, fighting spirit, great stamina. Built and engineered for speed. Big shoulders, plenty of room for internal organs, powerful thighs. Main source of blood in improving all warm-blood breeds for toughness and performance.

The most important characteristic of the horse is its speed. The fastest have always been the best, and the whole English Thoroughbred breeding industry is based on the recognition of this fact.

In the middle ages races were already being organized in England, with Galloway Ponies, some of which had received infusions of Arab or Barb blood. Pony mares of this type, proved for speed through generations, provided the female foundation stock for developing the Thoroughbred. The male foundation consisted of just three stallions: *Byerley Turk*, *Godolphin Barb* and *Darley Arabian*. Today, not only does the Thoroughbred dominate the racecourses of the whole world, it is also indispensable for the production of any high-performance warm-bloods.

The history of this breed is related in the introduction to the chapter on England.

French Trotter

Illustration: *Rigel*, born 1961, is stud-horse at Rosières-aux-Salines.
Description: Has a more harmonious general appearance than the American Standard Trotter. Straight, distinguished head, long neck, pronounced withers, very strong back, fine sinewy legs, steeply sloping shoulders. Good at the walk and the gallop, even greater staying-power than the American when trotting.

The basis for this breed was provided by the Norfolk Trotter. The actual foundation sire was one of these, *Young Rattler*, a stallion who also exercised a decisive influence on the development of the Anglo-Norman breed. Later on, Anglo-Normans were used for breeding Trotters, but this did not produce the hoped-for results. The renewed importation of Norfolk Trotters and of American and Russian Trotters finally led to the creation of the present-day outstanding 'Trotteur Français'.

About a third of all trotter races in France are still run under the saddle.

Frederiksborg

Illustration: Frederiksborg mare of modern sporting type, from an establishment near the former Frederiksborg stud.
Description: The old type was a parade horse with convex profile; the breeding system has now been switched to produce a type resembling the European sports breeds. Usually chestnut.

A product of Andalusian and Neapolitan horses bred in the former royal stud-farm at Frederiksborg in Danish North Zealand, this horse, the so-called 'Dane', was introduced to improve the horses at many European courts – even at Córdoba. The Frederiksborg stallion *Pluto* founded the Lipizzaner line bearing his name, and a Danish mare is supposed to have played a decisive part in the development of the Orlov Trotter. During the first half of the twentieth century the direction of breeding of the Frederiksborg was switched from use as leisure and riding-school horse to agricultural purposes. At present efforts are being made to satisfy the demand for versatile riding-horses by introducing Thoroughbreds and other breeds.

Gidran

Illustration: *Gidran II*, born 1959, at the Sütveny stud in Hungary.
Description: Extremely elegant Anglo-Arab. Closely resembles the Arab in many cases, as regards the dished profile, the short croup and the high set of the tail. Compact and muscular. Good in all gaits, and of course outstanding in the gallop. Nearly always chestnut.

Like the Hungarian Nonius and Furioso-North-Star breeds, the Gidran originated at the Mezöhegyes stud in the plain of southern Hungary. The mating of the Original-Siglavy Arab *Gidran Senior* with the Spanish mare *Arrogante* produced in 1820 the colt *Gidran II*, the actual foundation sire of the breed, who got horses of Arab type when mated with a wide assortment of mares. From 1830 onward English Thoroughbreds were often crossed in, and Arabs were later used again to correct the type. As typical Anglo-Arabs, Gidrans are above all excellent saddle horses, but they are also kept for carriage work and agriculture.

Outside Hungary it is mainly in Romania and Bulgaria that the Gidran is bred.

Hackney

Illustration: Hackney stallion on a stud-farm in California.
Description: Elegant, strong resemblance to the Thoroughbred; gives an impression of arrogance in its appearance. Steeply sloping (trotter) shoulder, almost straight croup, fine but very strong legs. Striking knee action.

The trotters from Norfolk and Yorkshire were well known in many parts as early as the seventeenth century. They carried Spanish blood, and later on Arabs were crossed in. Around 1760 the half-bred stallion *Old Shales*, a great-grandson of the renowned *Flying Childers*, set his stamp on the Hackney breed. Originally produced for riding, they were later used almost exclusively as coach horses. But Hackneys were also used to improve many other breeds, and these matings produced a number of world-famous sporting horses.

Early in the present century the breed had almost disappeared, but they have since been restored to favour as show horses much in demand in England, the Netherlands and above all in America, though their greatly admired knee action is often produced by dubious methods.

Freiberger

Illustration: *James*, born 1969, one of the Freiberger stallions at the Swiss Federal stud at Avenches.
Description: Lighter than medium-weight working horse with very harmonious conformation, small light head, neck well set, strong back and short, sound legs. Lively, extremely good-natured, robust, undemanding and with great endurance. Mostly bay, without markings.

This Swiss farm horse originated in the Jura. The breed was probably developed by crossing Norikers with Arab or Barb horses. Later on there were crossings with Ardennais, Anglo-Normans, English warm-bloods and Thoroughbreds. The type then became too light for the farmers, so they imported Bretons, Percherons and Shire Horses and thus redeveloped a powerful type of working horse which however is still on the light side; it is also excellent as a military pack-horse and for the production of mules.

More recent experiments in crossings with Arabs have produced pretty, compact horses for which, however, there is little demand.

Furioso-North-Star

Illustration: Furioso-North-Star at the Mezöhegyes stud in Hungary.
Description: Medium-sized horse, rather like an English half-bred. Distinguished-looking head, strong back, long sloping shoulders, very sound and correct legs and joints. Intelligent, docile, versatile horse for dressage, jumping, military purposes and in harness.

The English Thoroughbred stallion *Furioso* (not to be confused with the later famous French stallion of the same name) was acquired by the Hungarian state stud-farm at Mezöhegyes from the stud of Count Karolyi in 1841. Twelve years later they imported another Thoroughbred stallion from England: *The North Star*. Both were outstanding horses and potent progenitors who, with the tough Hungarian mares, laid the foundations of two equally good new blood-lines. From 1885 onwards the two lines were interbred, whence the hyphenated name.

At the present time this breed is produced mainly at Apajpuszta, between the Danube and the Tisza, but it is also bred in Czechoslovakia, Poland, Romania and Austria.

Haflinger

Illustration: Pair of Haflingers in Switzerland, where this breed is very popular.
Description: Small, powerful, beautifully built highland horse, standing 134 cm to 144 cm (about 13–14 hands). Compact, rounded shape, broad back good for pack carrying. Clean, sound legs and joints. Medium to small head with Arab-type dishing more or less marked. Does well in all gaits. Good-tempered, friendly and docile.

In the Tyrolese Alps there were already little pack-horses in Roman times; these must have constituted the foundation for the Haflinger. Various other breeds were crossed with them, the heavy Noriker giving added substance, while Arab or Barb horses transmitted muscular joints and lively temperament.

The foundation sire of the modern Haflinger breed, which originated at Hafling near Meran (Merano), was the stallion *Folie*, born 1874. His sire was the Arab *El Bedavi XXII*, from the Radautz stud-farm.

An undemanding, indestructible working horse, the Haflinger spread throughout Austria and Bavaria. With the increasing popularity of leisure riding in recent years, it quickly found a wide circle of fanciers. It is bred in more than twenty countries at present.

Hanoverian

Illustration: *Grande*, born 1958, stud-horse at Celle.
Description: The big frame and powerful but elegant appearance make this the ideal modern sporting horse. Aristocratic head of medium size, neck well set on long, sloping shoulders, good withers, strong back, slightly sloping, muscular croup. Good gaits, enormous jumping capacity, impeccable character. Stands 165 cm to 175 cm (about 16–17 hands).

The history of this breed begins with the establishment of the stud at Celle. Initially, twelve black Holstein stallions were stood there. Coach horses and English half-breds were brought in, as well as Arab and Barb stallions and stud-horses from Normandy. For some decades after this, Mecklenburgers predominated. Then followed a long period when English Thoroughbreds held sway, until about 1880, when selective breeding produced the heavy, native Hanoverian, which was soon afterwards again improved with additional substance. Under the slogan 'Nobility with substance' this new Hanoverian found its way into a large number of breeding regions and won many Olympic medals at sports.

Holstein

Illustration: *Granat*, ridden by Christine Stückelberger – the combination that won the Olympic Gold Medal for dressage in 1976.
Description: In contrast to the mighty Oldenburgers and East Friesians of former times, this was a native coach-horse of only medium weight, with well-marked withers and high trotter action. Its speciality is jumping. By a strong admixture of Thoroughbred blood, it has now been standardized in the type of a modern saddle-horse. Has recently gained Olympic successes in all events.

The fighting forces and postal services of Europe were using Holsteins for preference as early as 1700. It was from Holstein also that the first sires came for the Celle stud and the Hanover breeding region. Thereafter, this strong source of influence gradually receded, while English horses, Mecklenburgers and Hanoverians came to the fore.

The Holstein remained a wonderful coach horse and a trusty worker in agriculture. In addition, it developed great talent for jumping. After 1955 this breed, like others, became subject to the need for modernization, to suit the market for versatile saddle and sporting horses.

Irish Draught

Illustration: Irish Draught mare belonging to a Hunter breeder near Cork in southern Ireland.
Description: Medium-weight, powerful horse, standing about 155 cm to 165 cm (15–16 hands). Its appearance is distinguished not so much by any details as by the fact that, by and large, everything 'fits' – harmonious lines, good proportions, strong legs with good joints. Mostly grey or bay; feather undesirable.

The farmers of Ireland have never been blessed with material wealth, and hence have never been in a position to keep special horses for different purposes, such as work horses, cart-horses, hunters or saddle horses. Just one type had to serve for all requirements. In this way the Draught Horse was developed, which in spite of its name is not at all a cold-blood. This breed has inhabited the island for a long time. Its origin is uncertain, neither is it known with what breeds it has been crossed. Spanish and Oriental horses, Connemara Ponies and English cold-bloods, warm-bloods and Thoroughbreds have certainly been involved. The breed is famous on account of the fact that the universally known Irish Hunter was developed by mating Irish Draught mares with Thoroughbred stallions.

Kladruby

Illustration: Leading sire *Solo IV*, born 1957, has played an important part in Kladruby breeding at Slatiňany.
Description: Bred, like the Frederiksborgs and Lipizzaners, from Spanish and Italian stallions, as a parade horse of the Baroque period. Large, striking 'ram's head', neck carried high, inconspicuous withers, steeply sloping shoulders, long back, rounded lines. Short stride in walk and trot, with high action.

The court stud-farm at Kladrub, near Pardubitz, was established by the Emperor Maximilian in 1572; the coach-horses for the imperial stables were bred here. In 1764, after the Seven Years War, during which the buildings were destroyed, while the horses were evacuated in good time and sent to Hungary, the grey stallion *Pepoli*, from Italy, became the foundation sire of the *Generale* line of greys which still lives on. In 1799 the *Sacramoso* line of blacks was started with the stallion of that name. The Kladruby stallions *Maestoso* and *Favory* in turn founded two lines of the Lipizzaner breed.

Kladrubys are still bred today in Czechoslovakia: the greys at Kladrub and the blacks at Slatiňany.

Knabstruper

Illustration: A Knabstruper stallion – now very rare – at a private stud-farm in Danish North Zealand.
Description: Striking speckled coat. Similar to the older Frederiksborg type, from which it is directly descended.

Among the old Spanish horses there were many spotted ones. The Danish Knabstruper is descended from them, as are also the American Pintos and Appaloosas. A Spanish officer taken prisoner in 1812 in the Napoleonic Wars is believed to have sold his horse to a butcher named Flaebe. The latter, however, did not slaughter this remarkable mare, but sold it to Judge Lunn, who bred Knabstrupers on his estate. *Mikkel*, grandson of this mare, became the foundation sire of the Knabstruper breed.

Irish Hunter

Illustration: *Inis Cara* carrying the champion Irish rider Captain Larry Kiely.
Description: This is not a breed, but a so-called 'utility cross' with admixture of at least 50 per cent English Thoroughbred. Strong, harmonious appearance, well proportioned. Markedly noble head, rather long. Brisk in all gaits, great endurance in galloping, powerful jumper.

The Hunter was originally bred for that specific purpose. Anybody viewing the innumerable embankments and ditches in the Irish countryside can get an idea of the performance that will be needed from a horse in this country. No wonder, therefore, that more Irish Hunters than horses of any other breed have carried their riders to the highest peaks of fame. Examples are: *Gone Away*, *The Rock*, *Bellevue*, *Fulmer*, *Feather Duster*, *Ambassador*.

Four types are distinguished: The heavy Hunter is produced by mating a Thoroughbred stallion with an Irish Draught mare; medium-weight and light Hunters are bred mostly from Thoroughbred stallions with heavy Hunter mares; and lastly the small Hunter is produced by a Connemara Pony mare mated with a Thoroughbred stallion.

Jutlander

Illustration: This prize-winning stallion embodies the typical features of the Jutlander; the characteristic colouring is dark chestnut with light mane, tail and feather.
Description: Very powerful cold-blood of medium size. Medium-length, massive neck, broad breast, shoulders and croup especially muscular, sturdy legs, height 155 cm to 165 cm (about 15–16 hands), weight up to 900 kg (2000 lb or 140 stone).

This old Danish cold-blood breed, which has been in existence for well over a thousand years, was much desired by the knights of the middle ages for their tournaments. For many hundreds of years, however, its principal use was as a tireless and docile work horse for the farmers of the Jutland peninsula. There were times when this breed had such a good reputation that even the English and the French, who themselves bred excellent cold-bloods, imported Jutlanders. On the other hand the Jutlander received infusions of blood from other breeds, especially cold-bloods and warm-bloods from England. *Oppenheim LXII*, a stallion who was either a Shire or a Suffolk Punch, is supposed to have set his stamp on the present Jutlander around 1865.

Lipizzaner

Illustration: Four-in-hand team at the Lipizzaner stud at Szilvasvarad in Hungary.
Description: Very elegant medium-weight warm-blood. Head usually long, with a more or less convex profile, beautifully arched neck, inconspicuous withers, long back, muscular croup and shoulders. Extremely intelligent. Has a great aptitude for Haute Ecole. Most of them are greys, but some are bay or black.

The Greeks long ago treasured these excellent horses from the rugged Karst mountains of the Balkans, and many of their sculptures show an amazing likeness to the modern Lipizzaner. Karst horses also provided the female foundation for this breed. But the imported Neapolitan and Spanish stallions as well as the North Italian types undoubtedly exercised the stronger influence on the configuration of the Lipizzaner.

The Lipizza stud, near Trieste, was founded by the Archduke Charles of Austria in 1580, and it was here that the parade and show horses for the court were bred.

The history of the Lipizzaner is recounted in some detail in the descriptions of the Lipizza, Piber and Szilvasvarad stud-farms.

Morgan

Illustration: The Morgan stallion *South Ridge*, born 1967, is stood at Roswell in New Mexico.
Description: Very attractive appearance. Short head with broad forehead and strong jowls, neck muscular and carried well, short strong back, croup and shoulders long and well muscled. Courageous and intelligent, but with a gentle nature. Mostly chestnut and brown. Height hardly more than 150 cm (15 hands).

The foundation sire of this breed was one of America's most astonishing horses. He was a stallion standing only about 135 cm (13 hands); his name was *Figure*, and his sire was the Thoroughbred *Beautiful Bay*. His dam carried a high proportion of Arab blood as well as some Hackney and Fjord. *Figure* came into the possession of Justin Morgan, a teacher of singing in Vermont, who added to his meagre income by allowing the neighbouring farmers to send their mares to be covered by his stallion. *Morgan*, as the stallion was re-named, after his owner – as was the whole breed – proved to be extremely potent at transmitting his beautiful appearance, his speed, his stamina and his good character.

There are now more than 50,000 registered Morgans. They have passed on many of their good qualities to other breeds, especially the Standard Trotter.

277

Nonius

Illustration: A csikos – a Hungarian herdsman – mounting his Nonius. The csikos saddle lies loose on the horse's back, without any girth. For this reason the horses are often made to kneel, to facilitate mounting.
Description: Rather a rugged face. Tough, sound and well behaved. Occasionally, ribs not well 'sprung'. Mostly bay, without markings.

In 1814 Austrian cuirassiers occupied the stud-farm at Rosières-aux-Salines in France. Among the horses that fell into their hands was a splendid stallion named *Nonius*. In 1816 he was brought to the Mezőhegyes stud in Hungary. As well as Hungarian mares, Turkish, Arab, Spanish and Lipizzaner ones were sent to this stallion. The daughters and grand-daughters were in turn covered by *Nonius* who transmitted both appearance and characteristics with great potency.

Later on, two types were bred. The great Nonius, standing 160 to 168 cm (15 hands 3 inches to 16 hands 2 inches) is an elegant coach-horse whose appearance resembles that of the Lipizzaner; the small Nonius, with a height of 150 to 160 cm (14 hands 3 inches to 15 hands 3 inches), is a good-tempered, quite fast and versatile saddle horse.

Noriker

Illustration: *Wirt's Diamant*, a magnificent Noriker stallion at the Marbach main stud-farm.
Description: Medium-heavy cold-blood (600 to 700 kg, about 1300–1500 pounds). Well proportioned head on beautifully arched, muscular, rather short neck. Back and croup long and broad. Sloping shoulders, deep girth, strong legs with clean joints. Feather. Mostly chestnut and brown, exceptionally speckled grey.

Depending on the region where it is bred, the Noriker is also known as South-German Cold-blood, Pinzgauer or Oberländer.

The original home of this breed was probably Roman Noricum, the region of present-day Austria to the south of the Danube. These excellent work horses were systematically bred especially in the monasteries. This breed was not spared from the mania for experimentation which swept over Europe during the seventeenth, eighteenth and nineteenth centuries. Crosses were bred with Spanish, Italian and Belgian horses, with Kladrubers, Clydesdales, Normans, Oldenburgers, etc. From about 1885 the Noriker was developed as a pure breed and was consolidated as such. In the Austrian and Bavarian highlands these horses have remained indispensable up to the present day.

Palomino

Illustration: Palominos, working here as circus horses, at a rodeo in Nashville, Tennessee.
Description: Quite small, 140 cm to 160 cm (14–16 hands) tall, very high-class saddle horse, a member of the group of Western Horses. A striking characteristic is the gleaming gold-coloured coat with flaxen to silver-white mane and tail. Very refined head, beautiful neck, inconspicuous withers, noble proportions, very muscular legs.

This horse closely resembles the Arab in type and nature. As well as being extremely beautiful the Palomino is a wonderful family horse whose good temper and loyalty are probably not surpassed by any other horse. The Palomino is not yet a consolidated breed; however, the breeders' associations hope to attain this objective in the near future. The name comes from Don Juan de Palomino, who accompanied Cortez on a golden-coloured horse. Very little is known about the genealogy of these horses, but it is certain that a great deal of Arab blood flows in their veins. They are bred mainly in the south-west of the USA; other Palomino stud-farms exist principally in England.

Paso

Illustration: *Laurel*, at A.M. Pardue's stud in Hidden Valley, near Los Angeles, is reckoned to be the best and most beautiful Paso stallion in the USA.
Description: Rather small (140 cm to 155 cm (13 hands 3 inches to 15 hands 1 inch), very high-class, compact horse. Beautiful conformation, straight head, very muscular, superb carriage of neck, somewhat sloping, strongly muscled shoulders, strong back, rounded croup, outstanding gaits. Pacer gait comes naturally.

Various types of Pasos are distinguished, particularly the Paso Fino bred mainly in Colombia and the Caballo de Paso of Peru. Both of these are now bred in several countries, especially in the USA. Only in Peru, however, have Pasos been bred systematically for a long time, evidently since early colonial days. Their forebears were the Spanish horses brought to Peru by the conqueror Pizarro in 1532, as the first riding-animals to be seen in that country. Typical of the breed is the 'broken' pacer gait, a very brisk gait, extremely pleasant for the rider. Pasos have extraordinarily good stamina and are exceptionally sure-footed.

Oldenburger

More than 500 years ago, in the region
between the Weser and the Netherlands
border, horses of Friesian descent were being
bred, which were later to constitute the
foundation of the Oldenburger breed. Count
Anton Günther von Oldenburg aimed to
develop grand coach horses from this local
type and, as was the usual practice throughout
Europe, he obtained stallions from Spain and
Italy for this purpose. Thus there appeared,
around 1650, the Karossier, which resembled
the Frederiksborg and the Kladruby as
regards its essential features. It was crossed
with various other breeds, but not extensively
until the turn of the century. About twenty
years ago a start was made to switch breeding
to the modern competition type.

Ostfriese
(East Friesian)

In the year AD 200 Tacitus gave an account of
that country where 'the world came to an
end' and innumerable battles were fought on
horseback. In the middle ages, East Friesian
horses were regarded as trusty war-horses. In
1618 Count Enno established horse-fairs at
Emden. In 1754 the first selection decree for
stallions was issued and systematic breeding
was introduced. Heavy mares, nearly cold-
bloods, were mated with stallions from
North Africa, from Normandy, from
England and from Hanover. From 1816
onwards the Celle stallion centre sent out sires
to East Friesian covering stations. Since 1904
the North Zealand breeding industry has
been standing on its own feet.

Percheron

The excellent qualities of the Percheron have
made this horse well known and sought after
far beyond the limits of the Perche district. It
is nearly 150 years since the first Percherons
were taken to America, and by 100 years ago
their own breed society had been established
there. Even England, with her own very
good cold-bloods, imported Percherons; in
Russia they were used to improve the native
breeds; and a great many of these huge iron-
greys also went to Canada, Argentina,
Paraguay and South Africa.

Repeated crossing with Spanish horses, and
later especially with Arabs, mainly affected
the gaits without greatly reducing the weight
of the old heavy type.

Pinto

Among the Spanish horses there were many
piebalds and skewbalds. There are nearly
always some in the herds of wild mustangs,
and these distinctive colourings were particularly fancied by the Indians. It is from these
horses, with their animated history, that the
Pintos are descended, and they have retained
not only the blotchy coat but also the great
capacity for work. Although they have been
bred selectively for decades and have been
officially recognized as a breed since 1963,
they are not yet consolidated. Even so, they
are not only tremendous favourites as show-
horses in America but are equally excellent as
cowboy and family horses.

The American Paint Horse has in common
with the Pinto only its blotchy coat. Paint
Horses are always Thoroughbreds or Quarter
Horses.

Quarter Horse

Illustration: Quarter Horse at a carnival race in Nashville, Tennessee. For this kind of horseback sport, and for many others too, there is no better horse.
Description: Very compact and powerful but nevertheless refined overall appearance. Short head with wide forehead and powerful jowls; stout neck; short, solid trunk; well muscled shoulders and croup; impeccable legs with clearly defined joints.

A phenomenon. Probably the most versatile of all saddle horses. The only horse that has been able to beat the Thoroughbred over a short distance, it is also the best cowboy horse; it is excellent for hunting, jumping and polo; and, thanks to its problem-free and undemanding nature, it is an ideal family horse. Although the Quarter Horse Breeders' Society was founded only in 1940, there are now far more than a million registered animals, more than of any other breed.

The history of the Quarter Horse started about 350 years ago in the South-East States, when horses produced by crossing Atab, Turkish, English and probably also other breeds ran races over the quarter-mile (hence the name Quarter Horse).

Rhenish-German Cold-blood

Illustration: String of cold-blood stallions at the Warendorf stallion parade.
Description: Cold-blood breed similar to the Ardennais. Heavy but expressive head, arched neck of cold-blood type, short back, arched croup with marked cleavage, powerful chest, musculature excellent over-all, short legs, not much feather. Height 160 cm to 170 cm (about 16–17 hands), weight up to 1000 kg (one ton or over 160 stone).

Before World War II this mightiest of German cold-bloods was also the commonest, constituting over 80 per cent of the total stock of German cold-bloods and being encountered more frequently than any other breed. Nowadays it is almost a rarity.

In past centuries, German cold-bloods never attained the same high qualities as French, English and Belgian ones. Towards the end of the nineteenth century, particularly, efforts were made to improve the type by crossing mainly with Percherons, Clydesdales and Jutlanders. In the Rhineland, Belgians were used for this purpose, and a native German cold-blood horse was successfully developed as a result of this infusion of new blood.

Suffolk Punch

Illustration: Prizewinning stallion on a private farm in Suffolk, England.
Description: A particularly well rounded, substantial, short-legged horse with beautiful head, short thick neck, well placed shoulder, short back and powerful croup. Height 160 cm to 170 cm (about 16–17 hands), weight up to over 1000 kg (one ton or over 160 stone). Chestnut without markings.

Apart from its power and bulk, this third British cold-blood bears scarcely any resemblance to the Shire and the Clydesdale. It is more substantial and compact, has no markings or feather, and is moreover reckoned to make more efficient use of its fodder. It is said that Shires and Clydesdales would soon starve on its rations.

Its forebears were probably the war-horses of the Normans, and it has been known since the sixteenth century as the Suffolk horse. The breed became established towards the end of the eighteenth century, and a breed society has been in existence since 1877.

Suffolk Punches have been and are still being exported, above all to North and South America. A large number of mares have been shipped to Pakistan to produce mules for the mountain troops.

Tennessee Walking Horse

Illustration: Training for the big 1975 Walking Horse Show at Shelbyville, Tennessee.
Description: Rather large head, usually with slightly convex profile; thick neck, carried high; short, strong back; well 'sprung' ribs. All colours, blacks very common. Very placid nature.

The Tennessee Walker is descended from just about all the breeds that found their way to the southern States in the early days; it was originally a tireless saddle horse on the plantations, but has now been demoted to the role of show horse. At the widely attended show events it demonstrates not only the long stride but also the special 'running walk', a four-time gait in which the hind feet considerably overlap the prints of the fore feet. The abnormal knee action in all gaits is produced by attaching blocks, up to 12 cm (5 inches) high, to the hoofs by means of loose chains round the fetlocks; these strike the coronet at each step, causing pain and producing sore places. Alternatively the action may be produced by a type of intensive 'training' which might more properly be termed torture. The whole business is probably the worst form of fashionable stupidity that could be practised with horses.

Schwarzwälder

Illustration: The Schwarzwälder stallion *Militär* at the Marbach central stud-farm.
Description: Very handsome, rather small head; strong neck, short back, broad, sloping muscular croup, legs usually good, muscular. Height only 145 cm to 155 cm (about 14–15 hands). Chestnut with light mane and tail.

If a Noriker were crossed with a Haflinger, it would be expected that a horse like the Schwarzwälder would result from the mating. There is no doubt that the Schwarzwälder is closely related to the Noriker and has developed from the same foundation stock. It is probably the climate, the food and the nature of the soil in the upper Black Forest that has kept this horse smaller and lighter, so that it now looks more like a Cob than a cold-blood. It is an excellent, energetic and easy-going work horse, and will surely be giving good service in forestry and agriculture for a long time to come.

Shire

Illustration: Shire horses on a private farm in Norfolk, England
Description: The largest horse, normally standing 170–180 cm (17–18 hands), but many stallions are taller, up to 2 m or more (20 hands) and weighing up to 1300 kg (3000 pounds or 200 stone). Large head; well-proportioned, muscular; powerful chest, up to 1 m (over 3 feet) broad; medium-length neck, not very arched; sloping shoulders; strong back, croup narrower than chest. Luxuriant feathers. Black, bay, grey, occasionally chestnut.

The exact ancestry of the mighty Shire is not known, but it must certainly have developed from the heavy old war-horses, possibly of Flemish origin. In former times it was called the English Great Horse. After the age of chivalry, production of this type was concentrated in the region of the so-called Shires in the heart of England. From the war-horse there was developed a draught-horse for very heavy loads, capable of pulling the plough in marshy lowlands. On being crossed with Scottish Clydesdales the Shires acquired their luxuriant feather and characteristic markings on head and legs.

Shires are now bred not only in England but also in Ireland, in Canada and in North and South America, though of course only in relatively small numbers.

Trakehnen

Illustration: Leading sire *Pythagoras*, son of *Dampfross*, at the former East Prussian central stud-farm Trakehnen.
Description: Great class. Great charm. Short head, broad forehead, large eyes. Elegant neck carriage, fine nape. Beautiful conformation and impressive gaits. Many Olympic victors. Bred pure in western Europe since 1945, as an improver breed alongside the Thoroughbred.

The history of this East Prussian horse goes right back to the thirteenth century, the period when the Teutonic Order was founded; at that time both heavy war-horses and light farm-horses were bred. From the sixteenth century onwards many Arab and Barb horses were brought to East Prussia. The Trakehnen main stud was created in the reign of the Prussian King Frederick William I, and received no fewer than 1101 horses in 1732. In 1786 Count Lindenau started up systematic breeding with Arab stallions. From 1817 onwards the breed was greatly influenced by English Thoroughbreds.

In the winter of 1944/5, when the Russians marched in, a small number of the East Prussian horses were taken – under unimaginably harassing conditions – to the West, where breeding was developed anew after the war.

Württemberger

Illustration: Württemberger stallion at the Marbach main stud.
Description: Until about 1955 this was a utility and especially a farm-type heavy warm-blood. Since then it has been improved, mainly by the infusion of Trakehnen blood, and its characteristic features are approaching closer and closer to those of the modern riding and sporting horse of the 1970s.

Back in the sixteenth century Württemberg was already known for its good warm-blood horses, and its reputation was enhanced especially by the establishment of the Marbach court stud-farm at that period. As was the practice in those days, at Marbach all the available breeds of horses were crossed with one another. Spanish, Italian and Arab horses followed Brandenburgers, Mecklenburgers and Trakehnens, Anglo-Arabs, Thoroughbreds, Noniuses and even Clydesdales and Shires. It was only about a hundred years ago that systematic breeding of warmbloods was started, mainly on the basis of Anglo-Normans. It was chiefly the introduction of the outstanding Trakehnen stallion *Julmond* that brought about the evolution of the present higher-class type of Württembergers.

Horse breeding today

Connemara Pony foal. Expansion in the breeding of ponies and small horses is now greater than for any other type of horse. For this purpose the old traditional kind of stud-farm is not required, but a thorough understanding of the subject is of course just as essential as ever.

Around the middle of the twentieth century the demand for horses shifted from agricultural to saddle horses. In the USA this development was observed earlier, whereas in the countries of eastern Europe the change of direction in breeding objectives is still in full swing, and the demand for horses for agriculture is still relatively high.

State authorities in many countries continue to exert every effort to keep horse breeding going. In doing so they are performing or supporting an important cultural task and helping to promote equestrian sports and to make them more popular generally. States continue to run central and regional studs, stallion-testing institutes and stallion-rearing stations. Where necessary, the State helps private stallion owners with premiums and, by means of premium payments to organized breed associations, saves colts and three-year-old mares from being sold, so that the best can be kept for systematic breeding and continued improvement.

In the USA, as well as in the countries of the Commonwealth and some others, there are practically no State-run stallion centres or premium systems, and horse breeding in those countries has always relied on private initiative.

At the present time, stud-farms and farmer-breeders are competing to produce the ideal saddle horse – one whose character and external qualities satisfy the requirements of the rider as far as possible. At the same time, however, they are making big efforts to produce top-class horses for sport.

The bloodstock industry and racing, which must be regarded as the starting point for equestrian sports, have taken on increased importance in every continent. This applies also to the newer sport of trotter racing, now expanding at a tremendous rate in many countries.

Horseback games such as polo, Skijöring and pushball continue to be played, but in most countries by relatively small numbers only. On the other hand, interest in rodeo is on the increase in the USA as well as in Australia and New Zealand; it has long since ceased to be just the Sunday pastime of cowboys, and has caught on with all sections of the community. The same applies to the skilled equestrian sports, the gymkhanas, which originated in India and were introduced into Europe by the British; they continue to be much loved in the British Isles, and are now attracting more and more people especially in the western States of America.

Hunting also, in various forms, is becoming more widespread, and has for many years not been confined to privileged circles.

As a consequence of the mechanization of agriculture and transport, and of the reduction or disbandment of mounted troops in the army, stocks of horses have everywhere diminished greatly since the end of the war. However, during the last ten years or so there has been a distinct revival of interest in horse breeding. At the present time there is positive evidence that the breeding industry is again flourishing, though it may vary in strength, extent and objectives.

Cold-blood horses, which only a few decades ago accounted for 80 per cent of the stock in many countries, have almost disappeared. Except in the countries of eastern Europe there are now very few of these types, which may be useful to poor peasants in inaccessible mountain and forest regions, or may be kept out of loyalty to old traditions.

The biggest increase at the present time is in the numbers of ponies and small horses. On account of their robustness and their undemanding and friendly nature these small types, which many riders smile at, are of inestimable value for unambitious leisure riding and trekking, and well deserve their present triumphal progress.

Sources and further reading

Alcock, A., *Love of Horses*, Octopus, London, 1973

Alcock, A., *Love of Ponies*, Octopus, London, 1975

Ahnert, Rainer L., *Thoroughbred Breeding of the World*, Podzun Verlag, Dorheim, 1970

Baranski, A., *Geschichte der Tierzucht und Tiermedicin im Alterthum*, Georg Olms Verlag, Hildesheim and New York, 1971

Blendinger, W., *Psychologie und Verhaltensweise der Pferde*, Hoffmann, Heidenheim, 1971

Bräuer, C., *Gestütsbrandzeichen der Staats- und Privatgestüte Europas und des Orients*, 1877

Browne, Noel Philips, *The Horse in Ireland*, Pelham Books Ltd., London, 1967

Dent, Anthony, *The Horse through Fifty Centuries of Civilization*, Phaidon, London, 1974

Dossenbach, Monique und Hans D., Rüeger, M., und Meier, H.P., *Irlands Pferde*, Hallwag Verlag, Bern and Stuttgart, 1975

Froehner, Reinhard, *Kulturgeschichte der Tierheilkunde*
1. Band, Terra-Verlag, Konstanz, 1952
2. Band, Terra-Verlag, Konstanz, 1954

Gianoli, Luigi, *Horses and Horsemanship through the Ages*, Crown Publishers, Inc., New York, 1969

Gill, J. *Bloodstock*, Hamish Hamilton, London, 1977

Goodall, D.M., *Horses of the World*, David and Charles, Newton Abbot, new edn, 1973

Gorbracht, W., *Kennst Du Pferde*, Limpert, Frankfurt, 1975

Graham, Clive, *Hyperion*, J.A. Allen, London, 1967

Hancar, F., *Das Pferd in prähistorischer und früher historischer Zeit*, Herold, Vienna and Munich, 1955

Irish Sweeps Derby, Committee of the Irish Sweeps Derby, 3rd edn, 1963

Kapitzke, G., *Wildlebende Pferde*, Parey, Hamburg, 1973

Krüger, W., *Unser Pferd und seine Vorfahren*, Springer, Berlin, 1939

Krumbiegel, J., *Einhufer*, 1958

Löwe/Meyer, *Pferdezucht und Pferdefütterung*, Ulmer, Stuttgart, 1974

Longrigg, Roger, *The History of Horse Racing*, Macmillan London Ltd., London and Basingstoke, second impression, 1973

Mittler, R., *Eroberung eines Kontinentes*, Atlantis, Zürich, 1968

Monaghan, J., *The Book of the American West*, Bonanza, New York, 1963

Moody, T.W. and Martin, F.X., *The Course of Irish History*, The Mercier Press, Cork, 1967

Pacemaker and *The Horseman*, London

Persson, C., *Pferde und Ponys*, Keyser, Munich, 1972

Petry, E., *Die Flegeljahre Amerikas*, Nannen, Hamburg, 1963

Pferderassen, Südwest, Munich, 1975

Ryden, H., *Mustangs*, Viking, New York, 1972

Seth-Smith, Michael, *International Stallions and Studs*, W. Foulsham & Co. Ltd., Slough, 1974

Stable Management, Oct/Nov 1976, Vol. 13, No. 4

Török and Alapfy, *Das ungarische Pferd*, Corvina, Budapest, 1972

Traut, F., *Gestüte Europas*, Liebhaber, Verden, 1971

Trench, C.C., *A History of Horsemanship*, 1970

Winter von Adlersflügel, Georg Simon, *Neuer Tractat von der Stuterey oder Fohlenzucht*, Olms Presse, Hildesheim and New York, 1975

Wrangel, Carl Gustav, *Das Buch vom Pferde II*, Olms Presse, Hildesheim and New York, 1975

Index of horses

General index

287

Brand Marks

The brand-marks in the first ten rows are distinctive stud- and breed-marks from the second half of the nineteenth century. Rows 11 and 12 show brand-marks from around the turn of the century. In the bottom row brand-marks in current use are illustrated.

Row 1
1–18: Egypt
19–22: Palestine

Row 2
1–22: Moldavia

Row 3
1–22: Moldavia

Row 4
1–22: Moldavia

Row 5
1–22: Moldavia

Row 6
1–9: Breed and colour-type brand-marks of Count Gudowith, at the Black Sea.
10–22: Syria

Row 7
1–8: Syria
9–20: European breeders in the Near and Middle East
21–22: Polish private stud-farms

Row 8
1–22: Polish private stud-farms

Row 9
1–22: Polish private stud-farms

Row 10
1–22: Polish private stud-farms

Row 11
1–22: Austro-Hungarian stud-farms and stud-books: Tampaspuszta, Tordas, Valaszut, Bonczhida, Babolna, Tiszakürt, Arpadhalom, Hortobagy, Füzes Gyarmat, Tarsolya-Tanya, Berez-Surany, Vacs, Bobda, Darda, Folsoloperd, Baranya, Szirak, Debreczen, Dormand, Devecser, Kemenes, Fogaras

Row 12
1–22: Austro-Hungarian and German stud-farms and stud-books: Sziel-Szanacs, Hathalom, Kisber, Emilia Major, Paolgary, Sloboda, Radautz, Nagy Komlos, Biharillye, Feltorony, Hochwald, Torskie, Banlak, Dylegowka, Baranya, Posen stud-book for high-class half-breds, Silesian stud-book for cold-bloods, Holstein stud-book for high-class half-breds, Kanzlerhof, Stepperg, Saxony, Lopshorn

Row 13
1–22: Current Polish brand-marks. Gdansk cold-blood, Bialystok cold-blood, Koszalin, Olsztyn and Szczecin cold-blood, Bydgoroi, Kielce, Lodz and Warsaw cold-blood, small cold-blood foal brand-mark, small cold-blood registration brand-mark, Wielkopolska foal brand-mark, Wielkopolska registration brand-mark, Malopolska of Kielce registration brand-mark, Malopolska of Cracow foal brand-mark, Malopolska of Cracow registration brand-mark, Malopolska of Lublin registration brand-mark, Malopolska of Rzeszow foal brand-mark, Malopolska of Rzeszow registration brand-mark, Malopolska of Sadec foal brand-mark, Malopolska of Sadec registration brand-mark, heavy warm-blood foal brand-mark, heavy warm-blood registration brand-mark, Konik foal brand-mark, Konik registration brand-mark, Huzul foal brand-mark, Huzul registration brand-mark.

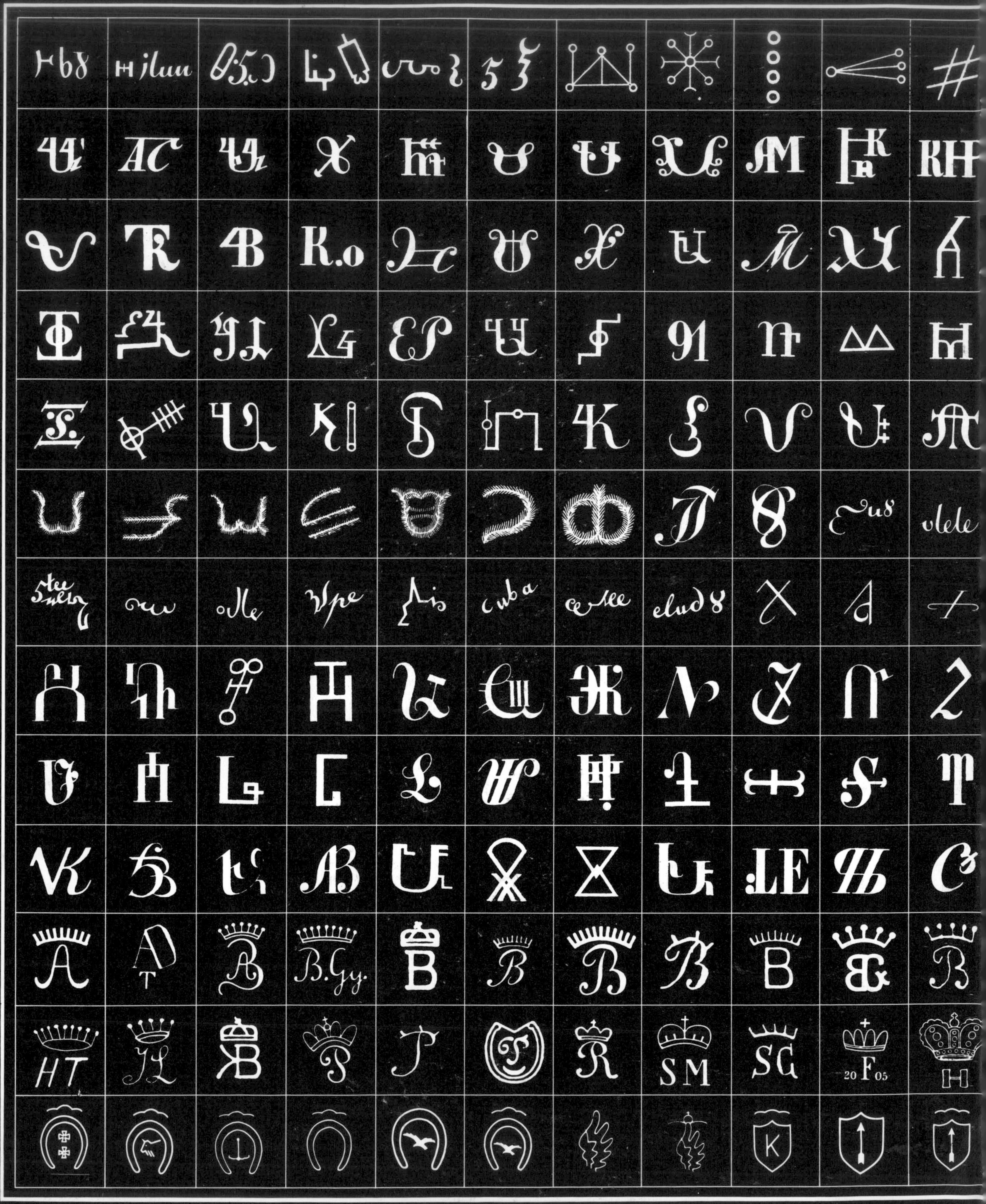
B.Gy.
HT
SM
SG
20 F 05